Baldev Raj □ C.V. Subramanian □ T. Jayakumar

Non-Destructive
Testing of Welds

Baldev Raj □ C.V. Subramanian □ T. Jayakumar

Non-Destructive Testing of Welds

The Materials
Information Society

Narosa Publishing House
New Delhi   Chennai   Mumbai   Calcutta

Baldev Raj
C.V. Subramanian
T. Jayakumar
Indira Gandhi Centre for Atomic Research
Kalpakkam 603 102, Tamil Nadu, India

Copyright © 2000 Narosa Publishing House
6 Community Centre, Panchsheel Park, New Delhi 110 017, India

Exclusive distribution in North America only by
ASM International, 9639 Kinsman Road, Materials Park,
Ohio, USA 44073-0002

ISBN 0-87170-678-4

Printed in India

Foreword

I am immensely pleased to write this 'Foreword' for the book on 'Non-Destructive Testing of Welds' authored by Dr. Baldev Raj, Shri C.V. Subramanian and Dr. T. Jayakumar. Welded components and structures are widely used in almost all industries and the engineering industry relies heavily on the weld integrity for adequate and reliable performance of components, structures and plants. Non-destructive testing and evaluation of welded components plays a crucial role in ensuring reliable performance of welded components. All the three authors are well versed with Welding Science and Technology and with the NDT techniques and I am glad that all their experiences and knowledge are converted into a comprehensive book on 'Non-Destructive Testing of Welds'.

Dr. Baldev Raj's contributions in the area of NDT covers a whole spectrum ranging from quality assurance and quality control, in-service inspection, ageing management to total quality management of engineering components. He has nurtured a school in NDT to pursue research and development in advanced NDT with many innovations for many challenging applications. He is the architect of developing intelligent welding processes in India. Shri C.V. Subramanian is an expert in NDT and in particular an authority in Ultrasonic Non-Destructive Testing and has vast experience of more than three decades in pre-service and in-service inspection of engineering components, especially welded components in nuclear, petrochemical and fertilizer industries. Dr. T. Jayakumar is a leading researcher in many advanced NDT techniques for comprehensive characterization of defects and microstructures and evaluation of residual stresses in welded components and has considerable experience in root cause failure analysis of weld related failures.

This book, which covers all aspects of weld testing and evaluation, is aimed at the undergraduate and graduate engineers, welding engineers, NDT professionals and materials technologists who need to know about various NDT techniques.

A detailed introductory chapter covers different types of welding processes, weld defects, fitness-for purpose approach, quality classes and choice of NDT techniques. A chapter each is devoted to all major conventional and advanced NDT techniques. Other interesting chapters are leak testing and in-situ metallography. Wide coverage has been given for residual stress analysis in weldments, automation and robotics in NDT and weld related failures. The chapters on intelligent welding, fracture mechanics concepts, quality control including total quality management and codes and standards add to the unique value of the book.

The whole book is structured in such a way that a lot of emphasis is given to basic principles, applications of each technique pertaining to weld inspection and related case studies.

I am sure that this book will be well received by undergraduate and post-graduate students and professionals in NDT and welding and will enhance the knowledge of the readers about the importance of non-destructive testing for evaluating welded components.

DR. PLACID RODRIGUEZ
Director
Indira Gandhi Centre for Atomic Research
Kalpakkam-603 102, India

Preface

Welded components and structures are widely used in almost all industries. With the realisation of the fact that weld is the weakest link and majority of failures of components are related to welding and weldment performance, more and more emphasis is being given for fabricating welded components with high quality and ensuring their performance reliability in service. Non-Destructive Testing and Evaluation of welded components (NDT & E) plays a crucial role in ensuring reliable performance of welded components. While welding engineers independently try to obtain high quality welds, NDT experts assure this quality by employing various NDT techniques. It has been felt that professionals with overlapping expertise in both welding technology and NDT are essential for a success in ensuring requisite performance of welded components. This aspect, inspired the authors to write a comprehensive book emphasising the need for non-destructive testing and evaluation of welded components, with due coverage of various welding procedures, possible defects, problems associated with inspection of welded components etc. Another motivating factor is that, such a book taking into account all aspects mentioned above is not available in the national or international market. This book on 'NDT of Welds' is written to meet this objective. This book along with other publications related to welding, would help welding engineers and professionals to achieve high quality welded components, through comprehensive understanding of the science and technology of welding.

NDT methods are required to obtain necessary information for evaluating the welds. The primary advantage of the NDT methods is that the product can be examined without destroying its usefulness. Non-destructive evaluation can be conveniently applied for ensuring that the weldments are fit for the purpose. Non-destructive Evaluation (NDE) places due emphasis on characterisation of microstructures, residual stresses and quantitative determination of size, shape and location of a defect or anomaly, thus enabling evaluation of structural integrity of a welded component.

Characteristics of weld defects such as cracks, inclusions, porosities, lack of penetration, lack of fusion, lack of bond, undercut and deficiencies in microstructures can be evaluated by NDT methods. Present range of NDT techniques and ever evolving capabilities of NDT techniques enable evaluation of weld joints of various materials and for various service conditions. The evaluation has to be correlated to performance and also should satisfy the criteria of cost effectiveness and time schedules.

This book is aimed at the undergraduate and graduate engineers, welding engineers, NDT professionals and material technologists who need to understand the basis of a wide range of NDT methods, so that the most appropriate one or a combination of a few techniques can be selected for a specific application.

In this book, a large number of case-studies on each NDT technique have been added so that the reader is exposed to the problems faced by industries and specific remedies to the problems by appropriate application of NDT methods to ensure the structural integrity of the component during service. All major conventional NDT techniques and their advancements have been highlighted. The book also contains information about the definition of a defect, various type of defects that are encountered during various welding processes which range from micro defects to gross defects and the significance that has to be attached in detecting the defects that may lead to loss of performance and even failure.

In addition to various NDT methods, the book contains chapters on residual stress analysis in weldments, automation and robotics which play a crucial role in weld inspection. A comprehensive chapter on various weld related failures with specific emphasis on the role of NDE in avoiding failures is included.

Quality control in production welding and Total Quality Management (TQM) are dealt in a chapter giving information about optimum quality level, quality assurance, quality control and statistical quality control. The concept of zero defect is being given prime importance as a part of TQM by incorporating suitable NDT methods in the total chain of TQM. The adoption of the technology of the Intelligent Processing of Material (IPM) with provision for feed back control to the process based on on-line measurements, understanding the vital correlations between measured parameters, process variables and quality specification is another step towards achieving TQM. A chapter giving information about intelligent welding is also included in this book.

Codes and Standards pertaining to weld inspection for all conventional NDT methods are also covered in this book.

We are thankful to Dr. Placid Rodriguez, Director, Indira Gandhi Centre for Atomic Research (IGCAR), for all his encouragement and to many NDT professionals at IGCAR for their useful suggestions, informations and help rendered in bringing the book.

We wish to thank Shri A.S. Ramesh (DPEND, IGCAR), for his keen involvement and dedication in bringing the book and Shri V Chandrasekar (DPEND IGCAR) for preparing illustrations. We also would like to thank M/s Narosa Publishing House, New Delhi for their interest and readiness to publish this book with excellent quality.

We hope that the readers will have a fruitful reading for success in their examinations and in their profession.

AUTHORS

Acknowledgments

The authors are extremely grateful and credit the following organisations for giving their permission to incorporate published informations like technical content, photographs, sketches etc.

1. Chief Executive, International Institute of Welding, Cambridge, UK for Quality classes, Fitness for purpose and Tables 1.1 and 1.2 etc.

2. Editor, American Welding Society, Miami, Florida, USA for Various welding processes, Fig. 1.1 etc.

3. General Manager, M/s. Sonaspection International, Lancaster, England for Types of weld defects and Fig. 1.3.

4. M/s H & R Optical Systems, Boulder, Co 80301 USA for Projection Microscopes, Fig. 2.1 etc.

5. M/s ITI/Institute Technology Inc. Westfield, MA 01086 USA for Borescopes and Fig. 2.2.

6. Fraunhofer Institute for NDT (IzfP), Saarbrucken, Germany for Inspection of austenitic welds, Multi-frequency ECT and for Figs. 5.6 and 5.7.

7. Editor, Materials Evaluation, The American Society for NDT, Columbus, Ohio, USA for TOFD technique and Figs. 6.33 and 6.34.

8. M/s P-Scan Systems, The Deutsche Welding Institute (Force Institute), Copenhagen, Denmark for P-Scan system details and Fig. 6.36.

Contents

Chapter 1

Non-Destructive Testing of Welds: An Introduction

Present day engineering industry relies heavily on welded components and structures. Therefore, weld integrity becomes important for adequate and reliable performance of components, structures and plants. Weld integrity is dependent on the base material, specifications and welding processes. Reliability of weld performance is evaluated by measurement and control of welds. It is widely accepted that testing, measurement and control of welds should be optimised based on fitness-for-purpose (FFP) approach taking into account the welding proceses and economical aspects of ensuring the desired levels of reliability. High technological demands have been met by recent advances in materials technology and availability of better and more reliable test techniques for ensuring the desired quality.

1.1 DEFINITION OF WELD

In the present day industrial world, welding is so pervasive and widespread that definition of weld seems to be unnecessary. However, for the purpose of completeness, a weld can be defined as localised coalescence of a metal wherein coalescence is produced by heating to suitable temperature, with or without the application of pressure and with or without the use of a filler metal. The filler metal has a melting point either approximately the same or below that of the base metals.

In order to produce a satisfactory metallic bond between two metallic objects, it is first necessary to dispel all non-metallic films from the joint faces. To minimize the magnitude of this problem, such films should obviously be removed by suitable mechanical and/or chemical cleaning prior to welding. Furthermore, the delay between cleaning and welding must be as short as possible to prevent reformation of the surface films by prolonged exposure to the ambient atmosphere. Therefore, for quality welding, adequate cleaning procedures must be carefully established and rightly enforced.

In ideal weld, there is complete continuity between the parts joined and every part of the joint is indistinguishable from the metal in which the joint is made. Although this ideal condition is difficult to achieve in practice, welds which give satisfactory service can be made in many ways. A skilled welding engineer recognizes the essential requirements that a particular weld must satisfy and the choice of the appropriate welding process. The welding process must fulfill the following conditions:

  (a) Supply of energy to create the weld joint by fusion or pressure
  (b) Mechanism for removing superficial contamination from the joint faces
  (c) Avoidance of atmospheric contamination
  (d) Control of weld metallurgy

Welding is a developing technology. New techniques are being devised to meet the latest needs and to solve problems encountered in fabrication. To the causal observer, this has led to a diversity of apparently unrelated practical techniques which rely heavily on the craft skill of individual welders. As the technology is based on established scientific concepts, the technologists, engineers and welders must understand these to respond to the demands of the modern industry.

Welding is used for making structures and repair work such as the joining of broken castings. The products obtained by welding are called "Weldments". Figure 1.1 shows a few welding processes based on the type of joint and the source of the heat input.

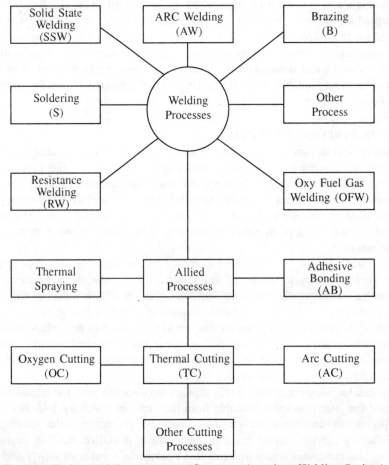

Fig. 1.1   Various welding processes (Courtesy: American Welding Society)

1.1.1 Types of Weld Joints

Different types of welding joints are butt, lap, corner, tee and edge (Figure 1.2). The choice of the type of joint depends on the weldment being made and the sheet thickness. The welding positions can be flat, horizontal, vertical and overhead.

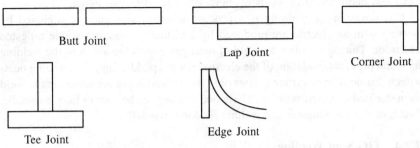

Butt Joint

Lap Joint

Corner Joint

Edge Joint

Tee Joint

Fig. 1.2   Typical weld joints

1.2   WELDING PROCESSES

1.2.1   Gas Welding

In gas welding, coalescence is achieved by directing a gas flame over metal where a filler rod may or may not be used to intermix with the molten puddle. The energy required for welding is generated from combustion of fuel with oxygen or air. The most commonly used fuels are acetylene, mapp gas (stabilized methyl acetylene-propadiene) and hydrogen. Arc welding has limited application for industrial production purposes because it is much slower than other welding processes. It is used for welding of metals having low melting point, and for performing operations such as brazing, soldering and metallizing.

1.2.2   Shielded Metal-Arc Welding

In this process, coalescence is achieved by generating an electric arc between a coated metallic electrode and the work piece. The heat produced by the electric arc melts the metal which mixes with the molten deposits of the coated electrode. The arc energy is provided by a power supply unit that furnishes direct or alternating current. The metallic electrode carries the current to form the arc, produces a gas which shields the arc from the atmosphere, and adds metal to control the bead shape. When an arc is struck with the electrode, the intense heat melts the tip of the electrode. The tiny drops of metal from the electrode enter the arc stream and are deposited on the base metal. As the molten metal is deposited, slag forms over the head which serves as an insulation against the contaminants of the air while cooling takes place.

The shielded metal-arc welding is used extensively in welding ferrous and non-ferrous metals. Arc welding is considerably used in ship building industry, girders, beams and columns for buildings/bridges.

1.2.3   Gas Tungsten-Arc Welding

The two main types of gas shielded-arc welding are gas tungsten-arc welding and gas metal-arc welding and are often referred as TIG and MIG, respectively. Both employ a shielding gas to protect the weld zone from the atmosphere. Since the shielding gas excludes the atmosphere from the molten puddle, welded joints will nearly possess the same chemical, metallurgical and physical properties as the base metal. As a consequence, welded joints are stronger, more ductile and have less distortion than welds made by other welding processes.

Gas tungsten-arc welding is a process where coalescence is achieved by heating with an electric arc produced by a virtually non-consumable tungsten electrode. During welding, a shield of inert gas expels the air from the welding area and prevents oxidation of the electrode, weld puddle, and surrounding heat-affected zone. The electrode creates only the arc and is not consumed in the weld as in shielded metal-arc welding. The actual welding can be semi or fully automatic. Much of the gas tungsten-arc welding is done manually.

1.2.4   TIG Spot Welding
The development of TIG spot welding makes it possible to produce localised fusion similar to resistance spot welding without requiring accessability to both sides of the joint. A special tungsten-arc gas is applied to one side of the joint. Heat is generated from resistance of the work to the flow of electrical current in a circuit of which the work is a part. The TIG spot welding has a wide range of applications in fabricating sheet metal products involving joints which are impractical to resistance spot welding because of the location of the weld or the size of the parts or where welding can be made only from one side.

1.2.5   Gas Metal-Arc Welding
In this process, coalescence is achieved by striking an electric arc between the work piece and a continuous consumable wire electrode which is fed through a torch at controlled speeds. A shielding gas flows through the torch and forms a blanket over the weld puddle to protect it from atmospheric contamination. The welding can be semi-automatic or fully mechanized. The important feature of gas metal-arc welding is the production of high quality welds at high welding speeds without using flux of any kind.

1.2.6   Submerged Arc Welding
In submerged arc welding, an electric arc is submerged or hidden beneath a granular material called flux. The electric arc provides necessary heat to melt and fuse the metal. The flux completely surrounds the electric arc, shielding the metal from the atmosphere. A metallic wire is fed into the welding zone underneath the flux. The welding process can be semi or fully-automatic.

1.2.7   Resistance Welding
Resistance welding is a process in which the required heat for fusion is produced by the resistance of the work piece to the flow of low-voltage, high density electric current. It is strictly a machine welding process and designed for mass production of metal products. The main resistance welding processes are spot, seam, projection, flash and upset.

1.2.8   Special Welding Processes

Electron beam welding: Electron beam welding is essentially a fusion welding process. Fusion is achieved by focussing a high power density beam of electrons on the area to be joined. The kinetic energy of the high velocity electrons, upon striking the metal, changes to thermal energy causing the metal to melt and fuse.

Laser welding: In laser welding, fusion is achieved by directing a highly concentrated beam to a spot about the diameter of a human hair. The word 'Laser' means light amplification by stimulated emission of radiation. The light beam has a higher energy concentration than the electron beam. The highly concentrated beam generates a power intensity of one billion or more watts per square centimeter at the focus point. Since the heat input to the work piece is extremely small, the size of the heat affected zone is minimized. Laser can be used to join dissimilar metals and other difficult to weld metals like copper, nickel, aluminium etc. Extensive applications of laser welding are in aerospace and electronic industries.

Ultrasonic welding: In ultrasonic welding, the interface between the work pieces is plastically deformed. This is done by vibratory energy which dispenses the moisture, oxide and irregular surfaces to bring the areas of both work pieces in close contact and form a solid bond. Vibratory energy is generated by a high frequency ultrasonic transducer. The bonding is established without applying external heat, filler rod or melting metal. This technique is adopted for joining electrical and electronic components.

1.3   WELD IMPERFECTIONS AND IMPORTANCE OF THEIR EVALUATION

Historically, welding has replaced riveted construction in many engineering structures. It is now scarcely possible to design an industrial structure without a welded joint. Though a lot of improvements have taken place in welding technology, there is still scope and need for further developments. In spite of this, inability to use appropriate testing, measurement and control procedures correctly may lead to unexpected and unforeseen problems. Occasional failures of welded joints that still take place support this view point. No weld is completely perfect. Welds may be compared to small castings except that weld metal cools much more rapidly mainly due to heat sink provided by the base metals. This results in thermal stresses which may lead to cracking (serverity depends on the microstructure) and entrapment of gases or foreign materials within the weld. These and other defects may cause premature failure of the weld during manufacture and/or in service.

1.4   DEFECTS IN WELDED JOINTS

A discontinuity is an interruption of the typical structure of a weldment such as lack of homogeneity in the mechanical, metallurgical or physical characteristics of the material or weldment. A discontinuity is not necessarily a defect. A defect is a discontinuity which by its nature or accumulated effect render a part or product unable to meet minimum applicable standards or specifications. Weld defects are broadly classified as cracks, cavities, slag inclusions, incomplete fusion or penetration, imperfect shape or unacceptable contour and other miscellaneous defects like spatter, arc strikes etc.

Cracks: Among the weld defects, cracks are considered as the most harmful ones, as they pose potential danger of growing under stress during service. Cracks can be defined as linear ruptures under stress. Cracks need considerable vigilance to be exercised to anticipate and avoid or at least detect and remove. Cracks occur in many forms and at many locations in a weld joint and over a wide temperature range. In size, cracks may range from large macro-sized cracks to very small micro cracks which need the use of microscope to detect. Location of cracks in a weldment is the first characteristic that has to be noted to investigate its cause. Based on the location and orientation of the cracks with respect to weld joint geometry, they are classified as longitudinal cracks, transverse cracks, toe cracks, crater cracks etc. Based on the tempeature of their formation, cracks are termed as hot cracks or cold cracks.

Hot cracking: Cracks occurring in a weldment during solidification or before the welding heat has completely dissipated from the joint are called hot cracks. Intergranular in nature, hot cracks are caused by the presence of low melting impurities such as sulphur, phosphorous, boron and selenium in the base metal. These low melting impurities remain in liquid state even after the main metal freezes and the impurities occupy the grain boundaries. Stresses developed during solidification of the molten metal act on these thin non-metallic films which are highly brittle and lead to cracks. Weld metal with a wide freezing range is more prone to develop hot cracking. With coarse grains, hot cracking tendency increases. In case of austenitic stainless steel, the elements responsible for hot cracking in the decreasing order of potency are: boron, sulphur, phosphorous, arsenic, tin, lead, zirconium, tantalum and copper.

Cold cracking: Cracks that occur in weldments after completion of solidification are called cold cracks. Cold cracking takes place at a fairly low temperature (below 573K) after completion of solidification of weld metal. In fact, cold cracks can occur hours or even days after the weld metal has equalised in temperature. Cold cracks are transgranular in nature. Essential conditions to cause cold cracking are: (a) hardening of the heat affected zone, (b) development of residual stresses in the weldment and, (c) presence of diffusible hydrogen in the weldment.

Hydrogen induced cracking: This is another type of cold cracking known as underbead cracking or heat affected zone cracking. The term embrittlement refers to abnormally low ductility being displayed by the weldment based on its structure and hardness.

Crater cracking: Crater cracks are caused by volumetric contraction of the molten weld metal during solidification, usually the result of abrupt interruption of the welding arc. Under such conditions, crater cools more rapidly than the remainder of the bead and because the crater solidifies from all sides towards the centre, shrinkage stresses are severe enough to cause cracks. If the base metal contains elements which are prone to segregate, such as carbon, sulphur and niobium, the susceptibility for crater cracking increases.

Lamellar tearing: If non-metallic inclusions like sulphides or silicates (products of deoxidation) are present in the ingot, they elongate while rolling and extend in a direction parallel to the plate surface. When such a plate is strained at right angles to the plate surface, i.e. through thickness direction, the inclusions seriously impair both the precentage of elongation and percentage reduction in area. While fillet welding, an attachment onto a plate (like welding of a set-on nozzle onto a shell), contraction due to welding sets up strains having a component at right angles to the plate surface. If the strains are sufficiently high, plate may fail by lamellar tearing. Cracks may start at the toe of the fillet and progress in step-like fashion underneath the weld.

Porosity: Porosity is the presence of gas pockets or voids (usually spherical in shape) in a weld which are caused by the entrapment of gases evolved during the solidification of the metal. Types of porosities include isolated pores, scattered pores, worm holes etc. Worm holes are the blow holes that result from progressive evolution of gases during freezing. Porosities can be classified as micro and macro-porosities.

Slag inclusion: Slag inclusions refer to oxides and other non-metallic solids entrapped in the weld metal or between the weld metal and the base metal.

Lack of penetration: It involves incomplete penetration of weld through the thickness of the joint. Since incomplete penetration reduces the load carrying cross section and corresponds geometrically to a crack, it becomes essential to design welding procedures that eliminate such defects.

Lack of fusion: Failure of adjacent weld metal and the base metal to fuse together completely is called lack of fusion.

Undercut: The following two conditions are termed as undercuts: (a) a grove melted into the base metal adjacent to the toe and left unfilled by the weld metal and (b) melting of the side wall of a weld groove at the edge of the layer or bead. Undercutting may range in size from a gross, readily seen, continuous furrow down to very small discontinuous rifts no more than a few microns in depth. Undercuts have proved to be the defects with the worst record for causing mechanical failures in weldments. Undercuts create 'notch-effect' at the weld toe.

Concavity: It is caused by the gravity sink of the molten metal or by the surface tension of the weld bevel pulling the molten metal into the bevel. Other term for this defect is 'Suck back'.

Mismatch: Mismatch represents misalignment of both the surfaces of the joint across the weld root.

Burn through: This refers to coalescence of the weld metal beyond the root.

Overlaps: An excess of the weld metal which extends beyond the limits of fusion over the surface of the base metal· is called overlap. Overlap is often associated with fillet welds than butt welds. It is caused by incorrect welding technique or welding currents.

Tungsten inclusion: During gas tungsten arc welding (GTAW) process, occasionally a portion of the tungsten electrode melts, drops off and is entrapped in the weld metal.

Distortion: While welding, the adjacent surfaces are heated to liquid state. During cooling, the liquefied areas shrink and move towards the direction of original heat application. This causes change in the relative positions of members and is called distortion.

The relevance and importance of defects are best understood by fracture mechanics concepts which show that the four important parameters are: defect size, defect shape, defect location and loading—both imposed and that arising out of presence of residual stress.

The objectives of a good and effective Testing, Measurement and Control (TMC) programme are to detect defects as specified by the design.

1.5   ACCEPTANCE STANDARDS (ASME SECTION VIII)

According to ASME Section VIII, indications with major dimensions greater than 1.6 mm are termed as relevant indications. Classification of discontinuities is made linear and rounded. Linear indication has a length greater than three times the width while rounded indication is either circular or elliptical in shape with length equal to or less than three times the width. Rounded indications up to 4.8 mm size are acceptable. However, four or more rounded indications in a line separated by 1.6 mm or less edge-to-edge are unacceptable. All relevant linear indications are unacceptable. Concavity is permitted when the resulting thickness of the weld is at least equal to the thickness of the thinner member of the two sections being joined. Different types of linear and volumetric defects are:

Linear type: Cracks, lack of fusion, lack of penetration, elongated slag inclusions, lack of side wall fusion and under cut

Volumetric type: Porosities and slag inclusions

The defects normally found in a welded joint are shown in Figure 1.3. With the progress in understanding the effect of various types of defects, the acceptance limits of volumetric defects are now largely enhanced. Among the linear type of

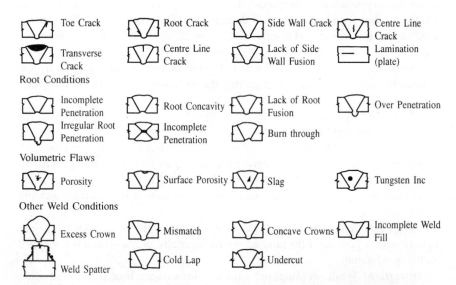

Fig. 1.3   Types of weld defects (Courtesy: Sonaspection International)

defects, their harmful nature would depend on whether the defect is situated on the surface or at the interior and more importantly on the sharpness of the defect. Cracks are the most harmful among the linear defects parlicularly when situated at the surface. Therefore, no code or a standard for a quality weld joint allows the presence of a crack in a welded joint. Recent developments in various TMC techniques aim at detection of cracks and crack like defects with more and more accuracy and reliability.

1.6 DEFECTS RELATED TO MICROSTRUCTURE

The microstructure in the weldment and/or in the HAZ is called defective if it is responsible for degradation in mechanical properties and for the generation of defects such as cracks/residual stresses during welding and cracks during service.

1.7 DEFECTS ASSOCIATED WITH RESIDUAL STRESSES

The two major causes of weld related failures in industrial structures are due to fatigue and stress corrosion cracking. Both these modes of failure depend to a large extent, on the presence of tensile residual stress on the surface of a component/ structure. Hence residual stress is a very important factor and requires accurate assessment.

1.8 TESTING, MEASUREMENT AND CONTROL (TMC) OF WELDS

1.8.1 Definitions and Scope

The meaning and scope of TMC of welds is broadly understood by those associated with the design, fabrication and quality assurance practices. In this context, TMC is defined in a manner that would put the subject matter in a proper perspective. Testing of welds implies the use of both destructive and non-destructive techniques which together assess the quality of a weld joint in terms of the design specifications.

Measurement of weld implies the measurement of various parameters associated with welding which affect the quality of a welded joint in terms of the design specification. These could be (i) pre-weld fitting parameters like bevel angle, dimensions etc., (ii) welding parameters such as welding current, heat input etc. and (ii) post-weld parameters like amount of delta ferrite as in the case of austenitic stainless steel weldments.

Post-weld measurements could be clubbed under testing since the measurement of delta ferrite is virtually a test for the quality of stainless steel welded joint i.e. a clear differentiation may not be possible. The term control implies the steps that are taken on the basis of developed practices so that a welded joint is made to serve the designed objectives. Thus, control of moisture in welding electrodes, used in high strength steel joints, avoid hydrogen embrittlement. Control of the chemical composition in the filler rods in the case of austenitic stainless steel welding avoids hot cracking in the welded joint.

The inter-relationship between testing, measurement and control is very important. The relationship between testing and measurement with respect to delta ferrite has already been mentioned. Take another example to stress this viewpoint. Tensile testing of a welded joint may indicate poor ductility that can be traced to poor control measures in terms of welding parameters, choice of chemical composition of electrodes/filler wires etc. Thus a strict categorisation in discussion on testing, measurement and control, however, does not seem rational. The categorisation helps to evolve total quality assurance schemes. It is in order to choose the important aspects connected with TMC at various stages of welding, and then proceed to examine the influence of these aspects on the quality of a welded joint which is required by a designer.

The most ideal method of evaluating a weld is to place it in service and determine whether it performs satisfactorily during its intended lifetime. Even though service testing may be a sure method of weld evaluation, economic and time limitations often preclude this. Therefore, accelerated performance or proof tests together with numerous destructive (qualification and acceptance criteria) and non-destructive tests and theoretical evaluation using fracture mechanics concepts are currently employed to predict the performance of a given weld or weldment. The extent of evaluation is often optimised based on fitness for purpose approach.

It is clear from the above discussion that however sincere we may be in evaluating the weldments for fitness for purpose, the feedback from the experience/ service behaviour is of paramount importance to improve the quality of weld on a consistent basis.

1.8.2   Fitness-for-Purpose (FFP) Approach

Fitness-for-purpose of a product means that the product functions satisfactorily in service during the expected lifetime. Geometrical defects in welds may influence the strength of the welds; large defects may lower the strength to an unacceptable level and render the product unfit.

Fitness-for-purpose quality requirements are, as a general rule, defined as the most severe defect configurations which may be present in the welds, without impairing the fitness-for-purpose of the product. In many cases, defect height is the essential parameter and fitness-for-purpose quality requirements define limits for defect height. Defect length usually is less important for elongated defects. However, defect type is also important; planar defects are considered more dangerous than volumetric of the same height.

1.8.3   Quality Classes

General: Table 1.1 shows the limits of the numbers, sizes and locations of the weld defects, for three quality classes (low, medium and high). For certain types of defects, different limits have been defined for local and continuous defects, respectively. In the evaluation, all defects not exceeding the limits for continuous defects may be disregarded. The remaining defects shall be local and should not exceed the limits for local defects.

1.8.4   Limitations in Total Defect Height

Unless more stringent requirements are defined in Table 1.1, the total height of the defects which reduce the cross section of the joint shall not exceed:

Low quality class   : 30 per cent of the nominal weld thickness, but not more than 10 mm.

Medium quality class : 25 per cent of the nominal weld thickness, but not more than 10 mm.

High quality class   : 20 per cent of the nominal weld thickness, but not more than 10 mm.

The values apply to any cross section of the welded joint, for each as well as several types of defects.

1.8.5   Quality Classes for Arc Welded Joints in Steel Materials

The three quality classes for welded joints relate to number and size of geometrical defects in the welded joints and mainly reflect the quality of workmanship. The quality classes are intended to be used for quality control of manual or mechanised arc welding of products in unalloyed or alloyed steels. It is applicable to butt welds as well as fillet welds.

1.8.6   Limitations

The quality classes do not directly relate to the fitness-for-purpose of the welds. The designer should, in each particular case, specify a quality class which results in a sufficient safety factor for all type of defects. For a fitness-for-purpose approach, the following prior conditions need to be fulfilled before acceptance on the basis of non-destructive evaluation (NDE).

(a) The requirement of design, access and surface preparation should be taken into account for account for carrying out various non-destructive testing (NDT) methods for the detection and evaluation of defects of structural concern. It must be understood that the root profile and weld cap significantly affect the capabilites of all NDT methods.

(b) There is a need to design and plan the fabrication and to set sufficiently high quality levels with future-in-service inspections in mind.

Table 1.2 shows a scheme for discussing the relations between quality control of weld defects, fitness-for-purpose and NDT. The following can be inferred from the table:

(a) The weldment must be designed to tolerate defects which are larger than the limits of NDT capability.

(b) Defects which are larger than the quality control acceptance level should in general be repaired.

(c) Fracture mechanics specialists should not put arbitrary large safety factors on the critical defect sizes as this can result in acceptance criteria which approach the limits of NDT capability.

1.8.7   Choice of NDT Techniques for Fitness-for-Purpose

For highly stressed components, failure can be in an elastic manner involving fast fracture. The capability to detect planar defects is the first criterion which decides the relative merits of various NDT techniques since fracture mechanics concept indicates the prime importance of detecting and measuring planar defects.

Table 1.1   Limits of Numbers, Sizes and Locations of Weld Deffects (Courtesy: R.S. Sharpe, IIW, FFP Document)

Defect ref. no.	Type of defect	Comments	Limits for:		
			Low quality	Medium quality	High quality
1	Cracks		Detectable cracks not permitted.	Detectable cracks not permitted.	Detectable cracks not permitted.
2.	Uniformly distributed porosity	Projection on a plane parallel to the surface of the joint over the length of weld.	Porosity not to exceed 4% of the projected area. Dimension of any single cavity not to exceed 5 mm.	Porosity not to exceed 2% of the projected area. Extent of any single cavity not to exceed 4 mm.	Porosity not to exceed 1% of the projected area. Extent of any single cavity not to exceed 3 mm.
3	Elongated cavities, wormholes, crater pipes	Only a few crater pipes permitted (no systematic defects).	Height and width of continuous defects not to exceed 2 mm. Height and width of local defects not to exceed 4 mm.	Detectable continuous defects not permitted. Height and width of local defects not to exceed 3 mm.	Detectable continuous defects not permitted. Height and width of local defects not to exceed 2 mm.
4	Lack of fusion		Detectable defects not permitted	Detectable defects not permitted	Detectable defects not permitted

(Contd.)

Defect ref. no.	Type of defect	Comments	Limits for:		
			Low quality	Medium quality	High quality
5	Incomplete penetration	Applies to butt welds in butt, corner, and 'T' joints. If the weld thickness has been prescribed to be smaller than the plate thickness, the defect height is the difference between thickness the nominal and actual weld thickness. If, for this type of welds, it is considered necessary to avoid actual weld thickness exceeding the prescribed values, supplementary requirements must be stipulated.	Detectable continuous defects not permitted. Local defects permitted if height does not exceed 2 mm, but not more than 20% of the weld .	Detectable continuous defects not permitted. Local defects permitted if height does not exceed 1.5 mm, but not more than 10% of the weld thickness.	Detectable defects not permitted.
6	Undercut		The height of continuous defects shall not exceed 0.6 mm. The height of local defects shall not exceed 1.0 mm.	The height of continuous defects shall not exceed 0.4 mm. The height of local defects shall not exceed 0.6 mm.	The height of continuous defects shall not exceed 0.2 mm. The height of local defects shall not exceed 0.4 mm.
7	Excessive penetration		The height of the penetration not to exceed 5 mm, but not more than 1 mm + 120% of the width of the penetration.	The height of the penetration not to exceed 4 mm, but not more than 1 mm + 60% of the width of the penetration.	The height of the penetration not to exceed 3 mm, but not more than 1 mm + 30% of the width of the penetration.

Table 1.2 Defect Size Ranges Covering Quality Control (QC), FFP and NDT Capability

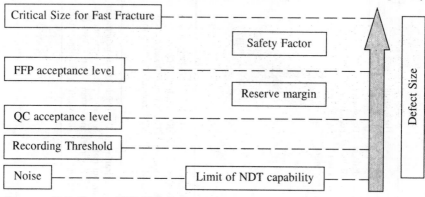

Courtesy: R.S. Sharpe (IIW, FFP, Document)

Thus, most appropriate NDT techniques used in conjunction with a FFP approach are: (a) which are sensitive to planar defects, whatever be their orientation and position, (b) those sensitive to surface breaking defects and (c) which are capable of discriminating planar from non-planar defects. Welding industry relies heavily on conventional NDT techniques to ensure quality of welds for meeting code requirements. Table 1.3 gives the applicability and capabilities of conventional NDT methods in relation to demonstrating fitness for purpose of welds.

1.9   TESTING OF WELDED JOINTS

The first test performed on any joint is Visual Inspection (VI). A good weld joint should have a neat appearance, even ripples, very little build up and no holes. Joints are further tested by destructive and non-destructive tests.

1.9.1   Destructive Tests

In a destructive test method, the weld is bent, twisted or pulled apart to check for flaws/mechanical properties. The five types of basic joints can be tested as follows:

1. Corner joint to be hammered until it is flat.
2. Butt-joint is bent until it takes a 'U' shape.
3. Tee joint should have the top or vertical piece hammered until it is flat.
4. Lap joint to be hammered until it resembles a tee joint.
5. The edge joint should be opened and bent until it forms a 'U' joint, similar to butt joint.

By its very nature, destructive testing (DT) makes a part unusable. Destructive tests have been used for routine inspection with the assumption that results derived from such tests are typical of the complete lot from which the test samples were selected. Destructive tests like longitudinal and transverse tensile tests, neck-break tests, root face and side bend tests, nil ductility transition temperature tests, drop weight tests, creep and fatigue tests, macro etch, corrosion tests and chemical analysis on welds are well established. The specimens used for the above tests are usually rather small and may or may not be representative of the actual production weld in question. Samples for examination are generally specially prepared test pads which are made by the same welding methods as the production weld or they may be samples machined/prepared from an actual production weld. Direct information may be obtained from such samples concerning the actual properties of the weld such as strength, ductility, and other mechanical properties. The disadvantages of destructive tests are that they are slow and costly and give information about the weld samples only.

The reliability of the destructive testing data can be greatly improved by employing statistical sampling techniques together with statistical analysis of the complete test data. Destructive tests by themselves are not sufficient to properly evaluate present day welds in critical components. Hence there is necessity for nondestructive testing.

1.9.2 Non-Destructive Tests (NDT)

NDT plays an important role in reducing the chances of weld failure, both through its application during fabrication and through its use in service. As the reliance on NDT increases, so does the need for a systematic approach to the planning of inspection techniques and their application in order to achieve the necessary reliability.

Role of NDT in prevention of failure: The importance of the role of NDT in preventing weld failure varies depending on the particular application.

Probability of weld failure = (Probability of flaw occuring) × (Probability of NDT missing the flaw) × (Probability of flaw growing)

The reliance placed on correct diagnosis by NDT is clearly greater if flaws are likely and if flaws could grow quickly. In the case of in-service inspection, reliance on NDT may occur twice in the above equation as NDT could have determined the probability of the flaw being present at the start of service. This shows how reliance on NDT varies depending on other factors.

NDT is an integral and the most important constituent of the Quality Assurance (QA) programme of any industry. The objectives of the QA programmes are safety, productivity, reliability and economy. Non-destructive evaluation places due emphasis on characterisation of materials including quantitative determination of the size, shape and location of a defect or abnormality assessment thus enabling evaluation of structural integrity of a component particularly in the context of fitness for purpose. NDT along with material properties and operating conditions is vital for successful prediction of damage and residual life.

Quality characteristics of welds having defects such as cracks, inclusions, porosity, lack of penetration, lack of fusion, lack of bond and undercut and alloy identification can be evaluated by NDT methods. Present range and capabilities of NDT techniques promise evaluation of weld joints for the most significant service conditions. However, proper choice of materials, welding processes etc. is a necessity to ensure building the quality in the product. Choice of a technique or complementary techniques should be carefully made to ensure structural

Table 1.3 Summary of Applicability and Capability of Various NDT Techniques used for Assessment of Defects in Materials and Components

Method	Materials Applicable	Applicable component geometrices		Detection capability			Dynamic detection @	Defect sizing		Defect characterisation	Numerical modelling
		Linear	Non-linear	Surf.	Sub-surf.	Internal		Length	Orientation (3D)		
VI	A	Y	Y	Y	N	N	N	Y	N	Y	N
LPI	A	Y	Y	Y	N	N	N	Y	N	Y	N
MPI	M	Y	*	Y	Y	N	N	Y	N	Y	*
ACPD	E	Y	Y	Y	N	N	N	Y	N	*	Y
DCPD	E	Y	Y	Y	Y	N	N	Y	*	*	Y
UT	A	Y	Y	Y	Y	Y	N	Y	Y	Y	Y
ECT	E	Y	Y	Y	Y	Y1	N	Y	Y1	Y	Y
RT	A	Y	Y	Y	Y	Y	N	Y	Y	Y	Y
AET	A	Y	Y	Y	Y	Y	Y	*	N	*2	N
IRT	A	Y	Y	Y	Y	Y	Y	Y	Y	*	*
MLFT	M	Y	Y	Y	Y	Y	N	Y	N	N	Y

Y – Possible
A – All Materials
1 – Less Than 6 mm
VI – Visual Inspection
UT – Ultrasonic Testing
RT – Radiography
N – Not Possible
E – Only Electrically Conductive Materials
2 – Only Harmful (Growing Defects)

LPI – Liquid Penetrant Inspection
IRT – Infrared Thermography
ECT – Eddy Current Testing
* – Feasibility Exist
M – Only Magnetic Materials
@ – Detected as and When Defect Initiates and Grows
MPI – Magnetic Particle Inspection
MLFT – Magnetic Flux Leakage Technique
PD – Potential Drop Technique

integrity during designed life of welded structures on a cost effective basis. Various NDT methods can be employed to evaluate a welded component depending upon the material, thickness, sensitivity requirement, accessability for inspection etc. Nondestructive testing over the years, in combination with operational experience, has led to well established routine NDT practice all over the world.

Further reading

5. Baldev Raj, Subramanian, C.V., Bhattacharya, D.K. An Overview of Status in Testing Measurement and Control of Welds-Report of Commission V. of Indian Institute of Welding, INC 1987.

12. Davies, C. The Science and Practice of Welding, Vol. 12, 8th edition, Cambridge University Press, 1984.

19. Farlay, J.M., Thomson, J.L. and Dikstra. B.J. Non-destructive Testing to Avoid Weld Failure, International Conference on Weld Failures, London, Edited by Harrison. J.D. The Welding Institute. 1988.

46. Kenneth Easterling, Introduction to the Physical Metallurgy of Welding, 2nd edition, Butterworth Henemann, 1992.

69. Paul, EMix, Introduction to Non-destructive Testing—A Training Guide, Wiley Interscience, John Wiley & Sons, New York, 1987.

84. Takeshi Kanazava and Albert Kobayashi, S. Significance of Defects in Welded Structure, Proceedings of the Japan-US Seminar, University of Tokyo Press, 1974.

95. Weld Imperfections, Proceedings of a Symposium at Lockheed Palo Alte Research Laboratory, California, Sept. 1966.

96. Welding Handbook, Vol. 1, Chapter 11, 12 and 15, American Welding Society, 550, N.W. Lejeune road, Miami, U.S.A., 1976.

97. American Society of Metals Hand Book, Vol. 6 and Vol. 11, ASM International. The Materials Information Society, Materials Park, Ohio, U.S.A., 1993.

104. The Singificance of Defects in Welds, Proceedings of the 2nd conferrence, The Welding Institute, London, May, 1968.

Chapter 2

Visual Inspection

Visual inspection (VI) is probably the most widely used among the non-destructive tests. It is simple, easy to apply, quickly carried out, and usually low in cost. Even though a component is to be inspected using other NDT methods, a good visual inspection should be carried out first. A simple visual test can reveal gross surface defects thus leading to an immediate rejection of the component and consequently saving much time and money, which would otherwise be spent on more complicated means of testing. It is often necessary to examine the weld joint for the presence of finer defects. For this purpose, visual methods have been developed to a very high degree of precision. With the advent of CCD cameras, microprocessors and computers, visual examination can be carried out very reliably and with minimum cost. Image processing, pattern recognition and automatic accept/reject choice are used when large number of components are to be assessed.

Visual inspection has wide applications for inspection of wrought, cast and weld materials. However, for welds, this is all the more important as at various stages of welding, it gives useful information. Many characteristics of a weld can be evaluated by visually examining a completed weld, but much can be learnt by observing the weld as it is being made. For many non-critical welds, integrity is verified principally by visual inspection. Even when other non-destructive methods are used, visual inspection still constitutes an important part of quality control. Visual inspection should be done before, during and after welding.

During the process of welding, various types of faults may creep in due to lack of skill and knowledge of the welder. In order to ensure that factors such as personnel fatigue may not affect the work of the skilled welder, it is necessary to have means of inspection and testing of welds so as to indicate the quality, strength and properties of the joint being made.

Visual inspection, made while the weld is in progress and afterwards, will give a good quality weld. Examination of a weld on its completion will indicate the following:

1. Has correct fusion been obtained between weld metal and parent metal?
2. Is there an indentation denoting undercutting along the line where the weld joins the parent metal?
3. Has penetration been obtained right through the joint, indicated by the weld metal appearing through the bottom of the single "V" or "U" joint?

4. Has the joint been built up on its upper side (reinforced) or does the weld have a concave side on its face, denoting lack of metal and thus weakness?
5. Are the dimensions of the weld correct, tested by gauges?
6. Conformity of welds to size, fit-up and control requirements.
7. Acceptability of weld appearance with regard to surface roughness, weld spatter, undercuts and overlaps.
8. Imperfections and cracks on the observed surfaces.
9. Lack of root penetration or excess penetration.
10. Pits, blow holes, end plate lamination.
11. Craters, uneven ripples etc.

A very useful multipurpose pocket size welding gauge has been designed by International Institute of Welding. It enables measurement of thickness up to 20 mm, preparation angle 0–60 degrees, excess metal capping size, depth of undercut, fillet weld throat size and leg length and high-low misalignment.

Although visual inspection is a very valuable method, it is unreliable for detecting subsurface flaws. Therefore, judgment of weld quality must be based on information from bulk material in addition to that from surface indications. Capabilities of VI can be enhanced considerably by using simple gadgets and instruments for viewing, dimensional measurements etc.

Despite many developments in visual aids, still there is no decision-making electronic computer that can emulate the human brain. The experienced eye is invaluable for an intelligent first inspection. A working knowledge of the engineering process is of a great help in focusing the inspection on critical or probable fault zones.

Many visual aids are available to enhance the inspection ranging from a pocket magnifier to microscope and monochromatic illumination to CCD-Camera colour video presentation. Intrascopes (rigid or flexible) are available to permit entry and inspection of internal surfaces through access openings (of less than 1 mm) and the human inspector is equipped to supply a wealth of primary NDT results. The convenience of visual aids is ergonomically warranted to reduce human fatigue and improve reliability.

2.1   BASIC PROCEDURE
The basic procedure used in visual NDT involves illumination of the test specimen with light, usually in the visible region. The specimen is then examined with eye or by light sensitive devices such as photocells. Though the equipment required for visual inspection is extremely simple, the adequate illumination is essential. The surface of the specimen should be properly cleaned before inspection.

2.2   THE EYE
The most valuable NDT tool is the human eye because of its excellent visual perception. The sensitivity of the human eye varies with light with different wavelengths. Under ordinary conditions, the eye is most sensitive to yellow-green light, with a wavelength of 5560 Å. The human eye will give satisfactory vision over a wide range of conditions and hence can not be a good judge for distinguishing the differences in brightness or intensity, except under the most

restricted conditions. For visual inspection, adequate lighting i.e. about 800-1000 lux is important. The time period during which a person is permitted to inspect should not be more than 2 hours on continuous basis to avoid errors due to decrease in visual reliability and discrimination.

2.2.1   Visual Inspection without Aids

Visual inspection of a component by an experienced inspector can reveal following informations: (a) general condition of the component, (b) presence or absence of oxide film or corrosive product on the surface, (c) presence or absence of cracks, orientation of cracks and position of cracks relative to the various zones in the case of welds, (d) surface porosity, unfilled craters, contour of the weld beads, and the probable orientation of the interface between the fused weld bead and the adjoining parent metal, (e) potential sources of mechanical weakness such as sharp notches, misalignment etc. and (f) the results of visual examination may be of great assistance in other tests.

2.3   OPTICAL AIDS USED FOR VISUAL INSPECTION

The use of optical instruments in visual inspection is beneficial and is recommended to: (a) magnify defects that cannot be detected by the unaided eye and (b) permit visual checks of areas not accessible to the unaided eye. In performing visual/optical checks, it is of utmost importance to know the type of defects that may develop and to recognize the areas where such failures may occur. Magnifying devices and lighting aids should be used wherever appropriate. The general area should be checked for cleanliness, presence of foreign objects, corrosion and damage. In many cases, area to be inspected should be cleaned before the visual examination.

2.3.1   Microscope

An optical microscope is a combination of lenses used to magnify the image of a small object. The object is placed close to the lens to obtain as high a magnification as possible. The distance from the lens to the object is adjusted until the object is at the depth of field of the lens and is in focus.

The simplest form of a microscope is a single converging lens, often referred as simple magnifier. Magnification (M) of a single lens is determined by the equation $M = 25/f$. In this equation, f is the focal length of the lens and 25 is a constant that represents the average minimum distance at which objects can be distinctly seen by the unaided eye. Using the equation $M = 25/f$, a lens with a focal length of 12.5 cm (5″) has a magnification of two or is said to be a two-power lens (2×). The focal length of a simple magnifier and its working distance are approximately the same. The field of view is the area seen through the magnifier. The diameter of the field of view of a simple maginfier is less than its focal length. Selection of a magnifier with the proper field of view is important. For example, if a large object is to be examined, the time involved in using a 20-power magnifier (with a field of view slightly greater than 9.5 mm) would be prohibitive. The proper procedure is to first use a low-power magnifier, marking questionable areas, and then examine the suspected areas in detail with a higher-powered magnifier.

The term depth of field is used to indicate the distance a magnifier can be moved towards or away from a subject with the subject remaining in good focus (sharply defined). At other distances, the subject is out of focus and not sharply defined. Depth of field varies with the power of the lens and is comparatively greater in lower-power magnifiers, decreasing as the power of the lens increases.

Minute defects and details of fine structure on a surface can be detected more easily with the aid of a microscope. The practical upper limit of the magnifying power of a simple microscope is in the region of 10×. Optical microscopes are used to evaluate the cracks with respect to their shape and orientation. In the first case, a low power microscope having a magnification of 2 to 20× is used, while in second, a magnification of 100 to 500× is used. In later case a magnification of 1500 to 2000× will be needed.

The development of projection microscopes has led to the incorporation of the common microscope into the inspection lines of many industries. The optical projector reduces eye strain and enables the operator to visually inspect large number of small parts at reasonable production rates. A 35 mm camera can be attached virtually to any projection microscope and many of them can project their images on walls in dark rooms. The magnification of both micro- and macro-projection microscope range from 3× to 3000×, depending on make and model (Fig. 2.1).

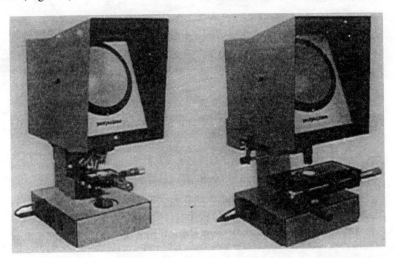

Fig. 2.1   Micro-macro style projection microscopes (Courtesy: H&R Optical Systems, Inc.)

2.3.2 Borescope

A borescope is an instrument designed for an observer to inspect the inside of a narrow tube, bore, or chamber. Borescope consists of precision built-in illumination system having a complex arrangement of prisms and plain lenses through which light is passed to the observer with maximum efficiency. The light source located in front or ahead of the object lens provides illumination for the part being examined. As the length of the borescope is increased, the image becomes less bright because of loss of light. Borescopes are available in numerous models from 2.5 to 19 mm in diameter and a few metres in length. Generally, the diameter of the borescope depends upon the diameter of the hole or bore to be inspected.

The length of the borescope is governed by the distance between the available access and the distance to the inspection area. Optical systems are generally designed to provide direct, right-angle, retrospective, and oblique vision. The choice of the inspection angle is determined by flaw type and location. In most borescopes, the observed visual area is approximately 25 mm in diameter at a distance of 25 mm from the object. For a given magnification system, the size of the visual field usually varies with the diameter. Straight in line and double swivel eye-piece borescopes (Fig. 2.2) have high resolution with 2× zoom capacity with a 35° field of view and a 80° (50 forward and 30 retro) capability.

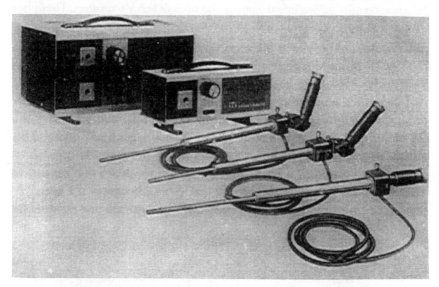

**Fig. 2.2   Straight in-line and double swivel eyepiece boroscopes
(Courtesy: ITI/Instrument Technology, Inc.)**

2.3.3   Endoscope

The endoscope is much like a borescope with a superior optical system and a high-intensity light source. Various viewing angles, as discussed in Sec. 2.3.2, can be used. A unique feature of endoscope is that objects are constantly in foucs from about 4 mm to infinity. Actually, when the tip is about 4 mm from the surface being inspected, a magnification factor of about 10× is achieved. The 'no-focusing' feature of the endoscope makes it easier to use whereas a borescope needs to be focused at the inspection area. Endoscopes are available in diameters down to 1.7 mm and in lengths from 100 to 1500 mm.

2.3.4   Flexible Fibre-Optic Borescope (Flexiscope)

Flexible fiber-optic borescopes can be used around corners and through passages with several directional changes. Woven stainless steel sheathing protects the image relaying fibre optic bundle during repeated flexing and maneuvering. These devices are designed to provide sharp and clear images of parts and interior surfaces normally impossible to inspect. Remote end-tip deflection makes it possible to thread the fibroscope through complex and series of bends. The end tip is deflected by using a manual rotating control system. Most of the devices have a wide-angle objective lens providing a 100° field of view and tip deflection of ± 90°. They have a fibre-optic image bundle and equipped with a focus control for sharp focus over a wide range of view. The working length is normally from 60 to 365 cm, with diameters from 3 to 12.5 mm.

High resolution CCD camera based fibroscopes are used to check inner surface of tubes. Cameras with direct or side view with minimum 50° field view with 4-way 120° articulation by joy stick or hand control are available. A suitable xenon/halogen lamp/metal arc light source and guide system illuminates the internals of the tube. Automatic light controls provide the adjustment in the brightness for optimum illumination. The images, displayed on a high resolution colour monitor and freezed for detailed observation are stored in an in-built hard disk. Images can be converted into file formats and imparted on to an IBM compatible PC. The data can be integrated into reports and documents through windows-based software. The image data can be processed to enhance the contrast and resolution.

2.3.5   Telescope
Telescope is used to obtain magnified images of objects at a distance from the eye and is useful for providing visual examination of the surface which is otherwise inaccessible. It consists of two lenses (or lens systems) called the objective and eye piece. The telescope can be used in conjunction with a periscope for viewing a concealed surface. Closed Circuit Television (CCTV) is also used for the purpose.

2.3.6   Diffracto-Sight (D-Sight)
D-sight is a method of visualising surface distortions, depressions or protrusions as small as 10 microns. It is a real time technique particularly applicable to rapid inspection of large structures. The optical setup for D-sight consists of a light source, a retro reflective screen, and the object being inspected (Fig. 2.3). Both flat and moderately curved surfaces can be inspected using this method, but the surface being inspected must be reflective. The D-sight technique is based on geometrical optical principles. If a flat surface with an indentation is inspected, the light striking the indentation is deflected. It strikes the retro reflective screen at a point removed from the light rays reflected from the area surrounding the indentation. The retro reflective screen attempts to return all these rays to the points on the inspected surface from which they were reflected. The screen consisting of numerous glass beads, returns a cone of light to the surface instead. This imperfection of the retro reflective screen creates the D-sight effect. By backlighting the defect, the technique increases the light intensity on one side of the indentation and reduces it on the opposite side. D-sight effectively locates invisible impact damage and cold worked holes, cracks and corrosion in metallic

welded components and has good correlation with ultrasonic C-scan images of the same structures.

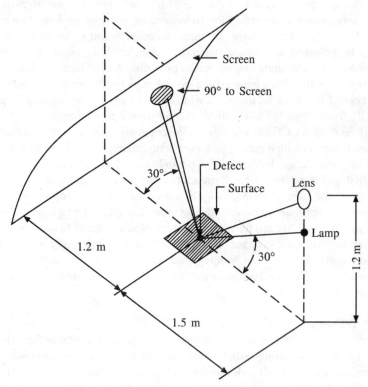

Fig. 2.3   Diffracto-sight set up

2.3.7   Laser Holography and Interferometry

Holography (*holus* in Greek means whole) records and reconstructs a complete optical wavefront. Holography is a lens-less recording technique using two-dimensional record of a subject to reconstruct subsequently a three-dimensional image.

The concept of coherence is the key to holography. A spatially coherent light beam allows hologram, to be taken over a large area, whilst temporal coherence provides depth of field since the two beams of light can be made 'to interfere even when large path differences have been introduced.

A parallel beam of light (Fig. 2.4) from a laser is split into two by reflection and refraction at a beam splitter. Each of these two beams is then allowed to diverse by separate spatial filters. One beam illuminates the subject and may split further with mirrors to illuminate the required areas. The second or the reference beam illuminates the photographic plate directly and interferes with the light reflected by the subject.

The hologram formed in the photographic emulsion contains the fringe configuration, information corresponding to both the amplitude and phase of the light wave reflected by the subject. After exposure which may last from a few

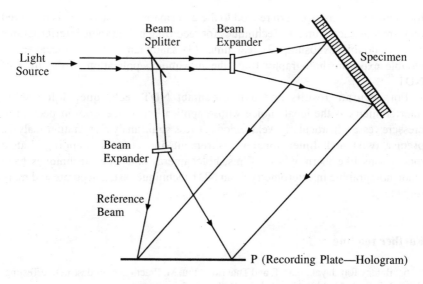

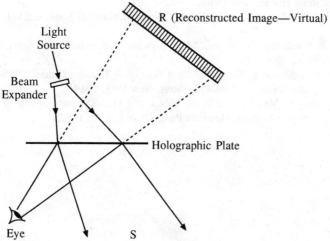

Fig. 2.4   Laser holography set up

milliseconds to a few seconds according to the intensity of the illumination used, the hologram is developed. Correct processing of the holographic plates is an art which has evolved in parallel with the holographic recording techniques. Results depend critically on the use of optimum procedures.

Reconstruction is effected by illuminating the hologram with the reference beam only, where upon the diffraction grating recorded in the emulsion causes an image of the original object to be reconstructed. The image obtained by illuminating the hologram is virtual. Holography, also records a set of wavefronts at different times and reconstructs them simultaneously. Once an object is recorded, a stimulus (load, temperature etc.) is applied to the object and then recorded again. Subsequently when these two wavefronts are reconstructed together, they interfere and a fringe pattern related to the deformation of the object is observed on its reconstructed image. Techniques for recording holographic interferograms are: (1) double exposure, (2) real time, (3) sandwich and (4) time average. Double exposure holography finds the maximum application in the field of NDT.

For accurate results and a non-contact NDT technique, holographic interferometry is the ideal choice whose applications range from inspection of pressure vessels (particularly weld regions), stress-strain analysis, vibration analysis, precise twist and dimensional measurement and contour mapping. Latest innovations like thermoplastic films, holocameras and video techniques have made holographic interferometry as an NDT technique faster, accurate and more reliable.

Further reading

6. Baldev Raj, Jayakumar, T. and Thavasimuthu, M. Practical Non-destructive Testing, Narosa Publishing House, New Delhi, 1997.
8. Bernd Rohloft, NDT methods. The South African Mechanical Engineer, Vol. 4, 1994.
31. Halmshaw, R. Nondestructive Testing, Metallurgy and Materials Science Services, Edward Arnold, London, 1992.
69. Paul, EMix. Introduction to Non-destructive Testing- A Training Guide, A Wiley Inter Science Publication, John Wiley & Sons, New York, 1989.
97. American Society of Metals Hand Book, Vols. 6 and 11, ASM International. The Materials Information Society, Materials Park, Ohio, U.S.A., 1992.

Chapter 3

Liquid Penetrant Testing

Liquid penetrant testing (LPT) is another NDT method to detect surface defects and also subsurface defects open to surface in welded materials. This method can be used in root pass and subsequent passes to detect surface defects and repair the defects in the weld. In this method, a liquid penetrant is applied to the surface of a product for a certain predetermined time during which the penetrant seeps through any surface opening defect by capillary action. Subsequently, the excess penetrant is removed from the surface. The surface is then dried and a developer is applied to it. The penetrant which remains in the discontinuity is absorbed by the developer to indicate the presence as well as the location, size and nature of the discontinuity. Figures 3.1 and 3.2 give the testing procedure and the sequence employed. Care should be taken so that chemical constituents of the liquid penetrant and developer should not affect the material.

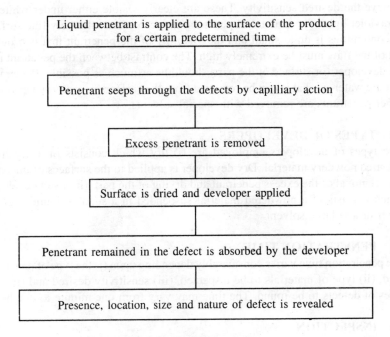

Fig. 3.1   Testing procedure

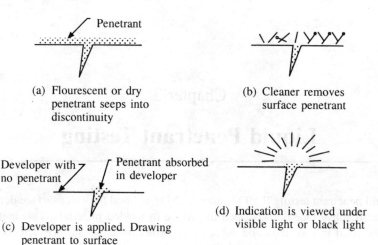

(a) Flourescent or dry penetrant seeps into discontinuity

(b) Cleaner removes surface penetrant

(c) Developer is applied. Drawing penetrant to surface

(d) Indication is viewed under visible light or black light

Fig. 3.2   Sequence of liquid penetrant testing

This method is best adopted to inspect all types of surface cracks, porosity, laminations and lack of bond at exposed edges or joined materials and leaks in welded tubes and tanks. It has been used with excellent success on ferrous and non-ferrous materials, ceramics, powder metallurgy products, weldments, glass as well as on some plastics and synthetic materials.

3.1   TYPES OF PENETRANTS

Liquids having good penetrating ability and potent coloured dyes are required to achieve the desired sensitivity. These are clearly visible either under white or ultraviolet light. The amount of penetrant that can enter extremely fine surface discontinuities is quite small and the visibility of the penetrant that is brought out of the flaw must be extremely high. The contrast between the penetrant and the developer (or surface of the part) should be as much as possible. Penetrants that are water-washable can be removed from the surface by ordinary tap water. Other penetrants are removed with special solvents.

3.2   TYPES OF DEVELOPERS

Two types of developers employed are (i) dry which consists of a dry light coloured powdery material. Dry developer is applied to the surfaces of the parts after removal of the excess penetrant and drying of the part. (ii) a wet developer which consists of a powdered material suspended in a suitable liquid such as water or a volatile solvent.

3.3   PENETRATION TIME

The penetration time varies considerably depending upon (i) the type of penetrant used, (ii) type of materials to be inspected, (iii) sensitivity desired and (iv) the types of defects to be found. The time may vary from one minute to one hour.

3.4   INSPECTION

Inspection is carried out by viewing the part for colour contrast between the penetrant drawn out from a defect and the background surface. In case of penetrants containing a visible dye, viewing is done under white light while for fluorescent dyes, viewing is done under ultraviolet or black light. It is important to look for small amounts of penetrant that indicates discontinuities.

3.5 POST-EMULSIFIABLE FLUORESCENT PENETRANT SYSTEM
It is the most sensitive of all penetrant systems. This procedure can locate wide and shallow flaws as well as tight cracks and requires only a short penetration time making it ideal for high production work. On the other hand, emulsification requires an extra operation which increases the cost and requires water supply and facilities for inspection under black light.

3.5.1 Solvent Removable Fluorescent Penetrant System
This employs a procedure similar to that used for the post-emulsifiable fluorescent system, except that excess penetrant is removed with a solvent. This system is especially recommended for spot inspection or where water cannot be conveniently used. It is more sensitive than the water-washable system but the extreme caution needed and the additional time required for application of the solvent often precludes its use.

3.5.2 Water Washable Fluorescent Penetrant System
It is the fastest of the fluorescent procedures. It is also reliable and reasonably economical. It can be used for both small and large work pieces and is good on rough surfaces. However, it can not reliably reveal open shallow flaws and in some instances, will not locate the very tight cracks because it is less sensitive than the two fluorescent systems described above. Inspection should be carried out where there is adequate water supply and a black light can be used.

Liquid-penetrant inspection is one of the procedures in which the penetrant testing materials can be brought to work site whenever the work piece cannot be brought to the inspection area. Portable penetrant inspection by the solvent removable system is used extensively to inspect welded joints where only limited areas are being examined and total immersion of the weldments would be impractical.

3.5.3 Low and High Temperature Penetrants
One of the recent developments in LPT is the availability of penetrants for operation at temperatures ranging from 261K (– 12°C) to 448K (175°C). High temperature penetrants are very useful for multipass welds and save time by eliminating part of waiting period required for welds to cool before inspection. Use of low temperature penetrant material enables penetrant application in places where ambient temperature goes to sub-zero level. However, ASME code (Part V Article 6) specifies qualification of the penetrant test procedure for use at non-standard temperatures (standard temperature range: 288-323K/15-50°C). While using penetrants for high temperature applications, care is taken to provide adequate ventilation, as irritating vapours are produced when volatile materials like cleaners, removers, or developers are applied to high temperature surfaces.

3.5.4 High Sensitivity Fluorescent Penetrant Examination

In certain field applications requiring weld inspection in a remote location, where spraying of penetrant or developer will affect the adjacent parts, high sensitivity fluorescent penetrant that can work without a separate developer is quite suitable. Such penetrants have been developed.

One such application is the fuel module assembly in aerospace industries in which weld seams between insulated bushings for instrumentation leads need critical inspection. The procedure for LPT is as follows:

The penetrant is applied to the localised area of the welds using cotton swabs. After a penetrant dwell time of 10 to 20 minutes, the excess penetrant is removed using dry cotton swabs, followed by cotton swabs dampened with solvent remover. The welds are then examined under black light. A minimum intensity of 30w/ sq.m (3 milli watts/sq. cm) is used. If developer is used, the minimum specified black light intensity would be 10 w/sq.m. The highest intensity of 30 w/sq.m helps to compensate for not using developer. The special procedure using high intensity fluorescent penetrant without developer solves the cleaning problem and provides increased flaw detection capability over the colour contrast solvent removable method used with non-aqueous wet developer.

3.6 ADVANCED LPT TECHNIQUES

3.6.1 Ultrasonic Pumping to Enhance Penetrant Performance

In an attempt to overcome the limitations of static processing, ultrasound at an optimized frequency can be used as a means of pumping the fluorescent penetrant into places it would not otherwise enter. Even it enters, but perhaps not in sufficient quantity to leak back at a useful rate through capillary action. The ultrasonic energy transmitted through a penetrant medium acts to

(1) shake loosely trapped adherents and flush out entrapped contaminants from the flaw interfaces by ultrasonic cleaning.

(2) deposit the flaw indicating fluid rapidly and minimizes the required penetrant dwell time.

Choice of ultrasonic frequency will depend on the size of the parts and their fragility. Lower frequencies produce greater penetrating power. Below 20 kHz, the "noise" is bordering on the audible and fragile part, as well as ears may get damaged at that frequency. The unique feature of ultrasonic cavitation is that it can be generated anywhere that a sound wave of sufficient intensity can penetrate, so that cleaning action might occur deep within the interstices of a part or assembly and may be effective in some parts with complicated geometric configuration.

The combination of supersensitive penetrants capable of fluorescence at very thin film levels with ultrasonic fluid excitation during precleaning and during penetrant application provides a method of reliably demonstrating the presence of fatigue cracks in precision weldments. On parts removed from service for routine examination, the presence of acids, chromates and combustion by-products contained within tight discontinuities hampers the mechanics of static penetrant process. No amount of precleaning by conventional methods adequately cleans the flaw interfaces. The contaminants remaining were observed to actually repel the penetrant material and in some cases negate the fluorescence.

3.6.2 Ultrasonically Enhanced Penetrant Inspection of Small Weldments

With ultrasonic penetrant inspection equipment embodying all steps of penetrant process, including the spray rinse and various associated timing devices, the time from beginning of the procedure to the dry and "ready to inspect" stage is maximum 5 minutes. The procedure lends itself well to automation. Thus, it permits inspecting a continuous flow of moderately sized precision weldments. Tests indicate that more penetrant gets deposited at a greater speed with ultrasonic excitation.

3.6.3 Mechanised Remote Liquid Penetrant Testing of Piping of Reactors

Special devices are used for liquid penetrant testing of pipings in nuclear reactor systems with radiation background, for detection of surface discontinuities.

Two basic problems involved in liquid penetrant testing of nuclear power systems are:

(a) lack of adequate access for operators and observers
(b) presence of high radiation fields in areas to be inspected.

Devices are available specifically for remote liquid penetrant testing of piping welds from the outside surface. This device cleans the surface, applies penetrant, removes excess penetrant, applies developer and presents images of the penetrant indications by means of fibre optics and a remote colour television monitor. Visual indications and positional data are recorded on a real time basis by means of a video recorder. The data on test indications may be recorded directly on the tape by using a key board and hard copies of the test indications can be obtained with the help of a printer.

Further reading

6. Baldev Raj, Jayakumar. T. and Thavasimuthu, M. Practical Non-destructive Testing, Narosa Publishing House, New Delhi, 1997.
8. Bernd Rohloft, NDT methods, The South African Mechanical Engineer, Vol. 4, 1994.
31. Halmshaw, R. Nondestructive Testing, Metallurgy and Materials Science Services, Edward Arnold, London, 1992.
69. Paul EMix. Introduction to Non-destructive Testing—A Training Guide, A Wiley Inter Science Publication, John Wiley & Sons, New York, 1987.
97. American Society of metals Hand Book, Vol. 6 and Vol. 11, ASM International, The Materials Information Society, Materials Park, Ohio, U.S.A., 1993.

Chapter 4

Magnetic Particle Testing

For detection of surface and sub-surface defects in welded components, liquid penetrant testing and magnetic particle testing (MPT) are being widely used. In case of ferromagnetic materials, magnetic particle technique is preferred as this will also detect sub-surface flaws which are not open to surface. Because of this advantage over liquid penetrant testing, it has become customary to specify magnetic particle testing for all ferromagnetic materials.

This method is based on the principle that 'when a ferromagnetic material under test is magnetised, discontinuities which lie in a direction generally transverse to the magnetic field will cause a leakage field around the discontinuity'. When finely divided ferromagnetic powder is sprinkled over the surface, some of these particles are gathered and held by the leakage field. This magnetically held collection of particles from an outline of the discontinuity indicates its location, shape and extent (Fig. 4.1). To get the highest sensitivity, fluorescent magnetic particles suspended in oil using full wave DC continuous technique is employed.

The test method consists of magnetisation of the component, applying magnetic powder, examination of powder patterns and demagnetisation of the component. The magnetic particle testing is a sensitive method of locating small and shallow surface cracks in ferromagnetic materials. Indications may be produced at cracks that are large enough. Wide cracks will not produce a particle pattern if the surface opening is too wide for the particles to bridge. If a discontinuity is fine and sharp and close to the surface, such as a long stringer of non metallic inclusion, a sharp indication will be produced. If the discontinuity lies deeper, the indication is less distinct. Magnetic particle indications are produced directly on the surface of the part, and constitute magnetic pictures of actual discontinuities. There is little or no limitation on the size or shape of the part being inspected. Ordinarily no elaborate pre-cleaning is necessary and cracks filled with foreign materials can be detected.

4.1 MAGNETISATION METHODS

In magnetic particle testing, the magnetic particles may be applied to the part while the magnetising current is flowing or after the current has ceased to flow, depending largely on the retentivity of the part. The former technique is known as the continuous method and latter as the residual method. The residual method can be used only on materials having sufficient retentivity. Usually the harder the material, the higher the retentivity. The continuous method is the only method

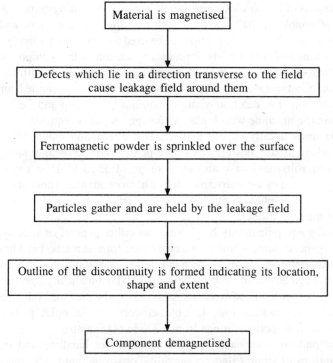

Fig. 4.1 Sequence of testing

used on low-carbon steels or iron having little or no retentivity and is frequently used with alternating current as it produces excellent mobility of the particles.

4.2 MAGNETISING CURRENT

Both direct current and alternating current are suitable for magnetising parts. The strength, direction and distribution of the magnetic fields are greatly affected by the type of current that is used for magnetisation. In magnetic particle inspection, fields produced by direct-current generally penetrate the cross section of the part, whereas the fields produced by alternating current are confined to the metal at or near the surface of the part which is commonly known as the skin effect. Therefore alternating current should not be used in detecting sub-surface discontinuities.

The most satisfactory source of direct current is the rectification of alternating current. Both single phase and three phase alternating currents are generated commercially. Alternating current which must be single phase when used directly for magnetising purposes is taken from commercial power lines and usually has a frequency of 50 or 60 Hz. When used for magnetising, line voltage is stepped down by transformers to the low voltages. Magnetising currents of several thousand amperes are often used at these required low voltages.

Portable equipments are available with light weight power source units that can be readily taken to the inspection site. Generally these portable units are designed to use 115, 230 or 440 volts alternating current and supply magnetising current outputs of 750 to 1500 amps in half wave or alternating current. Machines capable of supplying half-wave current and alternating current and having continuously variable current control can be used for magnetic particle inspection for a wide range of applications. Primary application of this equipment is hand held prod inspection utilising the half-wave output in conjunction with dry powder. The major disadvantage of the portable equipment is the limited amount of current available. For detction of discontinuities lying deep and for a coverage of large area, a machine with higher amperage output is required.

Mobile units usually supply half-wave or alternating magnetising current outputs and are usually powered by single-phase 50 or 60 Hz alternating current (230 or 440 volts) and have an output range of 1500 to 4500 amps, current control is provided by a power-tap switch or in more advanced units it is provided either by solid state phase control of the transformer or by use of a saturable core to control the transformer.

Stationary equipment may be obtained as either general or special purpose units. The general purpose unit is primarily used for wet method and has a built-in tank containing bath pump, which continuously agitates the bath and forces the fluid through hoses onto the part being tested. Pneumatically operated contact heads, together with a rigid type coil, provide capabilities for both circular and longitudinal magnetisation (Figs. 4.2a, b). Self-contained AC or DC power supplies are available in amperage ratings from 1000 to 6000 amps.

Special purpose stationary units are designed for handling and inspecting large quantities of similar items. Generally conveyers, automatic markers and alarm systems are included in such units to expedite handling and disposition of parts being inspected.

4.3   INSPECTION OF WELDMENTS

Many weld defects are open to the surface and are readily detectable by magnetic particle inspection using prods and yokes. For detection of subsurface discontinuities, such as slag inclusions, voids and inadequate joint penetration at the root of the weld, prod magnetisation is the best, using either alternating current, direct current or half-wave current.

Positioning of a yoke with respect to the direction of the discontinuity sought is different from the corresponding positioning of prods. Because the field traverses a path between the poles of the yoke, the poles must be placed on opposite sides of the weld bead to locate transverse cracks. Prods are spaced adjacent to the weld for parallel cracks and on opposite sides for transverse cracks.

For applications in which the holding of prod contacts by hand is difficult or tiring, prods incorporating magnetic clamps or laches that hold the prods magnetically to the part to be tested are available. The prods carrying the magnetising current are held firmly to the part by an electromagnet. Both prods may be attached by the magnets, or one of the prods may be held magnetically and the other by hand.

There is one type of weld in which the penetrating power of half-wave current results in non-relevant indications: a Tee joint welded from one or both sides for which complete joint penetration is not specified and in which an open root is permissible and almost always present. When half-wave current is used with prods, this open root probably will be indicated on the weld surface. This non-relevant indication can be eliminated by using alternating current instead of half-wave current.

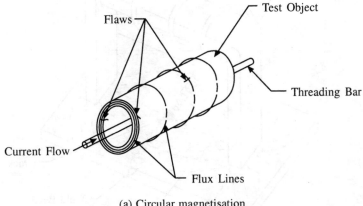

(a) Circular magnetisation

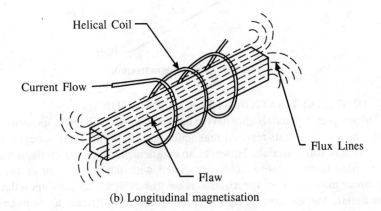

(b) Longitudinal magnetisation

Fig. 4.2

The detectability of subsurface discontinuities in butt welds made between relatively thin plates often can be improved by positioning a direct current yoke on the side opposite the weld bead. Magnetic particles are applied along the weld bead. Improvement is achieved because of the absence of extraneous leakage flux that normally emanates from the yoke's pole pieces.

4.4 AUTOMATED EQUIPMENT FOR SPECIFIC APPLICATIONS

Automation of magnetic particle inspection is often necessary to permit inspection at the required production rate. Loading, processing, conveying, rotating, demagnetisation and discharge can all be automated leading to consistent and effortless processing.

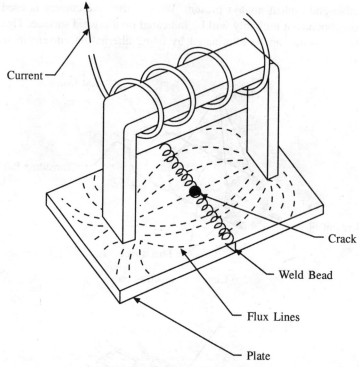

Current

Crack

Weld Bead

Flux Lines

Plate

Fig. 4.3   Yoke magnetisation

4.5   DEMAGNETISATION AFTER INSPECTION

All ferromagnetic materials after having been magnetised will retain some magnetic field which is known as residual magnetic field (B_x). This field is negligible in magnetically soft materials. However, in magnetically hard materials, it may be comparable to the intense fields associated with the special alloys used for permanent magnets. Demagnetisation is easy or difficult depends upon the type of material. Metals having high coercive force are difficult to demagnetise. There are many reasons for demagnetising a part after magnetic particle inspection. For example, during subsequent machining of a part, chips may adhere to the surface being machined and adversely affect surface finish, dimensions and total life. During electric arc welding operations, strong residual magnetic fields may deflect the arc away from the point at which it should be applied.

4.6 METHODS OF DEMAGNETISATION

4.6.1 Use of Diminishing AC Field

The coercive force H_c is always less than the magnetising force H_m (Fig. 4.4). Hence, if a part is initially subjected to a magnetising force greater than H_c, which is alternatively reversed in direction while being gradually reduced in magnitude, the magnitude of B_x reduces. Both H_c and B_x approach to a minimum as shown if Fig. 4.4. Frequency of reversals is an important factor for effective use of this methods. Very high frequency results in lower penetration of the magnetic field in the cross section of the part. For special cases, even a low frequency of around 12 Hz can be used.

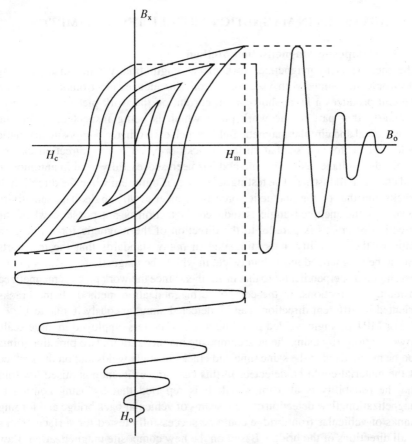

Fig. 4.4   Demagnetisation using AC field

4.6.2   Thermal Method
A ferromagnetic component can be demagnetised if it is raised above its curie temperature (e.g. 1023 K for iron) which is neither practical nor convenient. This can be employed where operation involves heat treatment to a temperature above curie temperature after magnetic particle inspection.

4.6.3   AC Circular Field Demagnetisation
This is useful for large parts and is similar to AC coil method as the field reversal is provided by the cyclic nature of the current. This method gives desired field by passing current through the part, where the current intensity is gradually reduced to zero.

4.6.4   AC or DC Yoke Method
This is suitable for parts having very high coercive force. Some yokes are

similar in operation to the AC coil method whereby the part is passed between pole faces and then withdrawn. A modified version uses a solenoid type electromagnet.

4.7   ADVANCES IN MAGNETIC PARTICLE TESTING (MPT)

4.7.1   Composite Magnetisation Method

The method is to magnetize work piece longitudinally with an alternating electromagnet wound with a secondary coil. The induced electromotive force on the coil produces a large short-circuit current on the work piece to magnetize circularly that part of the work piece which is being inspected. When the longitudinal and circular magnetic fields match each other, a composite magnetic field will be formed so that surface cracks oriented in any direction can be detected simultaneously. This method has been successfully used in automobile and chemical industries. The testing sensitivity is optimum when the direction of cracks and that of the magnetic force lines meet at 90° angle. The sensitivity lowers as the included angle is reduced. Detection is not possible when the direction of cracks is parallel to the direction of the magnetic force lines. To improve the reliability, it is stipulated in many standards that the test parts should be magnetized more than twice, in which the magnetic force lines in one test should be perpendicular to that in another. Since the work piece is magnetized in multiple directions, in the composite magnetization method all the cracks oriented in different directions can be detected simultaneously in one test.

For MPT of angle welded pipe line joints of boilers employed in large scale power stations (by using the new composite magnetization), two pipe line joints can be magnetized at the same time and cracks in angle welds and on the surface of the material could be detected. In this case, the efficiency is raised ten fold and the reliability is also improved. It is reported that by using composite magnetization, flaw detection of weld seams of vehicular back bridge and forging blanks of vehicular front bridge could be successfully tested for surface cracks in all directions of the bridge. Based on the new composite magnetization, flaw detectors can be designed as either portable, or large-scale fixed detectors.

Magnetic Particle Testing-Rubber Casting (MT-RC) is a new NDT technique for location of fine flaws in small holes. It is reported that magnetic rubber inspection (MRI) involves the use of a formulation of magnetic particles dispersed in a room temperature curing rubber. This material is catalyzed and applied into the holes and magnetized thus causing the particles to migrate through the rubber and accumulate at cracks in the holes. After curing, the solid replica casting is removed from the hole and viewed with high intensity light. MT-RC is considered to be the best and reliable method to inspect bolt holes of aircraft wing longeron for fatigue cracks.

An innovative magnetic flaw detector has been developed for inspection of roller bearing elements. Roller bearings are made of alloy materials which have to undergo a series of manufacturing steps. They work under harsh conditions, experiencing heavy loading and frequent impact in service. Therefore, the bearings having microcracks inherited from production history such as forging, machining or heat treatment will aid to initiate a fatigue crack and then the crack propagates and may lead to failures in service. So the elements in a roller bearing must be tested strictly and periodically both in manufacture and in use.

The underlying testing principle of the innovative magnetic flaw detector for roller bearings is as follows: the annular work piece to be tested is encased in an iron core acting as a single turn secondary coil. As a result of transformer effect, core induces high current at low voltage leading to an even distribution of magnetic flux on the exterior of the piece, thus demonstrating an uniform sensitivity at different locations of the surface of the piece.

Systems are available with automatic crack detection with computer vision and pattern recognition of magnetic particle indications. It is a connecting rod crack detection system which is a computer-vision based system with multiple solid state video cameras. The rod is passed through magnetic particle solution and then scanned in front of a camera. The video image is digitized and fed into a microcomputer. The computer analyses the image to detect crack indications based on their linearity and geometry properties. The pre-image processing and digital image processing techniques make automation of Fluorescent Magnetic Particle Inspection (FMPI) a viable plant operation tool. These techniques are employed for inspection of fluorescent crack indications for a variety of welded parts.

Magnetic particle inspection has been in existence for more than 75 years, all the while representing one of the most reliable, economical and safe non-destructive testing methods. Since its inception in 1922 and commercial introduction in 1933, simple iron and iron oxide magnetic powders have been gradually evolving resulting in sophisticated indicating media.

During and after World War II, innumerable new applications have been developed. Introduction of fluorescent magnetic particles satisfied an immediate demand for improvement in the reliability and sensitivity of the method. Furthermore, an option of utilizing water as a suspended carrier in place of oil, simplified and lowered the cost of magnetic particle inspection in general. The post-World War II era brought further significant growth not only with respect to the variety of materials but also in the better understanding of the involved technology.

Presently, the most general classification recognizes the structural differences between magnetic particles designed for dry applications and those for wet uses as suspensions in oil or water. In dry method application, particles need not exhibit great durability, whether the particles are expendable or re-used. Particles for the wet application methods, however, are constantly agitated and recirculated in the equipment to prevent them from their settling. The purpose for a wide variety of multicoloured magnetic particles is to create an optimum contrast between the colour of resulting indications and the surface of the tested metal.

With about 75 years of constant progress in the technology of magnetic materials, the MPI has an established range of applications, higher sensitivity and clear guidelines to achieve reliability of inspection as well as means of reduction in the operating costs.

Further reading

6. Baldev Raj, Jayakumar, T. and Thavasimuthu, M. Practical Non-destructive Testing, Narosa Publishing House, New Delhi, 1997.
8. Bernd Rohloft, NDT methods, The South African Mechanical Engineer, Vol. 4, 1994.
81. Song, H. Half A Century of Magnetic Particle by SEI, 11th WCNDT, Vol. 1, 1985–92. Yan Dawei, A New composite Magnetization Method, Proceedings of 7th Asian Pacific Conference on NDT, China, APC NDT-1993.
92. Yan Dawei, A New Composite Magnetization Method, Proceedings of 7th Asian Pacific Conference on NDT, China, APC NDT-1993.
93. Yen Fwn Chew, Automatic Crack Detection with Computer Vision and Pattern Recognition of Magnetic Particle Indications, Proceedings of 11th WCNDT, Vol. 1, 1985.

Chapter 5

Eddy Current Testing

Eddy current inspection is based on the principle of electromagnetic induction and is used to identify (or differentiate) between a wide variety of physical, structural and metallurgical conditions in electrically conductive materials and metal parts. This method does not require direct electrical contact with the part being inspected. The eddy current method is adaptable to high speed inspection and can be used to inspect an entire production if so desired. The method is based on indirect measurement. The correlation between the instrument readings and the structural characteristics and the acceptability of the parts being inspected must be carefully established with high reliability. The testing sequence is given in Fig. 5.1.

In ECT, an alternating current (widely used frequency: 1 kHz-2 MHz) is made to flow in a coil or probe which, in turn, produces an alternating magnetic field around it. This coil, when brought close to the electrically conducting surface of a metallic material to be inspected, induces an eddy current flow in the material due to electromagnetic induction (Fig. 5.2). These eddy current are generally parallel to the coil winding. The presence of any defect or discontinuity in the material disturbs the eddy current flow. These eddy currents, in turn, generate an alternating magnetic field (in opposite direction) which may be detected either as a voltage across a second coil or by the perturbation of the impedance of the original coil.

The impedance change is affected, mainly, by electrical conductivity, magnetic permeability and geometry of the material, test frequency and the spacing between the coil and the material. This impedance change can be measured and correlated with the changes in the above mentioned parameters.

Factors affecting the eddy current are:

(a) Test frequency related: (i) Frequency, (ii) Type and geometry of test coil(s) and (iii) Fill factor
(b) Test object related: (i) Electrical conductivity, (ii) Magnetic permeability, (iii) Dimensions and (iv) Temperature

Effect of test frequency: The importance of test frequency is that it determines the depth of penetration of eddy currents in the material. The eddy current density decreases exponentially from the material surface but the rate of decrease depends on the test frequency, the electrical conductivity and the magnetic permeability of the test material. The test frequency is the only parameter that can be varied by the inspector during inspection. Although higher frequencies

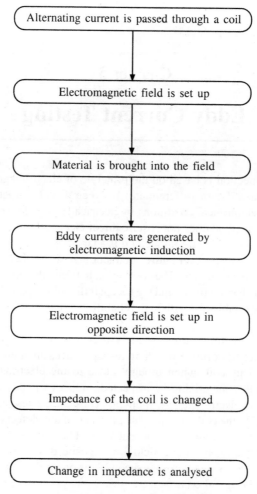

Fig. 5.1   Sequence of Testing

are suitable for achieving higher inspection speeds and better sensitivity to detect defects, they mainly increase the noise due to lift-off or fill factor to such an extent that sometimes even masking the signals due to defects. Similarly, lower frequencies yield reduced noise due to lift-off or fill factor but at the cost of sensitivity. In view of this, enough care should be taken while selecting the test frequency.

Depth of penetration and frequency: The depth of penetration of eddy currents in a material is a critical factor. For example, in the case of tube inspection, if the eddy currents do not penetrate the wall thickness of the tube, then it is possible to miss the defects. The depth of penetration of eddy currents can be found by the relation

$$\delta = \frac{500}{\sqrt{\sigma \mu f}}$$

(5.1)

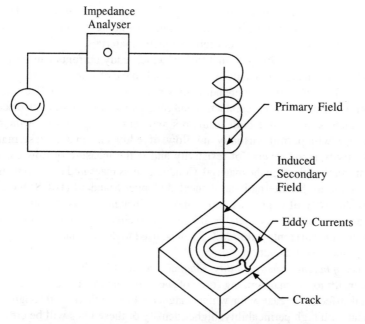

Fig. 5.2 Initial balance conditions of current and fields

where δ is the standard depth of penetration (mm), σ the conductivity (mhos/m), μ the relative permeability and f the inspection frequency (Hz).

The standard depth of penetration is the depth at which the eddy current field intensity drops to 37% ($1/e$ times) of the intensity at the surface of the conductor. It can be seen that higher the frequency, lower the depth of penetration. Thus a frequency must be chosen which permits penetration to the depth upto which defects are to be found. For general tube inspection, the frequency used is often the frequency at which the standard depth of penetration is equal to the wall thickness of the tube and is given by the equation

$$f = \frac{250}{\sigma t^2} \text{ kHz} \tag{5.2}$$

where t is the wall thickness of the tube (mm).

Effect of lift off: For a simple geometry like eddy current probe over a metallic plate, the distance between the probe and the plate being inspected is called lift-off (for encircling or inside coils used for inspecting rods or tubes, it is called 'fill factor'). As lift-off increases, the eddy current density in the material, in turn, the impedance change in the probe decreases.

For achieving better sensitivity, it is always desirable to set lift-off as minimum as possible. However, its adverse effects can be minimised by adopting special probe designs (e.g. differential pickup coils) and procedures that would yield enhanced phase separation between the signals due to wanted and unwanted parameters. It is interesting to note that lift-off is a function of coil diameter i.e. bigger the diameter of the probe, the smaller the lift-off.

Although lift-off signals are not preferred during routine defect detection, they are of great help in determining thickness of non-conducting coatings like paints on non-ferromagnetic and ferromagnetic materials.

Effect of conductivity: The material in which eddy currents can be induced should be of conductive in nature. All materials have characteristic resistance to the flow of electric current depending on which they can be classified into three categories: insulators, semi-conductors and conductors. We will limit our discussion to conductors only since both insulators and semi-conductors with their high resistivity will permit virtually no flow of eddy currents in test material. Conductivity is the reverse of resistivity and is the measure of how easily the current can flow through the material. Conductivity is measured most conveniently by referring to the International Annealed Copper Standard (IACS) which sets the conductivity of copper as 100% and for other metals as its percentage. In general, conductivity of a metal is affected by (i) chemical composition, (ii) heat treatment and (iii) temperature. ECT can be used to detect changes in any one of these properties in isolation.

Effect of magnetic permeability: Magnetic permeability is the ratio of magnetic flux density to the magnetizing force of the coil. The magnetic permeability of a metal affects the ease with which magnetic lines will flow through it. In a material with high permeability, higher density of these lines will be created for a given source and the lines will tend to concentrate in the material. This has two effects: firstly, a greater amount of magnetic energy can be stored in the coil which increases inductance and secondly plenty of eddy currents are generated which increase the 'lift off' effect. The tendency of the lines of force to concentrate in the material causes very little penetration.

Effect of geometry: The geometry of a component under test causes many difficulties in ECT. A curved piece of metal will have a different 'lift off' response compared to a flat one, and the edge effect can distort the eddy current field and produces a signal lag. Another feature of the geometry is on the actual thickness of the material under test. If eddy currents penetrate the full thickness, there will be some effect when the thickness changes. Signals from thickness changes are used to detect the loss of metal due to corrosion.

5.1   INSTRUMENTATION FOR ECT

In most inspections, probe impedance (voltage) changes only slightly, typically less than 1%, as the probe passes a defect. This small change is difficult to detect by measuring absolute impedance or voltage. Special instruments have been developed incorporating various methods of detecting and amplifying small impedance changes. The main functions of an eddy current instrument are illustrated in the block diagram (Fig. 5.3).

A sine wave oscillator generates sinusoidal current, at a specified frequency, that passes through the test coils. Since the impedance of any two coils is never exactly equal, balancing is required to eliminate the voltage difference between them. Most eddy current instruments achieve this through an AC bridge or by subtracting a voltage equal to the unbalance voltage. In general they can tolerate an impedance mismatch of 5%. Once balanced, the presence of a defect in the

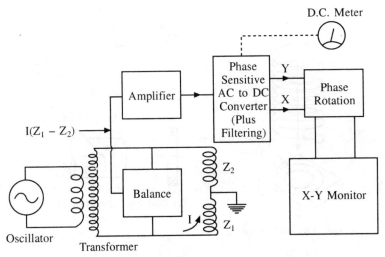

Fig. 5.3 Block diagram of eddy current test instrument

vicinity of one coil creates a small unbalanced signal which is then amplified, filtered and displayed on X-Y monitor (storage oscilloscope) after converting to DC signal. The coil output may vary in both amplitude and phase and the relative variation of the parameters may be important for evaluation of the material under test. There are many variations in the design of eddy current instruments.

Simple ECT instruments usually operate at a fixed frequency and have an analog meter output, thus having limited applications. Modern ECT instruments utilize both amplitude and phase information of the eddy currents. Such instruments permit test frequency to be varied over a wide range enabling selection of suitable skin depth. ECT is a comparative test; signals from real defects are compared with those from calibrated artificial defects to establish type and depth of defects. The calibration and inspection results are normally recorded on dual channel chart recorders and on magnetic tapes. The data stored on magnetic tapes can be played back at a later stage for further evaluation or documentation. Recently, personal computer based eddy current instruments have been developed. These are very compact, light in weight and very efficient in acquiring, processing and storing eddy current data.

Coils: Coils are necessary in ECT to produce sufficient magnetic field from a limited current or sufficient current from a limited magnetic field. A field from adjacent wires in a nearby coil adds to provide a total magnetic field depending on the number of turns in the coils. This type of magnetic field from a coil is similar to that from a permanent magnet.

Eddy current generation: When the coil is brought in close proximity with the conductive material, the alternating magnetic field (primary field) will pass through the material. The coil could be brought onto the material, or encircle it or be inside a tube, or sideways to the object (Fig. 5.4). Eddy currents will be induced into the material. It can be shown that they normally have circular paths at right angles to the primary field, in other words, parallel to the coil winding (Fig.5.2).

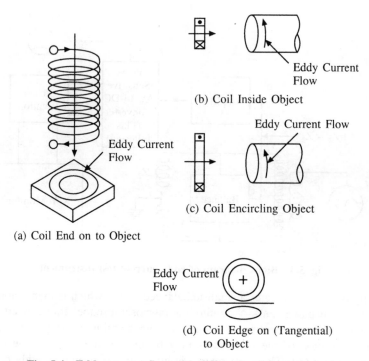

(b) Coil Inside Object

(c) Coil Encircling Object

(a) Coil End on to Object

(d) Coil Edge on (Tangential) to Object

Fig. 5.4　Eddy current flow with different coil arrangements

Eddy current detection: The eddy currents in the conducting material generate their own magnetic field (the secondary field) which in fact opposes and modifies the primary field. This in turn modifies the primary current usually in both phase and amplitude. If the current flowing through the primary field is shown on a display, then variations in it can be seen.

Coil arrangement: The same coil which is used for both generating the primary field and detecting the secondary field is called absolute coil (Fig. 5.5). Often it is useful to have two coils in close proximity which are electrically arranged to be in opposition i.e. wound in opposite directions. This arrangement reduces the effects which affect both coils, for example lift off, material variations and temperature. Signals which affect each coil differently, for example a crack sensed by one coil at a time, are enhanced. This arrangement is called differential

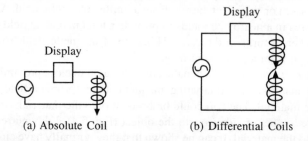

(a) Absolute Coil　　(b) Differential Coils

Fig. 5.5　Types of coils

coil mode. Table 5.1 shows the relative advantages and disadvantages of two most widely used eddy current probe types—absolute and differential.

Table 5.1 Comparison of absolute and differential probes

Absolute Probe	Differntial Probe
Respond to both abrupt and gradual changes in properties and dimensions	More sensitive to abrupt localised changes
Prone to drift due to temperature changes.	Immune to drift due to temperature changes.
Interpretation of signals is simple.	May yield signals difficult to interpret.
Can detect the length of defects.	Detects only the ends of long defects.
Sensitive to probe wobble.	Less sensitive to probe wobble.

Probe selection: The selection of a test coil (probe) is influenced by a number of factors, viz. (a) shape of test specimen (sheets, plates, tubes, rod, wires etc.), (b) likely distribution of variables affecting eddy currents and type of information required like crack detection, conductivity variation, permeability variation etc. and (c) accessibility (component location etc.).

Probe size requirements: The probe size requirements for ECT of tubes using bobbin type probes are determined by the 'fill factor' as follows:

$$\text{Fill factor} = \frac{D_1^2}{D_2^2} \tag{5.3}$$

where D_1 is the diameter of the probe, D_2 is the ID of the tube.

Ideally the fill factor should be as close to 1.0 as possible. A fill factor of 1.0 can never be achieved in practice since the probe would not travel down the tube. As a rule of thumb, the optimum fill factor for tube testing is approx. 0.7. This allows reasonable sensitivity to be achieved whilst still maintaining adequate clearance when dirt or dents may be present in the tube.

5.2 INSPECTION OF WELDS

Eddy current testing has been successfully used to locate defects like lack of fusion, incomplete penetration, cracks, oxidation and changes in chemical composition and hardness of welds. One of the difficulties in using eddy current testing is that the instruments are sensitive to so many variables that careful adjustments must be made to measure the desired weld properties without interference from non-critical characteristics. Many improvements in the latest electronic instruments have made ECT equipment suitable for evaluation of production welds.

For complete evaluation of welds, the alloy composition must be verified as there is always a possibility of wrong welding rod or wire accidentally used for a critical weld which may cause a premature failure of the weld. Many types of ECT instruments are currently available for sorting out various types of welding consumables and weld metal provided their electrical conductivity or magnetic permeability values are sufficiently different.

Longitudinal welds in welded tubing and pipes can be inspected for discontinuities using ECT with an external encircling coil and a probe-type detector coil. The inspection is performed by passing the tube or pipe longitudinally through the primary energising coil causing the probe-type detector coil to traverse the longitudinal weld from end to end. The primary coil is energised with alternating current at a frequency that is suitable for the part being inspected and induces the eddy currents in the tube or pipe.

For the inspection of ferromagnetic products, a direct current magnetic saturating coil is located concentrically around the primary energising coil. The direct current coil is energised at high current levels to magnetically saturate the tube or pipe. This improves the penetration of the eddy currents and cancels the effect of magnetic variables. Due to circumferential orientation of the eddy current flow, this type of inspection is effective in detecting most types of longitudinal weld discontinuities such as open welds, weld cracks, penetrators and pin holes.

It is important that the longitudinal weld be carefully positioned under the probe type detector coil before the pipe is passed through the tester. It is essential to provide good scanning equipment for the pipe so that, as the pipe is propelled longitudinally, the longitudinal weld will always be located under the detector coil.

5.3   ADVANCED EDDY CURRENT TESTING

The technique in its conventional form has a few limitations for in-service inspection (ISI) though it meets the requirements for inspection during manufacture and pre-service stages. The limitations during ISI are: interference from support structures, less sensitivity for circumferential cracks in a tubular structure, inspection of ferromagnetic materials and lack of methodologies for accurate defect characterisation. To overcome the above limitations, a number of developments have taken place making ECT more versatile, reliable and fast. The developments have come in the form of computer models, instrumentation for multi frequency, phased array ECT, remote field ECT, imaging, development of special probes and development towards automation in testing. With these advancements, significant progress has been made with respect to defect detection and characterisation.

5.3.1   Multi-Frequency ECT

It is the equivalent of operating more than one single frequency unit with a common coil and enables to eliminate unwanted parameters from test data. The basic approach relies on the skin effect phenomenon of eddy current flowing in the specimen that allows to obtain independent information at different frequencies. The test results from individual frequencies can be mixed in real time so as to obtain output signals which are free from certain unwanted parameters but preserve the desired test data.

Though there are various ways to mix outputs from various frequencies to cancel a given parameter, the more common way is the use of dual frequency. A popular application of dual frequency is the inspection of heat exchanger tubes for eliminating the signal due to support plate. Three or four frequency modes are used, if necessary, to suppress signals due to other extraneous sources.

The Multi-Frequency Eddy Current (MFEC) testing relies on the analysis of a signal in the impedance plane at different frequencies. The impedance-plane presentation is, in general, nonunique at a given frequency for certain material conditions. An analysis of signals at two or more frequencies and the monitoring of the rate of change of pattern-phase angle with frequency can provide information as to the nature of the signal. It has the advantage on defect detection, sludge profiling and dent sizing and the collection of data at different frequencies for the characterization of certain signal types which is not possible with single frequency testing.

K. Betzold has reported a typical problem in the inspection of austenitic stainless steel welded components where the properties of the weld and the base material differ (Fig. 5.6). The two fatigue cracks near the edges of the weld zone are measured by moving the coil over the specimen in several passes as indicated. The resulting coil impedance at each testing frequency is a function of the lift-off of the coil and the material properties of the weld and cracks. Typical variations of coil impedance caused by these parameters are shown in Fig. 5.6. In each inspection pass all effects are superimposed at different frequencies. The resulting impedances for two passes are also shown in Fig. 5.6.

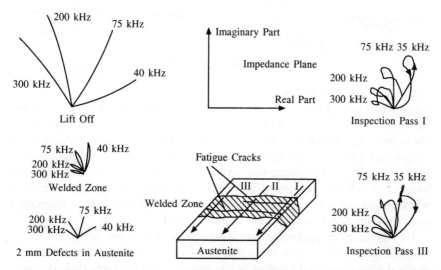

Fig. 5.6   Inspection of an austenite weld (Courtesy: IZFP, Germany)

It is difficult to recognise the contribution made by the defects. Figure 5.7 shows the two-dimensional measurement traces from the welded joint. The two upper plots show signals on the two read out channels after two frequency evaluation. For comparison, the real part of the coil impedance is shown in the lower part. While the first signal on the left side in pass III derives from the lift-off of the coil, it is suppressed in the other passes. The remaining disturbances caused by the weld zone are small. Near the end of the weld, a large indication represents a fatigue crack. In the two-dimensional display, all disturbances are reduced to a flat zero point, and only the signal representing the defect is traced out. In the second pass, the amplitude of this first defect is smaller, but at the begining of the weld, there is a second defect. In the two-dimensional picture both defects are presented. The greater depth for the second defect is found in the inspection pass I while the first is still indicated. In the corresponding plot, the first defect lies along the trace for the second.

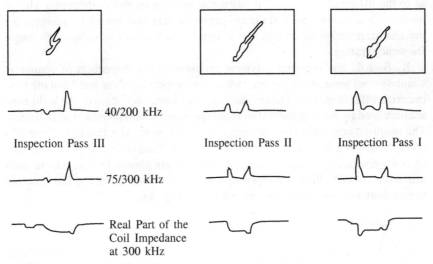

Fig. 5.7   Inspection of a welded joint

5.3.2   The 3D Phased Array ECT

All conventional eddy current instruments, now employed for tube inspection, use a two coil single phase bridge circuit similar to the one shown in Fig. 5.8a. The same bridge circuit or a variation of it is used in all single and multifrequency equipment for tubing inspection. The same bridge circuit is used even in surface inspection eddy current equipment. All types of probes, when used with this bridge circuit generate a magnetic field which is constant in direction and alternating in intensity. Even send-receive eddy current and pulsed eddy current techniques use a constant direction alternating magnetic field.

3D eddy current equipment uses a substantially different bridge circuit. as shown in Fig. 5.8b. In this, the probe that forms the bridge circuit has three identical coils connected together at one end. Each of the three coils is driven

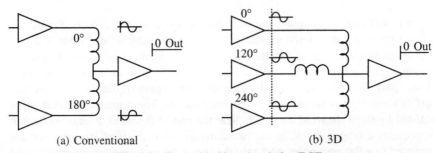

(a) Conventional   (b) 3D

Fig. 5.8   Typical bridge circuit for ECT

with a unique phase of the inspection frequency 0, 120 and 240 degrees. The result is a null output at the junction point of the bridge similar to the case of the conventional two coil bridge driven by 0 and 180 degrees. The magnetic field generated by this three coil configuration results in a constant magnitude rotating magnetic field.

When the three coils in this bridge circuit are energised with the three phases of the inspection frequency and the probe coils are positioned in air, there will be no output at the junction point of the three coils. The probe is balanced. Furthermore, if the probe is positioned centrally in a tube, each of the three coils responds to the tube equally and the system is still in balance. The impedance of each coil changes because of the presence of the tube but the impedance of each coil gets changed to the same amount. This feature of being balanced in the tube or out of the tube is similar to a differential probe which has no output whether the probe is located in the tube or outside the tube.

Consider the probe, balanced in the tube and now being withdrawn from the tube. Because each of the coils is located in the same axial plane in the tube, as the probe approaches the tube end, each coil senses the tube end equally and the bridge remains balanced. As the probe continues to move right past the end of the tube and into free air, the probe coil remains balanced regardless of the position of the probe. The 3D probe gives no signal as it is withdrawn from the tube. This is substantially different than a differential probe which would give an enormous signal as the probe is withdrawn from the tube. The above discussion explains why the 3D probe has no edge effect. The tube end is a symmetrical variation about the axis of the tube and each coil responds to it equally. Hence, the 3D probe will not be sensitive to any concentric variations such as an expansion transition zone, tube sheet or support plate. For this reason, a 3D probe can pass through the expansion transition zone in typical steam generator tube sheet without any response to the zone.

In order to help understand the responses of the 3D system to defects, we must understand the direction of current flow in the tube wall. Figure 5.9(a)

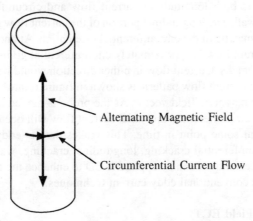

Fig. 5.9(a)   Magnetic field in conventional eddy current testing

shows the constant magnitude alternating magnetic field generated by a differential probe coil and the resulting circumferential current flow in the tube wall. As one coil leads the other as these two coils move along the tube, this differential probe coil responds to all concentric variations such as tube sheets. Also, the circumferential current flow has no sensitivity to circumferentially oriented cracks.

Figure 5.9(b) shows the constant magnitude rotating magnetic field generated by the 3D probe. The magnetic field is always in a direction which falls in the plane perpendicular to the axis of the tube. The constant magnitude magnetic field rotates in this plane. The current flow generated in the tube wall is a circular current flow that flows around the magnetic field vector and therefore flows in a pattern approximately circular (Fig. 5.9(b)).

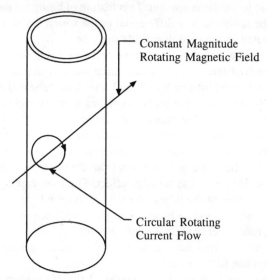

Constant Magnitude
Rotating Magnetic Field

Circular Rotating
Current Flow

Fig. 5.9(b)   Magnetic field in 3D eddy current testing

Figure 5.10 shows more accurately the actual current flow in the tube wall. Note that there is both longitudinal current flow and circumferential current flow in the tube wall. The longitudinal portion of the current flow gives sensitivity to cracks which may be in the circumferential orientation. At another location in the tube, the current flow is approximately circumferential giving senstitivity to axially oriented cracks. Current flow in either direction would be sensitive to pit type defects. The current flow pattern as shown in figure rotates around the tube with the rotating magnetic field vector. As the probe is moved along the length of the tube, both circumferential and axial current flow will occur at every point within the tube at some point in time. This makes the 3D eddy current probe sensitive to circumferential cracking, longitudinal cracking, wall loss and pits. Multifrequency techniques can be applied to 3D to enhance the technique in the same way as for conventional eddy current techniques.

5.3.3   Remote Field ECT
On ferromagnetic materials, poor results are obtained by conventional eddy

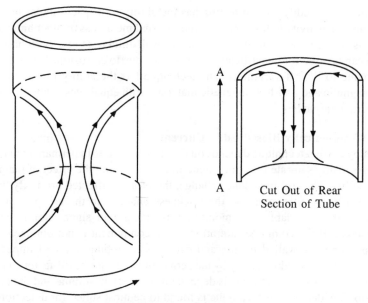

Fig. 5.10   3D Eddy current flow pattern

current methods. This is mainly due to poor signal to noise ratio due to permeability variations. Remote field ECT uses internal probes to inspect tubes. The internal electromagnetic field generated by an exciter driven with a relatively lower frequency sinusoidal signal can be divided into two distinct zones namely direct field zone and remote field zone. The secondary current generated in the tube wall travels along the tube length and enters the remote field zone when the intensity is greater than that of the field from the exciter. It is in this zone that the receiver coil is placed and the voltage induced in it is measured (Fig. 5.11). This voltage contains information from the double transit of the electromagnetic field. The wall loss is estimated by analysing the phase-lag of the receiver signals relative to the excitation signals of the exciter coil. Studies have indicated that the technique has detection capability of 10% wall loss and thus has great promise for inspection of small diameter ferromagnetic seam and seamless tubings.

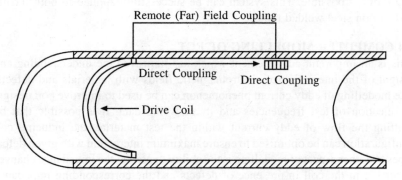

Fig. 5.11   Remote field eddy current drive and receive coil configuration

Remote field eddy current testing has the ability to inspect tubular products with equal sensitivity to both internal and external metal loss or other anomalies. There is a linear relationship between the wall thickness and the phase lag, which can be used for quantification of wall loss due to corrosion. The technique is immune to lift off variations. The technique has the ability to inspect both ferromagnetic and non-ferromagnetic materials with equal sensitivity to internal or external anomalies.

5.3.4   Magnetically Biased Eddy Current

This eddy current technique depends on the ability of built-in permanent magnets to magnetically saturate the component, thus minimizing the effect of magnetic permeability. The coil impedance change, therefore is affected primarily by the combined probe fill-factor and the thickness changes in the component. The effects of these variables are monitored as changes in signal amplitude and phase angle. If the complete saturation of the component is not obtained, as is the case for thick-walled ferritic and carbon steel tubing, the coil impedance change is affected predominantly by the permeability and probe fill-factor changes. In general, the signal amplitude is dependent on the flaw volume and the phase-angle-to flaw depth. This technique is found to be most suited for detection and sizing of ASME type flat-bottomed holes found in ferritic welded tubing of up to 0.90 mm thick. Because of the successful reduction of magnetic permeability to near unity when built-in magnets are used, a clear phase-angle separation in the 20–100% through-wall depth range is possible. By selecting an optimum operating frequency, a desired phase-angle spread could be obtained for estimating flaw depth.

5.3.5   Flux Leakage

With this technique, a permanent magnet built into the test probe is used to induce a magnetic field from inside the tubular component. A pair of coaxial induction coils detect stray flux from flaws in the tube wall. One induction coil, placed between the two poles of the magnet, senses active flux leakage from both OD and ID initiating flaws. A second coil, placed outside the poles of the magnet, detects only the residual flux leakage from ID flaws. By reviewing the information received from the two channels, discrimination of ID flaws from OD flaws is possible. This system can be successfully applied to both ferritic and carbon steel welded tubes.

5.4 COMPUTER MODELLING OF ECT

This is an important advancement which has improved the understanding and insight of the interaction of electromagnetic fields with materials and defects. The modelling of eddy current phenomenon can be used to improve coil design, in selection of test frequencies and in analysing data. It is possible that by plotting the flow of eddy current within the test material, the inducing coil configuration can be optimised to ensure maximum interaction with given defect types. Another aspect of modelling is the ability to predict the impedance changes occurring in the coil in presence of defects and the corresponding impedance trajectory on the oscilloscope.

Among the modelling techniques, the numerical approach using the Finite Element Method (FEM) is the most popular. Two dimensional FEM models suitable for axi-symmetric methods have been developed and applied extensively to design and optimise probes, predict signal trajectories for conditions like magnetic build up in steam generators and other applications.

5.5 DIGITAL SIGNAL PROCESSING (DSP)
A great deal of emphasis has been directed towards identifying procedures and processes that enhance both the reliability and the quantitative information of the signals obtained from conventional ECT. One such emphasis has centered on the application of Digital Signal Processing (DSP) and pattern recognition concepts.

Literature shows that the application of DSP together with artificial neural network analysis in ECT has led to a number of important advantages including improving inspection reliability, defect detection sensitivity and defect characterisation and also making the test process amenable to automation.

5.6 EDDY CURRENT IMAGING
By generating a two dimensional C-scan of the eddy current data in the form of an image and viewing, it is possible to substantially enhance the defect detection capability. Compared to conventional ECT, this gives a global perspective and allows balanced interpretation (Fig. 5.12). Imaging techniques are playing an important role in non-destructive evaluation. Eddy current imaging (ECI) is a recently emerging trend in the field of eddy current testing. In this ECT technique, images are formatted by scanning the surface of an object in a raster fashion, measuring impedance point by point and converting these data into gray levels. The images represent complete information about the extent of discontinuities in two dimensions. Images of notches, corrosion pits and cracks are presented. Imaging techniques have the potential for automating the measurement process, providing estimates of defect sizes from the image data and improving the probability of detection.

Humans are generally comfortable in interpreting images or pictures or two dimensional representation of the objects. By generating two dimensional "C-scan" of NDT data in the form of an image and viewing, one can substantially enhance the defect detection and the characterisation capability. It is stated that, in NDE, an image is worth thousand signals. Imaging techniques have been routinely applied for visual, X-ray and ultrasonic applications. However, they are reatively new to eddy current NDT. Also, it would be possible to extract the information regarding the depth of the features from the gray level variations in the images.

5.6.1 Eddy Current Imaging System
An ECI system has been built around a Personal Computer (PC) at the authors' laboratory to scan the object surface and create impedance changes in a laboratory environment. This consists of a PC controlled X-Y scanner which scans the object surface, point by point with an eddy current probe. The analog signals from the eddy current tester (EM-3300, Automation Sperry Inc., USA) are acquired

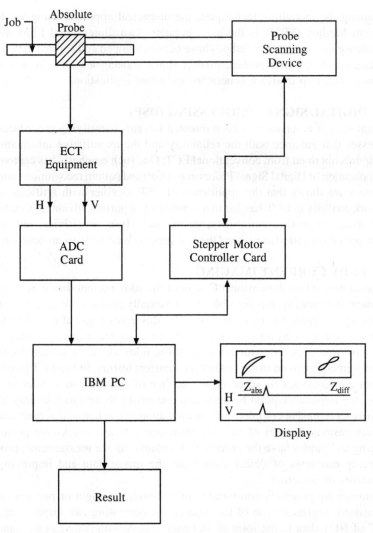

Fig. 5.12   Schematic sketch of eddy current impedance imaging system

using a 12 bit Analog to Digital Convertor (ADC) card. At each probe position, ADC acquires data 10 times and the average impedance value is stored in an array of data on the hard disk of the PC. This averaging is performed to increase the signal to noise ratio. These data are normalised with respect to lower and upper gray values to construct the impedance image. Since the probe impedance is a vector quantity, both in-phase and quadrature components have to be considered while formatting the impedance image. With these data, the four types of images that can be created are: in-phase quadrature amplitude and phase angle images and can be displayed using: (i) color code, (ii) 3-D (X-Y-Impedance) graphics or (iii) gray level images. Gray level images can be displayed by transferring the data to video memory of an image processor. However, in this case, since the studies are on laboratory scale and resolution and gray level range requirements are minimal, the PC screen itself was used to view the images for convenience. For this purpose, point clusters proportional to the gray levels are used.

5.6.2 Imaging and Characterisation of Defects

Using the above ECI system, fatigue cracks of 15 and 23 microns wide in aluminium compact tension (CT) specimens and 0.5 mm deep and 2 mm diameter corrosion pit in a 4 mm thick AISI type 316 steel plate were imaged. A ferrite cored probe of 0.8 mm diameter was used for imaging. The test frequencies used are 200 kHz for stainless steel plate and 100 kHz for the aluminum CT specimens. Close observation of the images clearly indicated that each image has a definite symmetry. The symmetry of the image is directly related to the defect/feature shape. Circular corrosion pit has produced a circular image and linear defects like fatigue cracks have produced images with a line of symmetry along the length of the defect. Hence from the images, it was possible to know the exact shape of the defect/feature. In the case of fatigue cracks, imaging is found to be capable of revealing the direction of growth of crack, an useful information for fracture mechanics studies. Also, when proper calibration procedures are followed, it would be possible to arrive at the exact defect size from the gray level information. Thus, from the above discussions, it is clear that ECI is an effective tool for detecting and characterising surface defects in metallic plates.

5.6.3 Detection of Weld Centre Line

Many a time it would be necessary to remotely inspect welds by ultrasonic testing. Identification of weld centre line is necessary for fixing the required skip distance ranges for ultrasonic testing. In the case of austenitic stainless steel welds, by making use of the presence of delta ferrite in the material, eddy current inspection can be employed for identification of weld centre line. Following is an example. The precise location of the weld centre line, in the inner vessel of Prototype Fast Breeder Reactor (PFBR), is required as a feedback information for remote operation of robots for detailed inspection of the weld by other NDT techniques. Feasibility studies have been carried out to precisely locate the weld centre line. Butt weld joints of 2 mm thick AISI type 316 stainless steel plates were studied to accurately locate the weld centre line. The ferrite cored probe was used at a test frequency of 100 kHz. The filtering techniques can be employed if the image data are of reasonable length (i.e. the scanned area is limited). These techniques are generally employed after acquiring the data. However, in the test object envisaged, the surface of the reactor vessel of a few meters in diameter is proposed to be scanned remotely with a crawler fixed with a probe scanner. Thus, continuous data is generated which is enormous. In such a case, employing filtering techniques may not be simple. Therefore, in this study, improved probe design was adopted to get better point spread function and image processing techniques were confined to those that could be implemented on-line/real time. Ferrite cored probe was used to get better point spread function giving reasonably resolvable images without filtering.

Figure 5.13 shows gray level impedance image of the weldment and the corresponding 3-D plot of the impedance along X and Y axis. Due to predominant variations in the electrical conductivity and magnetic permeability (due to the presence of delta ferrite) of the weld metal, this region is distinctly brought out. The changes in the material properties affect the probe impedance. The change in the impedance varies from the base metal-weld interface to the weld-base metal interface and reaches a peak at the centre of the weld. This peak is clearly observed in the 3D plot (Fig. 5.13). Thus the precise location of the weld centre line can be found from this plot by measuring the distance along Y axis from the origin i.e. the starting point for scanning. The accuracy of detection of the weld centre line is found to be ± 0.1 mm.

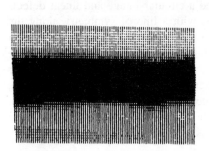 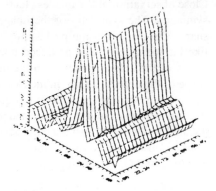

Fig. 5.13   Eddy current impedance imaging of SS 316 weldment and the 3D profile

The above studies clearly reveal the capability of ECI system for the detection and characterization of surface defects in metallic plates and also for precise location of the weld centre line in austenitic stainless steel weldments.

5.6.4   Eddy Current Array Instrumentation for Fixed Position Scanning

An eddy current array consisting of substantial number of individual coil elements, can greatly simplify scanning requirements when compared with those for a single probe. For example, in Offshore NDT, a single eddy current probe scanning a weldment under the control of a driver can easily miss significant defects unless great care is taken. A two dimensional array of coils which examines an area of the surface rather than a single point can greatly improve detection capabilities while allowing at the same time much coarser scanning pattern. Another advantage is that the responses from neighbouring coil elements can be compared to form a 2D map of the surface from which relevant crack responses can be differentiated from non-relevant material boundary changes.

Figure 5.14 shows an array probe which consists of a set of vertically mounted ferrite-cored coils arranged in a 4 × 4 square matrix. Each element coil has its own firing circuit and scanning of the array proceeds in a raster fashion with only one element active at a time to eliminate cross talk. The voltage output across each coil is passed to an analogue multiplexer and then to a fast peak detector with slew rate of 75 V/μ sec. This allows digitisation of the peak output and transfer of the same to the on-board computer for analysis. A zero crossing detector and fast 100 MHz clock are used to measure the "lift-off" portion of the detected wave form.

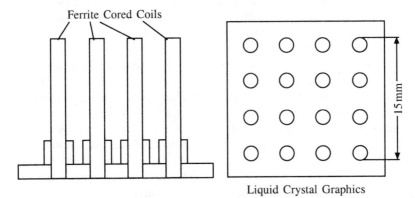

Fig. 5.14   **Coil elementary array**

The computer has the following functions:

(a) To control the firing of the array and multiplexing of the array data
(b) To analyse the array data and extract life-off and defect parameters
(c) To display the parameters

A liquid crystal graphics is used to display each array element as a circle which disappears with increasing coil lift off and whose centres become filled with dots as the flaw severity is increased. This 'Volcano display' presents crack like flaws in a welded component as a line of abnormalities across the imaged array.

Multi-frequency eddy current techniques are used to perform continuous on-line inspection of a seam weld in the steel jacket of a superconducting cable (Fig. 5.15). The inspection requirements are to detect both surface and internal weld defects in the presence of a large, highly conductive central conductor.

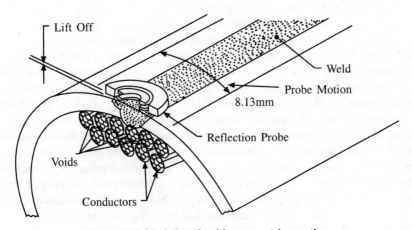

Fig. 5.15   **Steel sheath eddy current inspection**

Raw eddy current data are recorded on magnetic tape and the information such as discontinuity size and weld penetration are computed using co-efficients developed by mathematically fitting data obtained from representative standards. A sophisticated computer-controlled scanning technique is applied and a unique scanning device is employed to provide full coverage of the weld and the heat affected zone.

Harwell Offshore Inspection R&D Service (HOIS) has developed a new eddy current system for the inspection of welded steel jackets in offshore industry. The system has achieved a good defect detection performance and has an extremely low rate of false indications. A time saving of atleast 30-60% as compared to magnetic particle inspection for subsea inspection of typical uncoated welds, arising from both reduced cleaning requirements and faster inspection has been achieved. Savings for epoxy and paint coated welds are even greater, as coating removal is not required. The system has been designed for simple and quick linear scanning and will tolerate lift off from the surface upto 5 mm.

The system has so far achieved its target performance of detecting cracks deeper than 2 mm and longer than 10-15 mm with a high degree of reliability. Smaller cracks have also been detected but with a decreasing probability of detection. The system has major advantage of providing a permanent record of inspection data and the entire operation can be monitored by video cameras.

Instruments like eddy current guidance system for the automatic inspection machine used for the main vessel of the Superphenix Fast Reactor in France are available. These systems are based on understanding of physical phenomena and knowhow relating to high temperature conditions, experience gained on probe development, examination conditions, experience of electrical equipment construction and maintenance and signal enhancement techniques. The weld detector system is an eddy current measurement system consisting of four dual sensors (absolute + differential types) and a control cabinet with eight analog channels. The system delivers all the signals required for computing the correct track of automatic inspection machine along the welds irrespective of bend, temperature, width, type of the seam and junction of the seams.

The probe operates at a low frequency with separate emitting and receiving functions and with current injection so as to obtain a sine wave field inspite of the presence of ferrite (non-linear material) in an austentic stainless steel base material subjected to a hysteresis cycle. A relatively large inductor produces a field which is concentrated at the weld. A central receiver responds to the field concentration. The presence or absence of the weld is determined by the absolute measurement of that concentration. In the presence of a weld, two coils symmetrically located with respect to the probe and connected in opposition, detect sensor offset relative to the weld. It has been reported that the use of coils of different orientations for austenitic weld inspection using eddy current testing has demonstrated that the use of horizontal rather than vertical coils may be advantageous. This is because of the fact that horizontal coils are less sensitive to lift off and can be more sensitive to surface breaking defects if suitable coil is used. When inspecting large areas, much like those of nuclear reactor pressure vessels, the horizontal coil has the advantage because it is able to cover a large area in one scan because of its more spread out field. With a determined and streamlined effort for effective utilisation of the advanced techniques in ECT, it is possible to establish reliable quality assurance procedures and in increasing the availability of various welded components.

Further reading

6. Baldev Raj, Jayakumar, T. and Thavasimuthu, M. Practical Non-destructive Testing, Narosa Publishing House, New Delhi, 1997.
11. Bruce, J. and Nestleroth, Remote Field Eddy Current Detection of Stress Corrosion Cracks in Gas Transmission Pipelines, Review of progress in Quantitative Nondestructive Evaluation, Vol. 10A, Edited by Thomson. D.O. and Chimenti. D.E., Plenum Press, NY, 1991.
50. Krzywosz, K. and Dau, G. Comparison of Electromagnetic Techniques for Nondestructive inspection of Ferromagnetic tubing, Materials Evaluation, No. 48, Jan. 1990.
59. Monty, H. and Cornor, P. Phased Array Eddy Current Inspection of Expansion Transittion Zones in Steam Generator Tubing, Eng-ECT Report R. 8605.
73. Rao. B.P.C., Shyamsunder, M.T., Baburao, C., Bhattacharya, D.K. and Baldev Raj, Eddy Current Imaging of Surface Defects, 4th Asia Pacific Conference on NDT, Shanghai, China, 1995.
80. Smith, J.H., Dood, C.V. and Chitwood, L.D. Multi Frequency Eddy Current Examination of Seam Weld in Steel Sheath, Materials Evaluation, Vol. 43, No. 12, 1985.

Chapter 6

Ultrasonic Testing

Ultrasonic testing (UT) is a NDT method in which sound waves of high frequency (in MHz range) are introduced into the material being inspected to detect internal flaws (defects) and to study the properties of the material. The sound waves travel into the material with some loss of energy due to attenuation and are reflected at interfaces. In most of the applications, the reflected beam is detected and analysed to define the presence and location of defects and for quantitative evaluation.

The degree of reflection depends largely on the physical state of the matter on the opposite side of the interface and on specfic physical properties of that matter. The sound waves are almost completely reflected at metal-gas (air) interfaces, partial reflection occurs at metal-liquid or metal-solid interfaces. The reflected energy depends mainly on the ratio of certain properties of the matter (e.g. Impedence = Density × Velocity). Defects like cracks, shrinkage cavities, lack of fusion, pores and bonding faults which act like metal-gas interfaces can be easily detected by this method. Inclusions and other inhomogeneties in the metal can also be detected due to partial reflection or scattering of the ultrasonic waves. This widely used NDT method has a lot of applications like defining bond characteristics, measurement of thickness of components, estimation of corrosion and determination of physical properties, microstructure, grain size and elastic constants.

Ultrasonic inspection is mostly carried out at frequencies between 1 and 25 MHz. The inspection system includes.

(i) An electronic flaw detector having a sweep circuit, pulse generator, clock circuit and a cathode ray tube.

(ii) A transducer (probe or search unit) having a piezoelectric crystal that emits a beam of ultrasonic waves when bursts of alternating voltages are applied to it.

(iii) A couplant to transfer energy of the ultrasonic waves to the test piece (material).

The principal advantages of ultrasonic inspection as compared to other NDT methods are (i) superior penetrating power which allows inspection of parts of thickness as high as 5 m, (ii) high sensitivity permitting detection of extremely small defects, (iii) greater accuracy in determining the position of internal flaws, estimating their size and characterising their orientation, shape and nature, (iv) necessity for only one surface accessibility, (v) suitability for automation, rapid scanning, on-line production monitoring, process control and possibility for permanent record of results, (vi) volumetric scanning ability of objects, weldments, structures etc. and (vii) portability.

Ultrasonic inspection is used for quality control and materials inspection in many industries. In-service ultrasonic inspection for preventive maintenance is used for detecting impending failure of rail-road rolling-stock axles, mill rolls, earth moving equipment, mining equipment, welded pipe lines in chemical and nuclear plants, boilers, pressure vessels, nozzle welds etc.

Government agencies and standard making organisations (e.g. American Society for Mechanical Engineers (ASME), American Society for Testing Materials (ASTM), Bureau of Indian Standard (BIS), British Standard (BS) etc.) have issued inspection procedures, acceptance standards and related documents. These documents are mainly concerned with the detection of flaws in specific manufactured products but they also can serve as the basis for characterising flaws in many other applications.

Ultrasonic thickness measurements can be made on refractory and chemical processing equipment, submarine walls, aircraft sections and pressure vessels. Instruments with digital read-out are nowadays available. The technique is well suited for the assessment of loss of thickness due to inside corrosion in closed systems such as chemical processing equipment.

For successful application of ultrasonic inspection, the inspection system must be suitable for the type of inspection being done and the operator must be sufficiently trained and experienced. If either of these prerequisites is not met, there is a possibility of gross error in inspection results.

6.1 CHARACTERISTICS OF ULTRASONIC WAVES

In many respects, a beam of ultrasound is similar to beam of light, both are waves and obey the general wave equation. Each beam travels at a characteristic velocity in a given homogeneous medium—a velocity that depends on the properties of the medium and not on the properties of the waves. Like beam of light, ultrasonic beams are reflected from surfaces, refracted when they cross a boundary between two substances that have different characteristic sound velocities, and diffracted at edges or around obstacles. Scattering by rough surfaces or particles reduces the energy of an ultrasonic beam, comparable to the manner in which scattering reduces the intensity of a light beam.

6.2 TYPES OF ULTRASONIC WAVES

Ultrasonic waves are classified on the basis of the mode of vibration of the particles of the medium with respect to the direction of propagation of the waves, namely longitudinal, transverse and surface waves.

6.2.1 Longitudinal Waves

These are also called compressional waves. In this type of ultrasonic wave, alternate compression and rarefaction zones are produced by the vibration of the particles parallel to the direction of propagation of the wave. Figure 6.1 (a) represents schematically a longitudinal ultrasonic wave. For a longitudinal ultrasonic wave, the plot of a particle displacement versus resultant compression crest and rarefaction trough is shown in Fig. 6.1 (b).

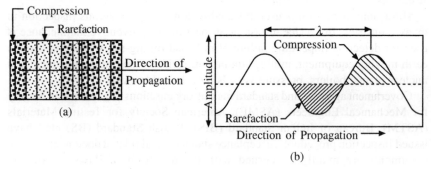

Fig. 6.1   Schematic representation of longitudinal waves

This type of ultrasonic wave is most widely used in ultrasonic testing because of its easy generation and detection. Almost all of the ultrasonic energy used for the testing of materials originates in this mode and then is converted to other modes for special test applications. This type of wave can propagate in solids, liquids and gases.

6.2.2 Transverse or Shear Waves

An ultrasonic wave is called a transverse or shear wave if the direction of particle displacement is at right angles or transverse to the direction of propagation. It is schematically represented in Fig. 6.2. For such a wave to travel through a material, it is necessary that each particle of the material is strongly bound to its neighbours so that as one particle moves, it pulls its neighbours with it thus causing the ultrasonic energy to propagate through the material with a velocity which is about 50% of the longitudinal velocity.

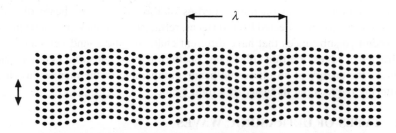

Fig. 6.2   Schematic representation of transverse waves

For all practical purposes, transverse wave can only propagate in solids. This is because, the distance between molecules or atoms, i.e. the mean free path is so large in liquids and gases that the attraction between them is not sufficient to allow one of them to move the other more than a fraction of its own movement. Thus the waves are rapidly attenuated. The transmission of this type of wave through a material can easily be illustrated by the motion of a rope as it is shaken, each particle in the rope moves up and down yet the waves move along the rope from its excitation point.

6.2.3 Surface or Rayleigh Waves

Surface waves, first described by Lord Rayleigh, are called Rayleigh waves. These types of waves can travel only along the surface bounded on one side by strong elastic forces of the solid and on the other side by nearly non existent elastic forces between gas molecules. Surface waves therefore, are essentially non-existent in a solid immersed in liquid, unless the liquid covers the solid surface only as a very thin layer. The waves have a velocity of approximately 90% of the shear wave velocity in the same material. These waves can propagate only in a region no thicker than about one wave length below the surface of the material.

In the case of surface waves, particle vibrations generally follow an elliptical orbit as shown in Fig. 6.3. The major axis of the ellipse is perpendicular to the surface along which the waves travel. The minor axis is parallel to the direction of propagation. Surface waves are useful for testing purposes because the attenuation they suffer for a given material is lower than that for a equivalent shear or longitudinal wave. As these waves can bend around corners, they can be used for testing complicated shapes. These waves enable detection of surface or near surface cracks and defects.

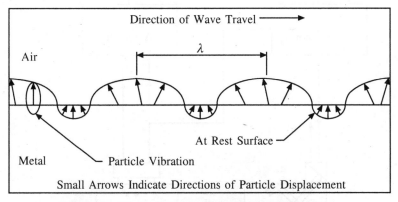

Fig. 6.3 Schematic representation of surface waves

6.3 GENERATION OF ULTRASONIC WAVES AND TYPES OF TRANSDUCERS

Conventionally, ultrasonic waves are generated by piezoelectric transducers that convert high frequency electrical signals into mechanical vibrations. These mechanical vibrations form a wavefront, which is coupled to the component being inspected through the use of a suitable medium. Several wave modes can be used for inspection depending upon the orientation and location of the discontinuities that exist. Longitudinal, shear and surface waves are used separately in different techniques to reveal discontinuities that are respectively parallel to, at an angle to and/or near the surface from which the inspection is performed.

These inspections are made with longitudinal wave transducers through pulse echo, through transmission, pitch-catch or delta techniques. Most of the inspections are performed using pulse echo straight longitudinal wave beams and angled shear wave beams from a single transducer. Figure 6.4 schematically illustrates the pulse echo shear wave and longitudinal wave systems. The working principle of the flaw detector is explained in Sec. 6.5.1.

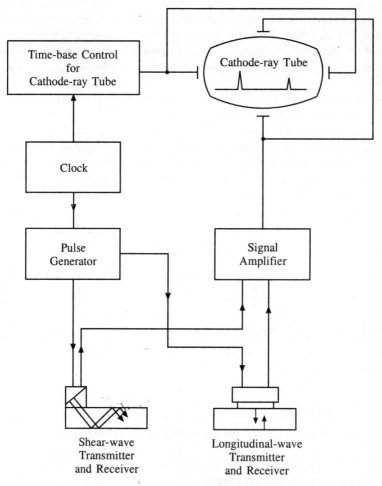

Fig. 6.4   Pulse echo longitudinal and shear wave systems

6.3.1   Materials for Probes

The three most common piezo-electric materials used in ultrasonic probes are quartz, lithium sulphate and polarised ceramics. Most common ceramics are barium titanate, lead metaniobate and lead zirconate titanate. The most important characteristics of ultrasonic probes are sensitivity, resolution, dead zone and near field effect. Nowadays quartz is not commonly used.

6.4 CONSTRUCTION OF PROBES

6.4.1 Construction of a Normal Beam Probe

Electrodes are fitted on both faces of the crystal and the wires from these electrodes lead to the connector socket of the probe (Fig. 6.5a). A damping material (sound absorbing material) can also be applied on the back of the crystal. Usually a wear plate made from a material of known acoustic properties is attached to the outer face of the crystal which protects the crystal from wear and tear. Probes for immersion testing are fitted in a watertight housing body.

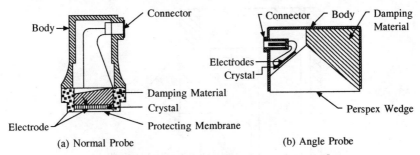

Fig. 6.5 Normal and angle beam ultrasonic transducers

6.4.2 Construction of an Angle Beam Probe

For an angle beam probe, the crystal is mounted on a perspex wedge (Fig. 6.5b) so that the beam of sound reaches the bottom flat surface of the probe at an angle of refraction in the material tested. The longitudinal wave after refraction from the interface changes its mode into transverse wave. The reflected sound beam in the prespex wedge is damped with a suitable damping material. The angle marked on the probe is the refracted beam angle in steel. For other materials, correction of this angle is to be made accordingly. Also, available are removable wedge type angle beam probes. These permit crystals of different frequencies to be used interchangeably with wedges of different angles (Fig. 6.6). It is to be noted that the anlge beam probe sends shear waves into the work piece which travel, for example, with a velocity of 3280 m/s in steel. For angle beam probes, change in material not only means a change in velocity but also a change in the (refracted) beam angle.

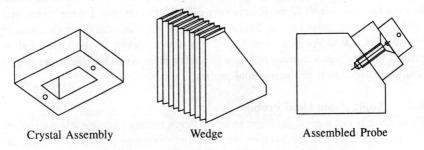

Fig. 6.6 Removable wedge type probe

6.4.3   Construction of a Transmitter-Receiver Probe

Handling of Transmitter-Receiver (TR) combination will be convenient if separate transmitter and receiver are incorporated in a single housing. Such probes are available and are called dual probes, twin probes, double crystal probes, T-R probes etc. The transmitter and receiver should be obviously of the same frequency. They must be slightly inclined towards each other (Fig. 6.7) if the reflected beam is to reach the receiver. This angle within the crystal that makes with the horizontal is called the 'roof angle'. Dual probes were developed to overcome. the problem of dead zone.

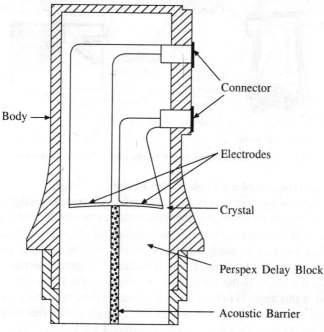

Fig. 6.7   T-R probe

Delay blocks usually of perspex are added to both the crystals. If the reflection from the probe front surface reaches the receiver, it will give rise to spurious signals. This is called 'cross-talk'. To prevent cross talk, an acoustic barrier is kept between the two. Since the probe has definite physical dimensions, it still can not receive signals from defects very close to the surface. Hence, even dual probes have dead zone but the dead zone is much less than that of single element transducers. Dead zones as small as 2 mm are achieved in the case of dual probes. Of late, highly damped probes with narrow pulse width have been developed and these are slowly replacing dual probes.

6.4.4   Angle Beam Dual Probes

Dead zone is not a great problem in angle beam testing because a large part of the dead zone goes in the perspex wedge. Also, the angle probes can be moved backward to see the defect at a greater distance. The improved signal to noise ratio (SNR) of the angle beam dual probes is useful in the case of highly scattering material like austentic steel welds.

6.4.5 Focused Beam Probes

Spherically and cylindrically ground acoustical lenses are commonly added to immersion type probes as shown in Fig. 6.8. Cylindrically ground lenses focus the sound beam to a line and spherically ground lenses focus the beam to a point. Sensitivity from a focused beam increases due to the increase in the intensity.

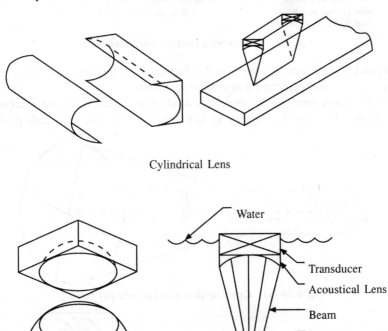

Cylindrical Lens

Spherical Lens

Fig. 6.8   Focused beam probes

6.4.6   Probes with Contour Corrected Soles

When testing specimens with small diameter (rods, pipes etc.), ordinary probes do not provide adequate contact. To ensure that sufficient sound energy is transmitted into the specimen, the probes are fitted with a sole of suitable shape. The matching sole is permanently fixed to the probe (Fig. 6.9).

6.5 ULTRASONIC FLAW DETECTOR

The most common technique employed is the pulse echo technique. The basic construction of the flaw detector ever since it was made in 1942, has not practically

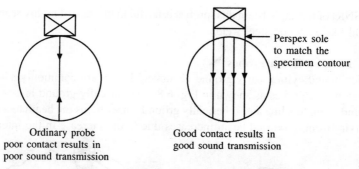

Perspex sole
to match the
specimen contour

Ordinary probe
poor contact results in
poor sound transmission

Good contact results in
good sound transmission

Fig. 6.9   Probes with contour corrected soles

changed. However, improvements in the electronic circuitry has made the system more versatile and capable for operation with ease.

The test equipment basically comprises an ultrasound pulse generator, a receiver, signal amplifier and the display system (Fig. 6.10 (a, b). The cathode ray

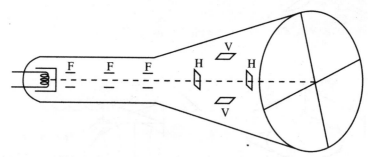

Fig. 6.10 (a)   Cross section of a cathode ray tube

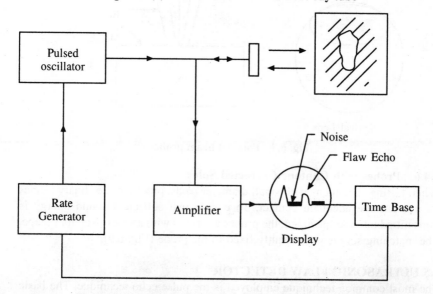

Fig. 6.10 (b)   Block diagram of an ultrasonic flaw detector

oscilloscope (CRT) is the main part of the flaw detector which comes under the display system and shows the information about the object under test. A "CRT" is an evacuated glass tube. When the cathode filament 'E' is heated electrically, it emits electrons. The emerging electrons are focussed as a thin beam by focussing coils 'F'. These electrons are accelerated by the anode by applying high voltage. The accelerated electron beam strikes on the screen which is in contact with a fluorescent material. The area where the electron beam strikes the screen will be seen as a luminous spot.

HH and VV are two sets of electrodes. If a voltage is applied on HH (horizantal) plates, the beam will deflect horizontally and a voltage on 'VV' plates will deflect the beam vertically. In the flaw detector, the horizontal distance is used to measure time. Hence, a voltage varying linearly with time is applied to these plates. Such a voltage is called a sweep voltage or a saw tooth voltage. When one cycle of sweep voltage is applied, the electron spot will travel at uniform speed from left to right and instantaneously reaches back to its starting point. Since the speed is uniform, the distance of the spot on X-axis is proportional to time. This cycle, repeated many number of times in a second can be seen as a line on the CRT due to persistence of vision. This line is called trace, sweep line, time base or base line. Simultaneous with a sweep voltage, if a voltage of short duration applied on the 'VV' plates, the trace on the CRT will also instantaneously deflect up and down. This vertical deflection, called as a 'pip', is also known as echoes, reflections, vertical deflections, reflected pulses etc.

6.5.1 Working Principle of Flaw Detector

The pulser gives out a high voltage electric pulse of short duration. This electric pulse excites the transducer and the transducer generates a short pulse of ultrasonic waves. This ultrasonic wave travels into the material under test and gets reflected by a defect or the back surface. The reflected wave reaches the transducer and gets converted into an electrical voltage/pulse. This voltage is amplified by the amplifier and fed to the vertical deflection plates of the CRT. This will make a 'pip' on the CRT as explained earlier.

The sweep circuit is simultaneously activated when the pulser emits a pulse and this sweep voltage is connected to the horizontal deflection plates of the CRT. Hence, the electron beam starts tracing the horizontal line on the CRT. The 'pip' appears after some distance on the X-axis. There is an interval of time between the start of the sweep circuit and the return of the ultrasonic pulse to the transducer and this time will be proportional to the distance of the reflector from the front or scanning surface of the specimen. A part of the pulse is sent (directly through) to the amplifier and therefore a fairly large vertical deflection is obtained at the start of the horizontal line on the CRT and is called as initial pulse or transmitted pulse. Depending on the display of the information, the pulse echo equipments can be sub-divided into three groups, namely, A scan, B scan and C scan.

6.5.2 'A' Scan

The information regarding the material being tested will be displayed on the

CRT. 'A' scan display indicates the depth of the discontinuities in the X-axis (time base) and the amplitude of the sound reflection from the discontinuity in the Y-axis which is a relative measure of the size of the discontinuity (Fig. 6.11).

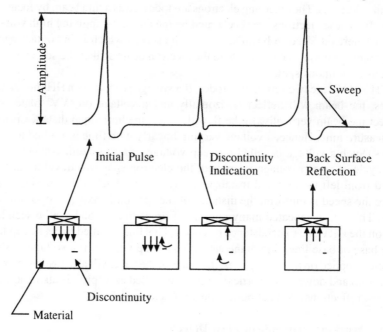

Fig. 6.11   Typical A-scan display

6.5.3   Test Techniques

Ultrasonic testing techniques are either of contact or immersion type. In contact type, the probe is placed in direct contact with the test specimen with a thin liquid film used as a couplant for better transmission of ultrasonic waves into the test specimen. In immersion type, a water proof probe is used at some distance from the test specimen and the ultrasonic beam is transmitted into the material through a water path or water column.

Contact type techniques are divided into three types, viz. normal beam, angle beam and surface wave techniques. Immersion testing techniques are mostly used in the laboratory and for large installations using automatic testing. It has the advantage that uniform couplant conditions are obtained and longitudinal and transverse waves can be generated in the material with the same probe simply by changing the incident beam angle. The three basic techniques used in immersion testing are immersion, bubbler and the wheel transducer techniques. In immersion technique, both the probe and the test specimen are immersed in water. The ultrasonic beam is directed through the water into the test specimen using either a normal beam technique (Fig. 6.12a) for generating longitudinal waves or an angle beam technique (Fig. 6.12b) for generating transverse waves. In bubbler or squirter technique, the ultrasonic beam is directed through a water column in to the test specimen.

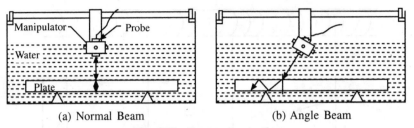

(a) Normal Beam (b) Angle Beam

Fig. 6.12   Immersion testing

6.6   ULTRASONIC TESTING OF WELDMENTS

The two aspects which distinguish ultrasonic testing of welds from UT of other products like forgings, castings, pipes etc. are (a) area of interest is defined and limited (weld and heat affected zone) and (b) knowledge of specific set of defects whose probable location and orientation are known. Most welds fall into one of the following categories: (a) Butt weld (b) Tee-weld and (c) Nozzle weld. Various weld configurations are shown in Fig. 6.13.

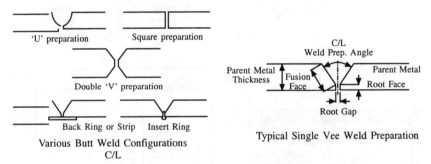

Fig. 6.13   Various weld configurations

Typical ultrasonic testing procedure for the examination of weld root and weld body is shown in Figs. 6.14 (a-c). The typical echo pattern from various types of weld defects are shown in Fig. 6.15. Weld defect sizing is done by either 6 or 20 dB drop method. Figure 6.14(a) shows the different types of probe movements (scanning) to detect a defect and also to find its nature, type and dimensions. Figure 6.14(b) indicates two probe technique (Tandem) to detect transverse cracks in a weldment. The weld centre line determination with angle beam is explained in Fig. 6.14(c).

6.6.1   Typical Test Procedure to Evaluate a Weld Joint

Specimen thickness: 25 mm (T)
Material: Carbon Steel
Weld angle: 60° single 'V' Butt joint
Weld cap width: 28 mm
From Figs. 6.16 and 6.17, calculate the following:

(1) Probe angle required = $90° - (\theta/2) = 90° - (60°/2) = 60°$
(2) Half skip distance = T (tan θ) = 25 × 1.73 = **43.25 mm**

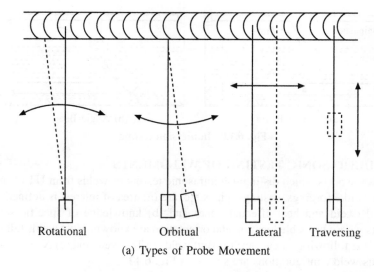

(a) Types of Probe Movement

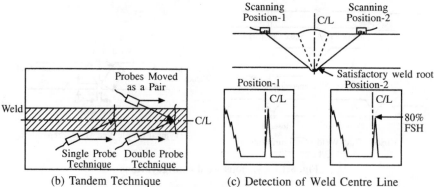

(b) Tandem Technique   (c) Detection of Weld Centre Line

Fig. 6.14   Typical scanning methods for weld inspection

(3) Full skip distance = 2T (tan θ) = 50 × 1.73 = **86.50 mm**
(4) Half skip beam path length = T/(cos θ) = 25 × 2.00 = **50 mm**
(5) Full skip beam path length = 2T/(cos θ) = 2 × 25 × 2.00 = **100 mm**

The scanning of the weld and the probe movement are shown in Fig. 6.17. The probe has to be moved from half skip distance to full skip +1/2 cap width distance from the centre of the weld (43.25 mm to 92.50 mm from the weld centre line). Draw the guide lines from 43.25 to 92.50 mm from the centre of the weld and scan the weld by moving the angle probe between the guideline limits and evaluate the weld and the heat affected zone for any defects. Figure 6.18 shows the scan directions of normal/angle beam examinations for various weld configurations (note: ↘ represents angle beam examination).

6.6.2   The 6 dB Drop Method

The basic assumption in this method is that the echo amplitude being displayed when the probe is positioned for maximum response from the flaw, will fall by

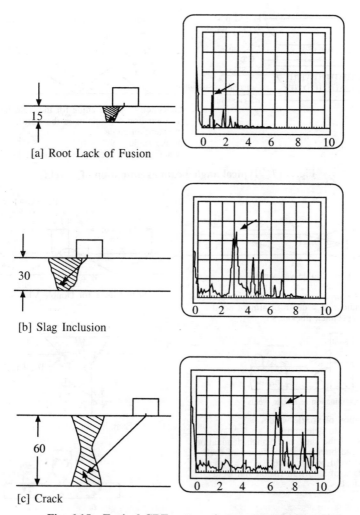

[a] Root Lack of Fusion

[b] Slag Inclusion

[c] Crack

Fig. 6.15 Typical CRT pattern from weld defects

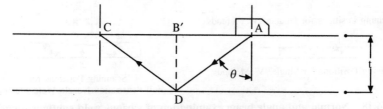

(a) Half ship and full skip distances and beam path lengths

AB – Half skip distance (HSD) = $t \times \tan\theta$
AC – Full skip distance (FSD) = $2t \times \tan\theta$
AD – Half skip beam path length (HSBPL) = $t/\cos\theta$
AD + DC – Full skip beam path length (FSBPL) = $2t/\cos\theta$

Fig. 6.16 Basic formulae in angle beam examination

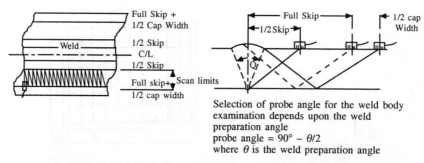

Selection of probe angle for the weld body examination depends upon the weld preparation angle

probe angle $= 90° - \theta/2$

where θ is the weld preparation angle

Fig. 6.17   **Typical angle beam examination of a weld**

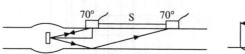

Root scan for double vee welds

$S = 2(t - d) \tan \theta$

where θ = probe angle, S = distance between probe indices, d = depth of aiming point and t = specimen thickness

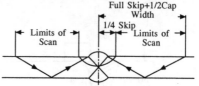

Scan Limits for Double VEE-welds

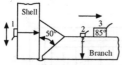

Examination of nozzle welds

Examination of nozzle welds
Scan 1 & 2 to determine
thickness of the shell and branch, lamination in shell and branch, lack of fusion of shell wall and weld body defects
scan 3-lack of side wall fusion and weld body defects

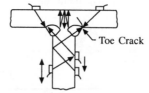

Examination of T-welds

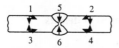

Scanning Positions for Double 'V' Methods

Scanning Positions for Single 'V' Methods

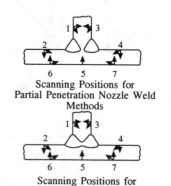

Scanning Positions for
Partial Penetration Nozzle Weld
Methods

Scanning Positions for
Full Penetration Nozzle Weld Methods

Fig. 6.18   **Normal and angle beam examination of various weld configurations**

one-half (i.e. by 6 dB and hence the name), when the axis of the beam is brought in line with the edge of the flaw as shown in Fig. 6.19. The procedure to determine the dimension of a flaw parallel to the probe movement i.e. the flaw length, is as follows.

1. Position the probe to get the maximum echo from the flaw.

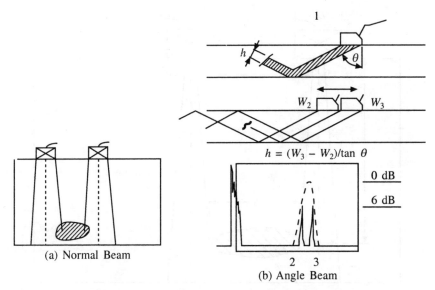

$$h = (W_3 - W_2)/\tan \theta$$

(a) Normal Beam

(b) Angle Beam

Fig. 6.19   The 6 dB drop method for defect sizing

2. Adjust the height of the echo to some convenient scale on the CRT screen by using the gain control of the flaw detector.
3. Move the probe across the flaw in one direction until the echo height falls to one half of the height adjusted in 2.
4. Mark the centre of the probe on the surface of the test specimen for this probe position.
5. Now move the probe in the opposite direction through the maximised echo position to the position when the echo height again falls to one half of the height adjusted in 2.
6. Mark the probe centre at this position as well.
7. The distance between the two marks gives the dimension of the defect parallel to the probe movement.

The 6 dB drop method is suitable for the sizing of flaws which have sizes of the same order or greater than that of the ultrasonic beam width. But this method will give inaccurate results when the flaws are smaller than the ultrasonic beam. It is therefore generally used to determine flaw length but not flaw size.

6.6.3   The 20 dB Drop Method

This method (Fig. 6.20) utilises, for the determination of flaw size, the edge of the ultrasonic beam where the intensity falls to 10% (i.e. 20 dB) of the intensity at the central axis of the beam. The procedure is as follows:

1. Position the probe to get a maximum echo amplitude from the flaw.
2. Adjust the echo amplitude to some convenient scale on the CRT screen using the gain control of the flaw detector.
3. Move the probe first across the flaw in one direction until the echo amplitude falls to 1/10th of its original height (i.e. by 20 dB).

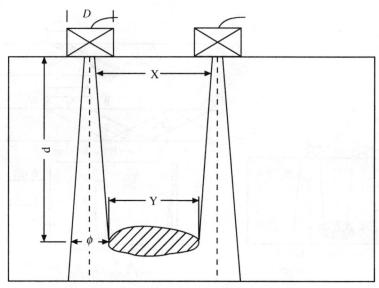

Dimensions of the flaw parallel to the movement of
the ultrasonic beam (Y)
$Y = x - \phi$
Where $\phi = D + 2 (d - X_0 \tan \theta)$
X_0 = near field length of the probe

Fig. 6.20   The 20 dB drop method for defect sizing

4. Mark the position of the probe index on the surface of the test specimen
   at this position.
5. Now move the probe in the opposite direction through the maximised
   echo position until the echo amplitude again falls to 1/10 th of its original
   height.
6. Mark the position of the probe index on the surface at this position.
7. Measure the distance between the two markings.
8. Determine the beam width at depth 'd' of the flaw from the equation
   given in Fig. 6.20 and calculate the dimension of the flaw parallel to the
   movement of the ultrasonic beam.

The 20 dB drop method gives more accurate result than the 6 dB drop method
because of the greater control one has on the manipulation of the ultrasonic
beam. However, size estimation using either 6 dB or 20 dB drop method has
inherent difficulties which must be considered. The main problem being that the
amplitude may drop for reasons like: (a) tapered defect (b) surface roughness,
(c) irregular defect etc.

6.7   PROBLEMS FACED DURING ULTRASONIC TESTING OF
WELDS OF CERTAIN MATERIALS

Welds of certain materils like austenitic stainless steel and nickel based alloys
pose serious problems for ultrasonic testing. These problems are primarily due
to the acoustic anisotrophy of these materials and the cast structure of the weld.

Heavy scattering of the ultrasonic beam, false indications and wrong judgement of position and size of the defect can be encountered in these materials. This results in heavy attenuation of the beam as well as 'noise' signals reaching the probe. The combined effect of these results is the loss of sensitivity and low signal to noise ratio. These problems are greatly minimised by the utilization of longitudinal wave angle beam probes for such applications.

6.7.1 Weld Structure

Unlike in the case of carbon steels, austenitic stainless steels neither undergo any phase transformation nor consequent recrystallisation during cooling. Hence, the austenitic stainless steel weld retains the coarse columner structure, typical of cast material. This coarse grain structure gives rise to scatter (Fig. 6. 21), which in turn results in low signal to noise ratio. It has been reported that one may be able to detect a notch with a depth of 3% of thickness in the parent metal whereas only a 7% notch could be detected in the weld regions. In addition to the loss of sensitivity due to scatter, the peculiar grain structure of the austenitic weld can generate pseudo-indications during UT and to distinguish them from real defect indications will be very difficult. These reflections are entirely different from the 'noise' or grass echoes. The echo dynamics of these pseudo indications are similar to genuine flaw indications. Whereas grass echoes are persistent when the probe is moved or swivelled, these pseudo-indications rise and fall sharply as the probe is moved, much in the same way as the echoes from genuine defects. Also unlike in the case of grass echoes, the pseudo indications are repeatable making evaluation more difficult.

Fig. 6.21   Coarse grain structure with an artificial defect.

6.7.2   Ultrasonic Examination of Austenitic Stainless Steel Welds

Austenitic stainless steel, due to its excellent combination of mechanical and corrosion properties, has become a largely used structural material in modern times. For any critical service, particularly for nuclear applications, it is essential to check the components at various stages of fabrication for their integrity. Depending on the geometry, size etc. different non-destructive tests are called for. However, unlike in the case of other ferrous materials, ultrasonic testing of austenitic stainless steels, particularly welds, present some formidable problems. Attempts to overcome these problems by manipulating conventional parameters like frequency and beam angle have met with a little success. This has necessitated recourse to improvements in instrumentation as well as applications of more sophisticated concepts like signal processing. Another line of attack is to study and identify the material parameters interfering with UT in the hope that the problems can be overcome by suitably manipulating these parameters. The main peculiarities of austenitic stainless steel are the acoustic anisotropy of the individual grains and in the case of weldments the cast structure of the weld. The effect of anisotropy is to produce anomalous refraction or beam skewing of ultrasonic waves. The skewing effect produces errors in locating the defect. The apparent defect location determined from oscilloscope screen range gets widely deviated from the actual defect location.

6.7.3   The Solutions

Solutions like testing at lower sensitivity levels, testing only those portions of the weld that do not give problems, or testing by other NDT methods or not using austenitic stainless steel at all are no solutions to these problems. Possible solutions for the problem can be broadly classified into three groups:

1. Improvements to the existing techniques
2. Applications of signal processing concepts
3. Controlling the weld structure

6.7.4   Typical Case Study

A study was conducted by the authors in their laboratory to locate defect accurately in austenitic stainless steel weldments. A geometrical model for austenitic weld structure was developed based on a computer programme for tracing the ultrasonic ray inside the weldment and thereby calculating the mislocation of the defects in the weld, taking into account the beam skewing phenomenon.

Model of the Grain Structure: The first necessity to assess the beam skewing taking place as a result of the orientation dependance and the successive deviations in the grains of an austenitic stainless steel weld is to develop a geometrical model of the grain morphologies. Towards the end, the cross section of a 50 mm thick single V weld was appropriately etched to bring out the grain structure with sufficient contrast. On the basis of this grain morphology, a geometrical model of the weld structure having the following characteristics was evolved (Fig. 6.22). The top region of the idealised traingular weld region in the model has been divided by vertical grains. Below this region, two vertical grains are extended upto the bottom area of the weld. In other areas, i.e. at the weld/parent metal interfaces, trapezoidal grains have been interposed with oblique grains. The angles (Fig. 6.22) at the vertices of the oblique grains have been kept equal. With this arrangement, a continuous grain rotation has been incorporated in the model.

Calculation of Beam Path and the Time to Reach the Defect: For the calculation of the beam path and the time to reach a defect, a geometrical model was

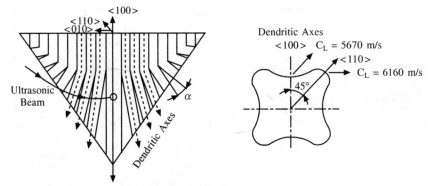

Fig. 6.22 Typical model of an austenitic stainless steel weld

evolved with the characteristics described earlier and with the following relevant parameters:

Angle of beam in steel	:	70°
Angle of weld	:	80°
Plate thickness	:	50 mm
Velocity of ultrasonic wave in parent metal	:	5730 m/sec
Total angular variation of the axis of grains between bottom and top edges of weld region	:	45°

The variation in the acoustic velocity in various directions which is relevant inside the weldment was taken from literature. For each refraction at successive boundaries, the phase velocities of the incident wave and the refracted wave have been matched. Under the conditions mentioned above, computations have been developed for tracing the path of the ultrasonic beam after it crosses the weld/parent metal boundary. At the same time, the time taken by the beam to reach the defect is also calculated. This is the time which would be shown by the oscilloscope as the time taken for travelling the straight line path to the phantom defect. Number of trapezoidal and oblique grains have also been varied. Calculations were made taking into account refraction and beam skewing in two dimensions only. Acoustic beam was considered as a ray for this modelling and calculations purpose. The phenomenon of beam skewing is illustrated in the computer output (Fig. 6.23) which indicates the enormisity of the problem and the corrections made on the basis of: (a) refraction at weld/parent metal interface only and (b) due to beam skewing caused by anisotropic dendritic structure of the weld.

6.7.5 Improvements to the Existing Techniques
(a) Use of longitudinal waves instead of shear waves: It is well known that compressional waves are attenuated less than shear waves. Also, in case of scattering, the scattered waves contain a lesser proportion of longitudinal waves than shear waves. These two facts together lead us to the conclusion that use of longitudinal wave angle beam can considerably improve the SNR. This has been tried successfully and such longitudinal wave angle beam probes are now

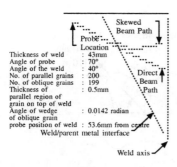

Thickness of weld : 43mm
Angle of probe : 70°
Angle of the weld : 40°
No. of parallel grains : 200
No. of oblique grains : 199
Thickness of : 0.5mm
parallel region of
grain on top of weld
Angle of wedge : 0.0142 radian
of oblique grain
probe position of weld : 53.6mm from centre
Weld/parent metal interface

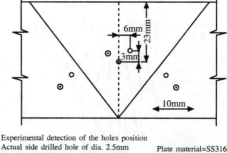

Experimental detection of the holes position
Actual side drilled hole of dia. 2.5mm
Corrected position of hole considering
refraction at weld/parent metal interface
Corrected theoritical position of hole
considering beam skewing

Plate material=SS316
Arc welded with
Philips RS 316B
electrode

Fig. 6.23   Computer plot showing beam skewing and corrections of defect locations

commercially available. It has also been reported that attenuation is minimum when the longitudinal beam is inclined at 45° to the grain axis and this can be taken advantage of during testing. However, one has to guard against indications due to the shear wave component which always accompanies refracted longitudinal wave component.

(b) Use of double crystal angle beam probes: Since double crystal probes (both normal and angle beam) 'focalizes' the beam to a narrow band of material thickness, scatter from other parts of the weld does not interfere in the testing. This results in enhanced SNR. Obviously probes with different 'focalization depths' will have to be used for the same weld to cover the entire thickness.

6.7.6   Signal Processing Concepts

In conventional ultrasonic testing, only one parameter of the reflected signal, namely, amplitude is studied. In the case of austenitic welds, because of poor signal to noise ratio, it is difficult to depend upon or even measure this single parameter. Hence only the other parameters such as frequency spectrum content can give reliable information. Signal analysis by correlation techniques has also been attempted with various degrees of success. However, it must be realised that signal processing needs automation for fast and repeatable data acquisition.

6.7.7   Controlling the Weld Structure

Whereas the above methods try to overcome the problems, methods of eliminating them by understanding and suitably modifying the weld parameters, which give rise to the problems, are attracting the attention of the investigators. Of the many metallurgical parameters like segregation, stress distribution etc. that contribute to scatter, the dendritic structure contributes to spurious or pseudo-indications in addition to 'noise'. Effects of welding procedure on the orientation of grains have been studied with respect to weld preparation angle etc. It must be known that, while all of the above three approaches help in the reduction of noise, they cannot identify and distinguish pseudo-indications from a 'true' defect indication.

The problems of ultrasonic testing of austenitic stainless steel welds are still far from having been reliably solved. Sophisticated methods of signal processing can be applied only on production lines which lend themselves to automatic ultrasonic testing. Modifications to probing techniques can solve the problem to some extent.

Conventional ultrasonic testing (A scan) has limitations in providing the exact size, contour and image of the defects in objects. Due to the demand for quality products, and the necessity for imaging and quantitative sizing of the defects for extending the life of components, advancements have taken place in the field of ultrasonic testing. This has led to certain extent precise assessment of defects in materials.

6.8 ADVANCED ULTRASONIC TESTING TECHNOLOGY

6.8.1 Defect Detection with High Sensitivity and Reliability Using Advanced Signal Analysis Concepts in Ultrasonic Testing

Industrial components in many chemical, petrochemical, process and nuclear industries are made of stainless steels and sometimes with maraging steels in critical aerospace applications. As indicated earlier, detection of defects in welds made in these materials using ultrasonic testing poses great difficulty because of poor signal-to-noise ratio of the ultrasonic signals. The noise due to grain scattering dominantes over the signal corresponding to a defect. Therefore, advanced signal analysis concepts like spectral analysis, pattern recognition, neural network analysis etc. are employed in such cases. Dendritic (hence anisotropic) microstructures of these weldments, especially in the thickness range of 10 to 40 mm, pose problems for ultrasonic testing. Considering these facts, the ASME boiler and presser vessel code has recommended that in the case of austenitic stainless steel weldments, any defect that is 10% of thickness should be recorded and monitored. In some cases, it may be desirable to detect defects of much less than 10% of the thickness. In this connection, signal analysis (SA) procedures, by using effective cluster and pattern analysis algorithms have been developed. These enable detection and characterisation of defects down to 1% of weld thickness (14.0 mm weld thickness) in austenitic stainless steel welds (Fig. 6.24). In case of maraging steel weldments used in the rocket motor casings by the aerospace industry, tight cracks (3 mm × 1 mm) produced by fatigue loading have to be detected and characterised and this is possible by using cluster and pattern analysis principles. Detection of such small defects for this application, enhances the payload capacity of the rocket motor, resulting in significant economic and technological gains.

Signal Analysis and Pattern Recognition

In order to enhance the capabilities of NDE techniques for detection with high sensitivity and quantitative characterisation of defects, advanced signal analysis (SA), image processing (IP) and knowledge based systems have been employed. Use of these approaches also helped in understanding the interaction between the interrogative medium and the material. These approaches help in appropriate decision even if the raw information obtained for NDE methods is unprecise, incomplete or uncertain. Signal analysis methodologies include power spectrum analysis, wavelet transforms, frequency domain deconvolution, Fourier descriptors

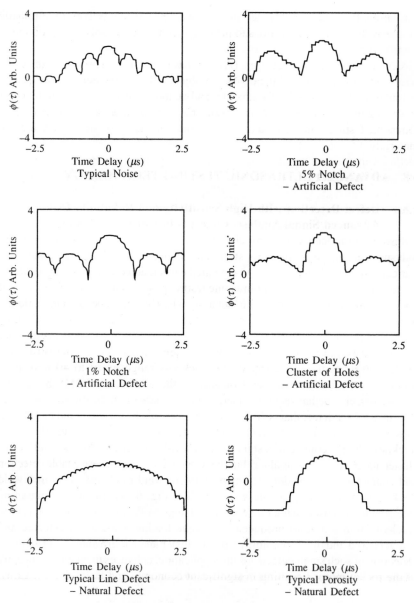

Fig. 6.24   Ultrasonic signal patterns of typical noise, porosity, notches and a crack

etc. If the information related to defects is concentrated in specific frequency ranges, then spectral analysis would enable defect detection with high sensitivity. Wavelet transform can be used for performing multi resolution analysis of the signals. This consists of signal decomposition over a set of special functions generated by translation and dialation of a basic function well localised in both time and frequency domain. These functions include Gaussian Morlet, Mallet and Mexican-hat and this transform enhances SNR.

Pattern recognition can be defined as the categorisation of input data into identifiable classes via the extraction of significant features or attributes of the data from a back ground of irrelevant detail. The features can be selected from time, frequency, power, phase, cepstral and auto correlation domains. One of the pattern recognition techniques employed for improving defect detection sensitivity is demodulated auto correlogram (DMAC). The Pattern in the demodulated autocorrelogram function is obtained by taking log of square of the autocorrelogram function of any signal. Cluster analysis deals with partitioning of data with an aim to make the data presentable and easier to interpret. The success of this method depends on the inherent ease with which clustered objects can be classified and identified. Selection of signal parameters that would result in cluster formation such that the average intra-cluster distance is much smaller than the average inter-cluster distance.

Cluster and pattern analysis methods use the cross-power spectrum (between signals from weld noise and those from the defects), to obtain the cluster elements. The pattern analysis method generates a pattern called demodulated auto-correlogram (DMAC) from the autocorrelation function of a signal. Feature of DMAC are studied for interpretation and evaluation. The DMAC pattern for the noise has more number of lobes as compared to the pattern of the defect signal. The physical interaction of ultrasonic waves with the complex material microstructure manifests itself as a number of lobes in the signal processed DMAC pattern. The exact nature of the interaction and the model based approach to understand the DMAC patterns have not yet been established. It is reported that the cluster analysis of the cross power data for maraging steel weldments shows that the coordinates of centroids for the noise-defect signals are higher than those for the noise-noise signals. Another example where advanced signal analysis concepts can be employed is for ultrasonic inspection of end-cap weld joints in fuel elements of pressurised heavy water reactors (PHWR).

In PHWR, uranium dioxide fuel pellets are encapsulated in Zircaloy-2 cladding tubes of 0.37 mm thickness and sealed with end caps. Resistance welding of the end cap with the cladding tube leaves a material upset both inside and outside on the joint. The outside upset is machined off leaving only a tiny step between the end cap and the cladding tube, but the inside upset remains. Generally helium leak test on all the weld joints and destructive metallographic tests on a sampling basis are carried out to ensure the integrity of the weld joints. These techniques have their own limitations. Helium leak test detects only those defects which have passed 'through' the tube wall thickness. Metallography is a destructive test and reveals only the cut section, and cannot be carried out on all the joints. The quality assurance procedures do not give enough confidence when the target is zero failure rate with the objective of keeping the coolant of nuclear reactors as less radioactive as possible. Ultrasonic testing aided by advanced digital signal analysis can solve this problem. Ultrasonic testing of the end-cap weld joints poses several difficulties due to: (i) small dimensions (diameter of the tube and the wall thickness etc.) involved, (ii) abnormal weld contours and (iii) stringent sensitivity requirements. The use of signal analysis technique on the ultrasonic echoes was expected to overcome these difficulties.

A study was carried out at the authors' laboratory to this effect. In order to simulate the idealistic conditions, reference defects (holes) of 0.1 mm dia. and depth of 5, 10 and 20% of the wall thickness (W_t) were introduced at the ID region and also on the OD region of the weld joint using spark erosion machining. The reference defects were selected in order to find the level of detection sensitivity achievable and extract information on the defect sizes. The ultrasonic testing of the weld region is based on angle beam with shear waves using immersion pulse echo method.

Since the signals from the geometrical features of the weld joints were found to vary between 17 and 35% full scale height (FSH), only OD defects of 20% wt. and above could be detected reliably by conventional UT technique. In case of 10 and 5% wt. defects, the signals from the defects were fully masked by the signals due to geometrical feature. Hence, in order to increase the sensitivity of defect detection down to 10% wt. or less, digital signal analysis technique, particularly auto power spectral analysis, was explored. The auto power spectra of signals from the defects have a broad envelope pattern with or without small fluctuations in the spectrum envelopes (Fig. 6.25).

In case of auto power spectra of signals due to the geometrical upset, the spectrum envelope has large fluctuations in its power (a number of narrow packets), often attaining zero or near zero values (Fig. 6.25), which is not observed in the case of defect signal auto power spectra. In case of signals from geometrical upset, a large number of reflecting points from the boundary of the geometric upset causes signals with similar spectral content but with a change in the phase dut to temporal variation (different time of flight values of the ultrasonic signal reflecting from different points of the geometric upset) and the same can be explained as follows:

The spectral content from any two points on the geometric upset giving identical amplitude but with 180° phase difference would get cancelled. Thus, the spectral pattern from the geometric upset manifests as large fluctuations in its power, i.e. a number of narrow packets. Presence of a defect which shadows a portion of the geometric upset leads to reduced chances for obtaining signals with 180° phase difference thus reducing the chance for observing extensive fluctuations. Even with a defect (0.034 mm) much smaller than the wavelength

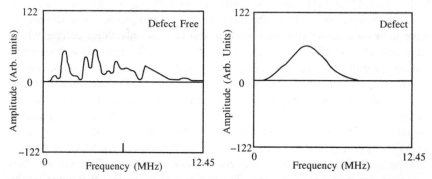

Fig. 6.25   Autopower spectra of ultrasonic signals from geometric upset (defect free) and a defect

(0.236 mm), it is possible to detect the defects because of the shadowing effect. This explanation suggests that even when the defect is of the order of wavelength also, it is possible to detect the defects, without having the problem of multiple echoes and fluctuations in the power spectrum. It should be noted that the methodology adopted is essentially for detection of defects much smaller than the wavelength of the ultrasonic beam used. For defects of the order of wavelength, the conventional ultrasonic approaches without resorting to advanced signal analysis would be adequate. After establishing this approach with the help of fine artificial defects, a large number of production end cap welds which passed helium leak testing were subjected to digital ultrasonic signal analysis tests. The results from these studies were in confirmation with the earlier studies on artificial defects, thus establishing the validity of the signal analysis approach for defect detection in these weldments. This approach also paved the way for design and use of an automated workstation through which probe scanning, signal acquisition, digitation and analysis, and classification can be performed.

6.8.2 The B Scan Display

It is a plot of time versus distance, in which one orthogonal axis on the display corresponds to elapsed time while the other axis represents the position of the transducer along a line on the surface of the test piece relative to the position of the transducer at the start of the inspection. Echo intensity is not measured directly as in A-Scan but often indicated semiquantitatively by the relative brightness of echo indications on an oscilloscope screen.

B scan display can be similar to an imaging cross section through the test piece, where both front and back surfaces are shown in profile. Indications from reflecting interfaces (defects) within the test piece are also shown in the profile and the position, orientation and depth of such interfaces along the imaginary cutting plane are revealed. A typical 'B' scan system is shown in Fig. 6.26. The chief value of B-Scan presentation is its ability to reveal the distribution of flaws in a cross section of a part. Although B-Scan techniques have been more widely used in medical applications than in industrial, it can be used for the rapid scanning of complete welding parts or portions of certain parts.

6.8.3 The C-Scan Display

It records echoes from internal portions of test pieces as a function of the position of each reflecting interface within an area. Flaws are shown on a readout, superimposed on a plan view of the test piece and both flaw size (flaw area) and position within the plan view are recorded. Flaw depth is not recorded. In a basic C-Scan system (Fig. 6.27), the search unit is moved over the surface of the test piece in a search pattern. The search pattern can be a series of closely spaced parallel lines, or a fine zig-zag pattern or a spiral pattern. Mechanical linkage connects the search unit to X- and Y-axis position indicators which in turn feed position data to the X-Y plotter. Each recording system varies—some produce a shaded-line scan with echo intensity recorded as a variation in line shading while others indicate flaws by an absence of shading so that each flaw shows up as a blank space on the display.

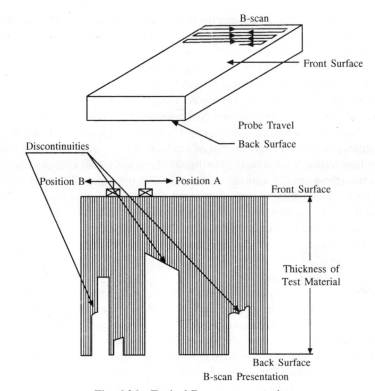

Fig. 6.26   Typical B-scan presentation

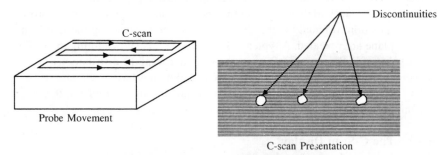

C-scan Presentation

Fig. 6.27   Typical C-scan presentation

An electronic depth gate is another essential element in C-Scan systems. It measures time of flight data and allows only those echo signals that are received within a limited range of delay times following the initial pulse to be admitted to the receiver-amplifier circuit. Some C-Scan systems incorporate additional electronic gating circuits for marking, giving alarm or recording. These gates can record or indicate information such as flaw depth or loss of back reflection, while the main display records an overall picture of flaw distribution.

6.8.4   Synthetic Aperture Focussing Technique (SAFT)
A major application of this technique is to characterise the defect for quantitative

evaluation and also to enable application of fracture mechanics based concepts for estimation of the remaining life of a welded component. In this method, analysis of the received ultrasonic signals is done either by stationary methods, where at fixed probe positions, all the echoes from a defect - direct as well as satellite echoes - are compared with the results of calculated or measured echoes of typical defects (modelling) or by moving the probe along the surface and picking up the echoes for all probe positions thus synthesising an aperture. The basic idea of a synthetic aperture is to measure the complete sound field scattered by a defect on an orbit S_m around the defect as shown in Fig. 6.28. During re-construction, this sound field is calculated back into that region where the scattering occurred, making use of well known scaler wave propagation formulae. The result is the three dimensional amplitude distribution of the sound field inside the orbit. In an ideal case, this will be non-zero only on the surface of the scatterer, thus enabling an image of the defet by describing its surface. Since a 360° scanning around a defect may be possible only in a few cases like rods or turbine rotors, one is forced to reduce the aperture to that part of the surface which is accessible. Therefore only that part of the defect may be imaged which could be insonified during scanning the aperture.

To maximize the illuminated area of the defect, probes with large beam opening angle have to be used, that is small probes or the defocussed part of the farfield of focus probes. In addition, it is possible to synthesise the scanning around the defect using different insonification angles and different inspection

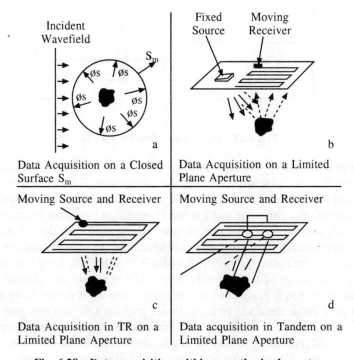

Fig. 6.28 Data acquisition within a synthesized aperture.

techniques like pitch-catch or tandem. Data acquisition involves scanning of the probe on the surface and recording complete rf-echo signals coming back from the specimen. That is, for each probe position (X, Y) inside the scanned aperture, the complete received ultrasonic signals are stored as an input for the SAFT— algorithm as shown schematically in Fig. 6.29. By using suitable algorithms, three dimensional amplitude distribution inside the specimen (D-Scan) is obtained. When scanning is done in one direction (X), we get only two dimensional amplitude distribution corresponding to the area below the scanned line and perpendicular to the scanned surface thus performing a side view (B-Scan).

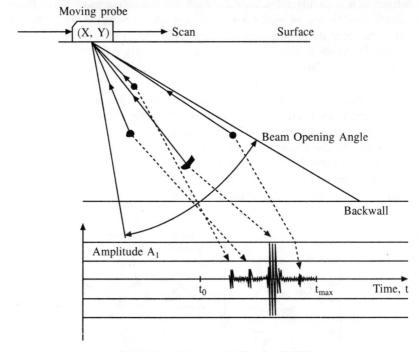

Fig. 6.29   Data acquisition for SAFT.

Typical case study: A study was carried out in the authors' laboratory on a carbon steel 'TEE' joint with stainless steel weldment (Fig. 6.30). The 'TEE' joint contained four side drilled holes at different depths in the stainless steel side. Conventional ultrasonic angle beam examination could not be carried out successfully due to poor signal to nose ratio. Strong echo from the carbon steel/ stainless steel weld overlay interface was obtained thereby reducing the sensitivity of detection of the holes. Using SAFT with a 2.25 MHz frequency longitudinal probe, a clear image of the reference holes (defects) could be obtained at the expected depth. Angle beam examination using shear wave probes of 45 and 70 degrees gave better results in terms of image contrast and with less gain in dB (Fig. 6.31). Based on the standardized test parameters, actual testing was carried out on a 'TEE' joint using 45 and 70 degree angle beam probes using a manual scanner. Figure 6.32 shows the SAFT pattern obtained from a 3 mm diameter hole in the SS weldment.

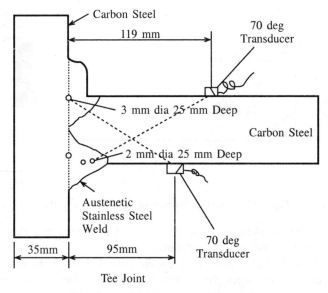

Fig. 6.30 Dissimilar weld (Tee joint).

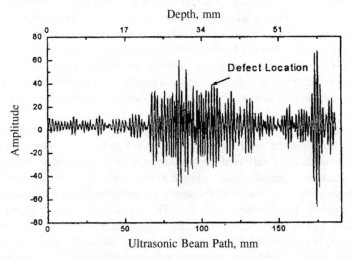

Fig. 6.31 Typical A scan pattern.

6.8.5 Time of Flight Diffraction Technique (TOFD)

This has the ability to capture high resolution, low amplitude signals and perform real-time processing to carry out crack tip diffraction examination by using the acclaimed time of flight diffraction (TOFD) technique. It lends itself ideally to fast volumetric detection applications where inspection results need to be of sufficient quality to enable decisive on-line action. This speed is achieved by virtue of the fact that a wide beam, tandem array of transducers and scanned parallel to the weld, are usually sufficient to achieve full coverage and scan rates upto 50 mm/s. This approach overcomes the need for comprehensive raster

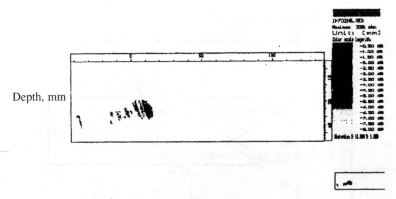

Fig. 6.32   SAFT pattern from a 3 mm dia hole.

scanning and probe skewing to optimise signal responses and thus massive reduction in the amount of data generated.

As TOFD technique relies solely on the time separation between signals diffracted only from the edges of the defects (Fig. 6.33)—rather than conventionally reflected energy—it can be performed almost independently of amplitude response and thus the coupling quality, material attenuation and defect orientation are much less critical than with conventional pulse-echo methods. It is for this reason that the TOFD method of inspection is now recognised as one of the reliable and accurate means of defect detection and sizing. The major advantage of the TOFD mode of operation is the on-line graphic display of inspection data. This presents the operator with a real-time radiographic-type image, representing a through wall section along the weld axis with defects shown in their true length and accurate sectional location and size.

One possibility for improving the decision making capability, based upon the size of the defect in the depth direction, is to move away from techniques based upon the amplitude of reflected signals towards such concepts as the time of flight diffraction techniques as developed at National NDT Centre, Harwell.

The basis of this technique relies on the measurement of the transit time of ultrasonic echoes from defect extremities. The interaction of an ultrasonic beam with a crack like defect gives rise not only to a specular reflection from the face of the crack but also to two cylindrical diffracted waves from the crack tips. Since these waves effectively have their origin at the defect extremities, it is clear that their time delay or phase relationship can provide data on the separation

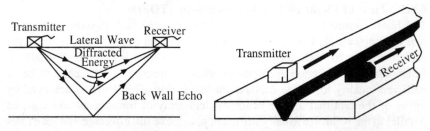

Fig. 6.33   TOFD technique.

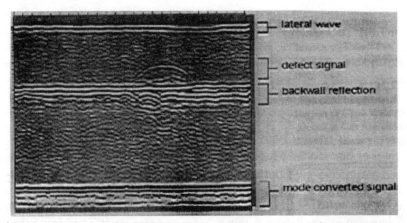

Fig. 6.34 Typical TOFD image (Courtesy: The American Society for NDT).

of the crack tips and thus on the size of the crack. Single probe and two probe examination using both compressional and shear wave ultrasound have been carried out and the data are analysed directly in the time domain or by the use of spectral techniques.

Single Probe Time-of-Flight Techniques: This approach, irrespective of use of compressional wave or shear wave, works well for the nearer (upper) crack tip but less well for the most distant tip. Normally the crack tip location is calculated from the range of the echo and the angle of the probe. To gain sufficient accuracy, the beam spread must be limited so that angle is well defined. This means that the probe should be scanned in two dimensions which makes the technique more useful for hand scanning work than for automated studies.

Two Probe Shear Wave Time-of-Flight Techniques: In the two probe approach, the relative times-of-flight of the echoes from the defect extremities provides an indication of the defect depth. Since only time delay is used in the analysis, broad beam probes can be used to cover greater depths of materials. With shear waves, no greater efficiency is obtained with steeply angled probes and close separations between the probes. This gives rise to two practical problems; firstly the energy diffracted from the lower extremity of the crack may interact again with the crack producing a weak or misplaced signal; and secondly lateral scanning is again required in order to accurately define the crack depth. An additional problem is that the mode converted energy can produce interfering pulses which arrive earlier than the pulses of interest. This could be a serious limitation if the technique is used to locate defects.

Two Probe Compressional Wave Time-of-Flight Techniques: This approach utilises the earliest arrival of pulses thus minimising problems due to mode conversion. In addition, the probes can be more widely spaced which allows a single linear scan to be used to accurately size defects in the through-thickness direction. This mode of operation has been the most commonly used among the various alternatives mentioned above.

Data Analysis: Broadly, the analysis of the data in the time domain is favoured since information on the order of arrival of the pulses is retained. This information is lost in frequency domain analysis. In addition, it is generally true that the resolution is not improved by frequency domain analysis because there is an underlying link between bandwidth and pulse length. However, spectral analysis in conjunction with these probes could provide additional information on defect characterisation.

In terms of defect sizing, the time-of-flight technique has been used to examine specimens, containing both crack-like and volumetric defects. There is also a development in AERE-Harwell of using multi-probe system (instead of two probe system) capable of inspecting the given weld region of the pressure vessel as well as building a prototype nozzle scanner based on the same technique. The multiprobe system will be capable of detecting and locating defects in the given weld region throughout the full thickness of the pressure vessel. It uses sixteen probes controlled by a computer with automated data acquisition and processing. It is intended to size defects within ± 2 mm and size all defects greater than 5 mm in depth below the interface between the stainless steel cladding and the carbon steel plate.

6.8.6 Phased Array Probes

The general test procedure followed for pre and in-service inspection of reactor pressure vessels is the use of 0 and 70° longitudinal wave probes, 45, 60 and 70° transverse wave inspection with single and T-R (SE) probe technique as well as the Tandem technique. These techniques employ a large number of transducers in a multiprobe arrangement (Fig. 6.35). The possibility of replacement of most of these probes by an optimized linear array has been explored by Fraunhofer Institute for NDT (IZFP), Germany. Because of the high flexibility due to the electronic steering feature, the advantages of the linear array probe are obviously two fold: (a) reduction in preparation time and (b) amelioration of the system performance with regard to defect detection and defect analysis.

With linear array probes, the sound field can be steered in one plane, and perpendicular to this plane, the field parameters are determined by the geometry of the active area of the probe.

In the case of complicated shapes of the components, it may be necessary to steer and focus the ultrasonic beam not only in one plane but rather three dimensionally (example: inspection of the perforated area of the bottom and top portions of pressurized water reactors). The inspection of the web and the weldments requires the variation of the angle of incidence, the focus depth and the orientation to the plane of incidence. The optimal solution to this problem is a planar array. For the computerized design and optimisation of linear and planar array probes, extensive software packages have been developed.

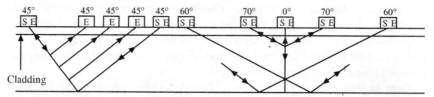

Fig. 6.35   Multiprobe arrangement for reactor pressure vessel inspection.

The important array probe parameters are: (1) frequency, (2) wave mode (longitudinal, transverse, and surface waves), (3) beam width, (4) near field length, (5) bandwidth, (6) pulse length, (7) dead zone, (8) sensitivity, (9) electrical and acoustical cross coupling and (10) gain reserve. The parameters (2) to (4), at a given centre frequency, are dependent on the dimensions of the total aperture, the centre-to-centre spacing of the transducer elements, element number, size and shape of the elements. The parameters (5) to (10) are also influenced by the geometry of the transducer elements. In addition to this, the electrical parameters, the electrical matching and the acoustical matching are of importance.

6.9 AUTOMATED PIPE SCANNER FOR ULTRASONIC INSPECTION OF WELDMENTS

The primary objective of the development of automated pipe scanner is for the inspection of welds in nuclear piping systems whereby eliminating human (manual scanning) errors. This will significantly improve the accuracy and repeatability of ultrasonic data obtained during plant inspections. These scanners are designed to meet a set of requirements that include easy portability, rapid installation and removal and accurate and repeatable positioning during the data-acquisition process.

Inspection of Boiling Water Reactor (BWR) safety class systems using these scanners led to detection of numerous transverse and longitudinal cracks near welds in the austenitic stainless steel piping. Many of these cracks were detected by ultrasonic testing technique during field inspection. In some cases, the cracks were detected not by ultrasonic inspection but because of water leaks.

Problems associated with detection of intergranular stress corrosion cracking are numerous. Differentiating between geometric reflectors and cracks is often difficult. Resolution of flaw signals may be difficult because of the weld root signal and the weld crown may interface with positioning the ultrasonic search units. Also, because most pipe inspections are conducted manually, the skill and consistency of the inspectors are significant factors. The effectiveness of the operator is often reduced by an undesirable working environment like high radiation levels, elevated temperature, high humidity and poor accessibility.

The successful development of a scanner and search head has provided solution to a number of problems encountered during inspection by the personnel who operate the mechanical scanning equipment. The field inspection problems are: (1) physical limitations, (2) environmental considerations, (3) operational requirements and (4) ultrasonic requirements.

Physical parameters that must be considered in the establishment of pipe scanning requirements include the spatial constraint available around the weldment where the scanner must operate, scanner weight and size of the pipe and weld surface conditions, installation prerequisites and time.

Weight and size of the scanner must permit relatively fast transport into and out of containment building. The physical size limitation is defined by the volume of components that can be transported, installed and removed quickly by one or two people. An operator independent system would consist of a scanning device which could be used on various pipe geometries by workers with minimal training.

Once installed, the device would automatically scan the weld and transmit all the necessary position and ultrasonic data to a central processing unit for monitoring and/or storage. Such a controlled system removes the shortcoming of uncertainty in the skill of the operator during manual scanning in the acquisition of data. All parts of the system would be reliable both in recording and/or displaying data, and in the physical sense of being rugged and maximum availability with minimum maintenance.

The data displayed must offer high resolution and precision necessary to accurately detect and size the smallest flaw without misinterpretation due to the physical nature or microstructure of the material being examind. The system should allow permanent storage of all data in an easy to use format. This storage should allow for recalling the data at any time in the future to compare subsequent examination results to base line data. The system should allow for all forms of data manipulation desired to fully characterize the nature of indication and measure the size of a flaw. If the data manipulation allows for these goals, the display will be easy to interpret. A system which exists today that meets many of the features described above is the P-Scan system originally developed by the Danish Welding Institute. Det Norske Veritas (DNV) in Norway, Independent Testing Laboratories (ITL) in the United States have developed the FLAG system and demonstrated many practical uses such as corrosion mapping and IGSCC detection in piping systems in nuclear power plants.

The FLAG system (Fig. 6.36) consists of: (1) precision scanners for guiding the ultrasonic probes along the weld with position encoders continuously transmitting the position of the probes and the beam direction to the data processor, (2) high resolution, dual-channel signal transmitter and processor utilising logarithmic amplifiers for wide dynamic range and direct conversion of echo amplitudes to the logarithmic dB scale, (3) computer and interface unit for temporary storage of scan parameters, echo signals and probe position signals. The computer is the heart of the system, controlling the transmitter and receiver circuitry, as well as storing and displaying signals on the cathode ray monitors. Software and data are recorded, permanently stored and read by two cassette tape drives, (4) control of the system by the operator is via a keyboard with system settings and operations under software control and (5) prints of P-Scan displays are available from a hard copy unit (Fig. 6.37).

Automatic scanners have been developed to allow rapid inspection of pipe welds and for use in radioactive environments to minimize occupational radiation exposure. Provided the drive strip and the guide chain are securely anchored, the scanner can also operate on large diameter vessels or tank bottoms. In this type of scanner, two angle beam probes scan the weld from both sides simultaneously in a rectangular or zig-zag pattern. Depending on the thickness, surface conditions and resolution required, scan speeds may vary from 10 to 36 m/h. A toothed belt, slipped around the circumference of a pipe, holds the scanner in place and serves to drive the probes. A circumferentially mounted metal chain is used to guide the scanner and provide a reference point. The scanner has two motors for providing X and Y motion viz. position encoders, which transmit the X-Y coordinates of the probes to the processor. Hardware and software for recording and displaying transverse defects are incorporated suitably in the system.

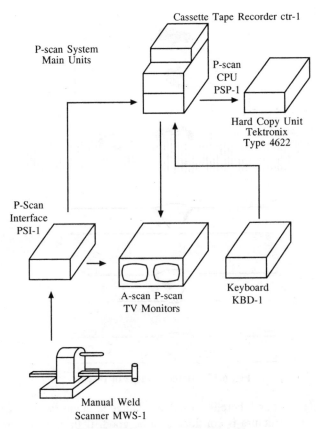

Fig. 6.36 P-scan system (FLAG)

6.10 DRY COUPLANT TECHNIQUE

In the field of ultrasonics, the advent of dry scan techniques has widened the horizon of applications (Fig. 6.38). It is now possible to inspect reliably adhesive bonds in non-metallic materials such as composites and honeycomb structures, and weldments with complex geometries where conventional ultrasonic techniques do not give satisfactory results.

The basic principle of this method is the transmission of ultrasonic energy into the material at one point and the reception of the energy at another point after it has travelled through the material. The interpretation of the differences in the received energy levels and the displacement time, indicates the presence or absence of flaws within the material under test. The two main factors governing the technique are Intensity and Displacement. The system must be tuned by the discriminator with the appropriate frequency range selected on the flaw detector. The CRT pattern will show a number of cycles over a known time. The received signals have a typical "beat pattern". The condition of the material is decided from the intensity of the received signal, the displacement or the point of start of the first half cycle of this wave on the time base and the shape of the interference pattern. If the beat pattern looks normal that is the first group has between seven

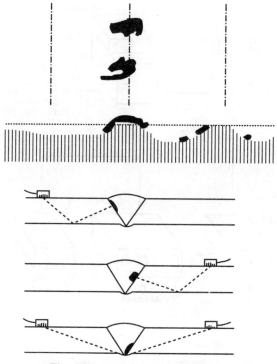

Fig. 6.37   Defect images of P-scan

and ten cycles in it and there is no sudden change in intensity between adjacent cycles then the structure is considered to be good. If there is a change in the intensity of the beat pattern then this can be seen as flaws lying within the zone of the beam spread which causes part of the beam energy to be redirected away from the receiver. Complete loss of signal indicates crack or lamination at the point of test.

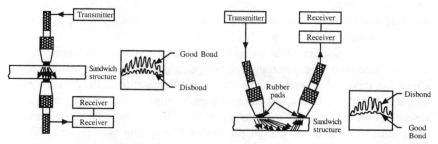

Fig. 6.38   Principle of dry-couplant technique through transmission and pitch catch

6.11   ACOUSTIC HOLOGRAPHY

Holography is a method used in optics to provide an accurate three dimensional image of a given object. It is carried out in two stages. In the first stage, a permanent record in the form of a two-dimensional pattern of optical fringes, called the hologram, is obtained on a photographic plate. In the second stage, the image of the original object is reconstructed from the hologram.

Ordinary photography records only the intensity distribution of light from an object while the phase information is lost and therefore no feeling of depth is obtained. Holography records both phase and intensity distribution. With the optical technique, a coherent monochromatic beam (a very long train of light waves having a single frequency as obtained from a laser source) is incident partly at a mirror and partly at the object under examination. Interference of light reflected at the mirror (the reference beam) with light scattered from the illuminated object takes place at the photographic plate. The plate is developed after exposure and a complicated system of optical fringes (the hologram) appears on the surface. Two 3-D images, one real and the other virtual, are obtained from the hologram as a result of diffraction of the laser beam by the plate. The virtual image can be observed with the naked eye. This image is three dimensional and is entirely free from aberrations. With ultrasonic holography, an optical hologram is prepared using a technique different from the optical holography, but the method of viewing the final image is the same.

Utrasound is a wave motion and, like light, can be made to form images in a similar manner. That is, an object is illuminated with ultrasound and the scattered ultrasound is collected by an ultrasonic lens or mirror which focuses the image in some convenient plane, where it is converted into an optical image by a suitable sensor. Since ultrasound penetrates opaque bodies, the idea of being able to see their interiors and measure their internal structures is very attractive and has significant advantages over the more usual A, B and C scans. In late 1940s, Gabor demonstrated that it is possible to record a three dimensional image on a two dimensional photographic plate using coherent light.

Two transducers driven from the same generator are placed in a water tank and oriented so that their beams overlap at the water surface. In addition to the surface displacement, the interference pattern of the beams produces a static ripple pattern. When an object is placed in the path of one of the beams, the other beam serves as the reference, with the result ripple pattern is modified by the sound scattered by the object. The resultant static surface displacement is the ultrasonic hologram. This is then used as an optical phase hologram and the ultrasonic images are viewed by means of coherent light reflected from the hologram. Use of different methods of acoustical holography in non-destructive inspection work is being conducted very intensely. The capability of imaging of defects in the form of foreign inclusions, cracks in metals, weld joints and tubing and defects in large forgings has been demonstrated.

6.12 TOMOGRAPHY

Tomographic imaging is the reconstruction of a tomographic plane or slice of an object by a computer. Several types of energy including ultrasound are used to obtain such imaging. Tomograph of an object is a two-dimensional picture of a thin cross section of an object. This can be at any location and orientation. This cross sectional method eliminates the superposition of features that occurs when a three-dimensional object is displayed in a two-dimensional imaging format. The use of computers provides facility for image enhancement.

Reflective and transmission are the two types of tomography. Reflective ultrasonic tomography is used to locate and size defects. Transmission type is used to find out differences in density, residual stress and composition of materials. Reflection tomography is an outcome of the transmission technique and is designed for providing quantitative images displaying a specific acoustic parameter of the test material. The amplitude and time of flight of the signal give information about the size and location of the defects detected. The shape of the discontinuity can be estimated by successive scans around the defect.

Tomography requires more computer hardware and software than conventional ultrasonic techniques. The main constituents of the hardware system are data acquisition and storage, data processing and image display of the processed data. The transducers used for data acquisition are either single or phased arrays immersed in a immersion tank. Both normal and angle beam types are used. During scanning, the transducer is moved across the plane of the test object with several degrees of freedom to follow the contour of the object even it is irregular. The raw scanned data is stored and processed. Calculations are made on the data acquired to get the two dimensional cross sectional image of the object.

Ultrasonic tomography has many advantages for nondestructive tests. It gives increased spatial resolution by an order of magnitude which is limited by the ultrasonic pulse length, less imaging errors, and has wide dynamic range. In addition, computed tomographic images are providing quantitative and qualitative information since the data are mathematically derived. Since the images are digital, image enhancement algorithms can be used.

The technique has many applications like testing of complex geometries and assembled components, capability of detecting linear and planar defects and determining the size and location of defects. It is used for detection of debonds, stress corrosion and erosion in pipe and weld anomalies.

6.13   ELECTROMAGNETIC ACOUSTIC TRANSDUCERS (EMATs)

Ultrasonic NDT techniques employing Longitudinal (L) or Shear Vertical (SV) waves generated by piezoelectric transducer are widely used for pre-service and in-service inspection of industrial components and structures. One of the essential requirements of piezoelectric transducer based ultrasonic NDT is ensuring acoustic coupling between the transducer and the object under examination. This is in general achieved by placing the object in a tank filled with water/fluid or by applying a thin layer of couplant between the transducer and the object surface. Accidental discovery in 1967 that electromagnetic radiation can excite acoustic resonances in single crystal discs of Bi and Al at liquid Helium temperatures without making any contact to samples and with apparently strong coupling to the conduction of electrons in the crystals led to a number of investigations on the properties of "Electromagnetic Acoustic Transducers (EMAT)" and their application to NDT. Significant progress took place in the last three decades and a variety of inspection problems were elegantly solved by the use of EMATs, among others, worth mentioning are the inspection of moving, hot objects and the difficult-to-inspect anisotropic welds. A brief description of the structure, design and features of EMATs is given in the following sections.

6.13.1   Structure and Design of EMATs

EMATs are the devices that essentially consist of a stack of wires and magnets to excite and detect ultrasonic waves in an electrically conductive material, be it magnetic or non-magnetic. When EMAT transmitter is placed near an electrically conducting material, not necessarily in contact with, ultrasonic waves are launched into the material through the reaction of induced eddy currents and static magnetic fields. This eliminates the problems associated with acoustic coupling to the metal part under examination as the electromechanical conversion takes place directly within the electromagnetic skin depth of the metal. Thus, EMATs allow operation without contact at elevated temperatures and in remote locations. When a wire is placed near to the surface of an electrically conducting object and is driven by a current at the desired ultrasonic frequency, eddy currents will be induced in a near surface region called skin depth. In the presence of a static magnetic field, these currents will experience Lorenz forces,

$$f = J \times B_0$$

where f is a body force per unit volume, J the induced dynamic current density and B_0 the static magnetic induction. Through a variety of interactions, these forces are transmitted to the lattice and serve as a source of ultrasonic waves. The internal structure of an EMAT and its radiation pattern are shown in Fig. 6.39. The interaction is different in non-magnetic and magnetic materials. EMATs are reciprocal devices i.e. they can be used for receivers as well as transmitters of ultrasound. By reciprocal processes, the receiver EMAT generates a voltage when the surface of the metal underneath is set into motion by an incident ultrasonic wave.

The finite sets of wires and magnets that comprise EMATs can be arranged in various combinations to excite a variety of ultrasonic wave modes. The overall practical EMATs generally fall into one of the following types (Fig. 6.40):

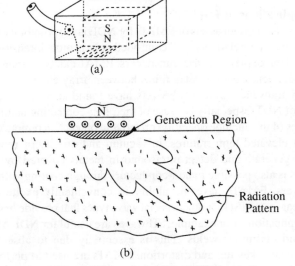

Fig. 6.39   EMAT probe and its radiation pattern.

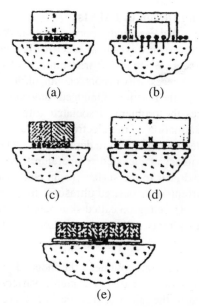

**Fig. 6.40   Various EMAT configuration (a) spiral (b) Tangential field (c) Normal
field (d) Meander coil (e) Periodic permanent magnet.**

(a)   Radially polarised shear waves propagating normal to the specimen surface.

(b)   Longitudinal waves propagating normal to the specimen surface.

(c)   Shear plane polarised waves propagating normal to the surface.

(d)   Longitudinal or vertically polarised shear waves propagating at oblique
      angles, Rayleigh waves or guided wave modes of plates.

(e)   Horizontally polarised shear horizontal (SH) waves propagating at oblique
      angles or guided SH modes of plates.

6.13.2   Applications of EMATs

One of the most important assets of EMATs for NDE is the possibility of producing
an ultrasonic beam of relatively well controlled polarization, intensity and angular
distribution. Unlike piezoelectric transducers, EMAT can be scanned in an angle
by varying frequency and/or delay times between array elements in the case of
phased array transducer systems. EMATs have found attractive applications in
many areas of NDT, especially because of their non-contacting nature. Important
consequences of this include operation on moving objects, in remote or hazardous
locations, at elevated temperatures, in vacuum and on oily or rough surfaces.
EMATs can generate and detect ultrasound in metals covered by a protective
coating. This is also possible in non-conductors through coating with conducting
skins or layers. EMATs have the ability to conveniently excite horizontally
polarised shear waves (SH) or other special wave types that provide best advantages
in certain applications. For example, SH waves are useful for NDE of anisotropic
austenitic and dissimilar welds. This is essentially due to absence of mode
conversion, beam skewing and distortion. EMATs are used to perform absolute
measurements on the sound field and are more reproducible than the piezoelectric

transducers. For these reasons, the EMATs are used extensively in the calibration of other types of transducers. Because of the ability of EMAT to operate at high speed and elevated temperatures, thickness gauging is well suited for on-line measurements, during material processing.

6.13.3 EMAT Generated Shear Horizontal Waves for NDE

Ultrasonic waves generated by EMATs are gaining importance in many industrial applications. One ultrasonic wave mode that has provided solutions to many inspection problems is SH waves. SH waves can be generated by using conventional piezoelectric transducers as well as by using EMATs. In the former case, though it is possible in principle, in practice these transducers are not effective due to coupling problems. In the latter case, it is quite easy and the transduction is effective enough to use these waves for practical applications. Different EMAT configurations are used to launch SH waves in non-ferromagnetic materials, as the interaction is different. In non-ferromagnetic electrically conducting materials, the EMAT configuration consists of an arrangement of Periodic Permanent Magnets (PPM) as illustrated in Fig. 6.41 and the SH waves are excited by Lorentz forces. For ferromagnetic material, EMAT configuration consists of an rf coil arrangement in a meander fashion and an U-shaped electromagnet is used and the SH waves are excited by magnetostriction. The angle of incidence α is varied by suitably changing the frequency f, thereby the wavelength λ_s. However, the non-segmented permanent magnet based EMATs of the end-fire type suffer from inadequate side lobe suppression and have the disadvantage of bidirectional radiation and narrow band waveforms. Beam steering can only be performed by changing the frequency of the transmitted wave and therefore also the wavelength. To overcome these disadvantages, angle beam EMATs are designed as phased arrays by dividing the whole transducer aperture into multiple segments which are excited with appropriate time delay. Essentially, phased array EMATs consist of several small, discrete elements rather than the series connected meander, multi-period radio-frequency coils that excite narrow band, obliquely propagating bulk waves. When the discrete elements are appropriately driven, the EMAT phased arrays exhibit a

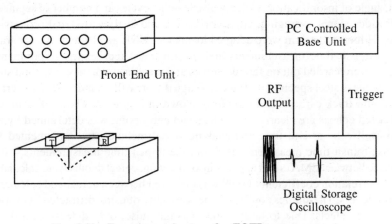

Fig. 6.41 Experimental set up for TOFD measurements

unidirectional directivity pattern and produce broad band signals of controlled direction and focusing. The phased array EMATs provide a greater flexibility in both the selection of wave modes and angles of propagation. The time delayed transmitted signals interfere constructively in the far-field under a pre-selected angle α given by the relation

$$\alpha = \sin^{-1} (C_t \, \Delta t/D)$$

where Δt is the time delay, D the spacing between the segments and C_t the shear wave velocity of sound in the material. Due to the smaller aperture of the array-elements, shorter ultrasonic pulses are radiated, yielding a short pulse of the interfered signal in the far field. This phased array principle helps to enlarge the beam width, furthermore it improves the signal-to-noise ratio. Further, given the ability to operate when the test object is moving past the EMAT at production speeds, it would be possible with phased arrays to be able to rapidly change the characteristics of the interrogating radiation, to obtain as much information as possible.

6.13.4   Defect Characterisation using EMAT Generated SH Waves

Considering the many advantageous features of SH waves over Longitudinal and Shear Vertical (SV) waves, experimental studies were carried out at IZFP (Germany) to detect and characterise defects in materials. Sizing of defects using reflected signal amplitude based methods such as 6 dB and 20 dB drop methods etc. is most common. However, in many situations under or oversizing is reported. On the other hand, the time-of-flight based methods are found to size the defects more accurately. One such method is the TOFD method which uses the timing of pulses diffracted from the tips of a defect to determine the size of the defect (Sec. 6.8.5). Experimental investigations were carried out using the SH waves generated by EMATs for defect sizing by TOFD method. Two 8-segmented EMATs were designed for their use as transmitter and receiver in pitch-catch mode (Fig. 6.41). Test and instrument parameters were optimised for high sensitive detection of diffracted signals.

The optimum parameters arrived at were: distance between EMATs was 40 mm, angle of insonification 52 deg, pulse length 2 cycles and number of segments 4. Besides signal averaging, cross-correlation and analytical signal processing using Hilbert transform were adopted to enhance SNR and to improve accuracy in the transit time measurements and in turn the defect sizing. Experimental studies were carried out on fatigue cracks and machined notches in carbon steel and stainless steel specimens. Typical rf signal from a 28 mm deep fatigue crack in 56 mm thick carbon steel sample is shown in Fig. 6.42. The back wall and diffracted echoes are clearly seen. The beam entry point was determined by the back-wall echo arrival time and analytic signal method was implemented for precise transit time measurements. From the transit time measurements, using distance between EMATs and angle of insonification, defect depths were calculated and a correlation coefficient of 0.99 was observed between actual and calculated defect depths. The studies confirmed the feasibility of using diffracted SH waves for sizing defects. Due to large initial leakage pulse, only defects with depth exceeding 12 mm could be detected.

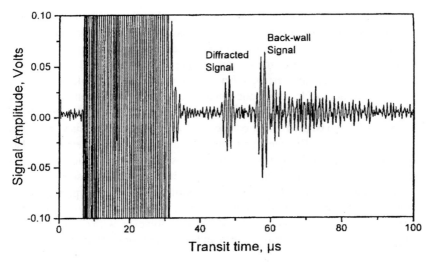

Fig. 6.42   Typical RF signal from a fatigue crack

Another study pertains to detection and characterisation of fatigue cracks and machined notches in anisotropic stainless steel welds which is rather difficult using L or SV waves due to beam skewing and mode conversion problems. However, the situation is different for SH waves. Experimental studies were carried out using SH waves. Four segment T/R EMATs operating at 1 MHz were scanned along the length of the weld at a predetermined distance from the weld center line. The rf signals from defect locations were digitised and stored in a personal computer. Signal envelopes were generated using analytic signal method. Considering the variations in the envelopes of the analytic signals from defects at top and bottom locations, a set of representitative parameters were computed and processed by a feed-forward error back propagation Artificial Neural Network (ANN) methodology to characterise defects. The parameters chosen are: rise time, fall time, peak height, full-width-at-half-maximum, mean, standard deviation and skewness. During the training phase of the ANN, the interconnecting weights of the network were adjusted in such a way that the network learned the relationship between the eight parameters generated from the envelopes and the desired output i.e. defect top (0) or bottom (1). With a mere 50 iterations, convergence was observed and a success rate of 100% was achieved, confirming the exactness of the chosen parameters. This methodology is particularly attractive for high temperature and radioactive components and also for components with limited access, primarily due to the fact that EMATs do not need couplant to transfer ultrasonic energy. Further, when the experimental conditions are fixed, it would be possible to implement this methodology on-line and to find location and size of the defects precisely.

6.13.5 Limitations of EMATs
Two major limitations in using EMATs for a number of practical applications are the physical size of the source of magnetic field (a few tens of millimeters) and the low transduction efficiency (due to weak Lorenz and magnetostrictive driving

forces) as compared to piezoelectric transducers. However, with the availability of high energy rare-earth magnets, it is now possible to construct small and high sensitive EMATs. Due to low transduction efficiency (commonly quoted as about 50 dB), only a small part of the rf energy entering the metal will be converted into acoustic energy, the rest being normally dissipated as Joule heat in the metal. The problem of low transduction efficiency can be overcome by the use of high transmitting currents, low noise receivers and careful electrical matching. Though EMATs can be used in non-contact manner, higher lift-off values drastically reduce the EMAT's efficiency and alter the directivity characteristics. Also, EMATs exhibit lower driving point impedances than piezoelectric transducers and are inductive rather than capacitive in character. Because of these differences, most commercially available ultrasonic instruments designed primarily for piezoelectric transducers will produce dynamic responses which are far-from-optimum when used in conjunction with EMATs. However, with simple redesign or augmentation, the same instruments can be adapted for use with EMATs with near-optimum results.

Further reading

1. Alers, G.A., Huebschen, G., Maxfield, B.W., Reblinger, W., Salzburger. H.J., Thomson, R.B. and Wilbrand, A. Electromagnetic Acoustic Transducers-Non-destructive testing handbook, ASNT, Columbus, OH 1991.
3. Baikee, et al, Ultrasonic Inspection of Austenitic Welds-Proceedings of International Conference on Non-destructive Examination in Nuclear Industry, ASM, Tests 1978.
4. Barat, P., Baldev Raj, Subramanian, C.V., Bhattacharya, D.K. Estimation of ultrasonic beam skewing in thick austenitic stainless steel weldments—A comparative study, Proceedings of 12th WCNDT, Navada, 1988.
15. Dijkstra, F.H., de Raad, J.A. and Boumen, T., TOFD and Acceptance Criteria, A Perfect Team,. Insight, Vol. 39, No. 4, 1997.
21. Gebhardt, W., Banity, F. and Woll, H. Defect Reconstruction and Classification of Phased Arrays, Materials Evaluation, Vol. 40, 1994-95.
37. Hubschen, G., Salzburger, H.J. and Kroning, M. UT of Bimetallic Welds by Shear Horizontal Waves and Electromagnetic Ultrasonic (EMUS) Probes, 12th International Conference on NDE in Nuclear and Pressure Vessels Industries.
60. Muller, W., Schmitz, V. and Schafer, G. Reconstruction by the Synthetic Aperture Focussing Technique, Nuclear Engineering and Design, North Holland, Amsterdam, 1994.
74. Rao, B.P.C. Internal Report No. 980133-TW, Frunhofer Institute for NDT-Saarbrucken, Germany, March, 1998.
82. Subramanian, C.V., Thavasimuthu, M., Rajagopalan, C., Kalyanasundaram, P. and Baldev Raj, Ultrasonic Test Procedure for Evaluating Fuel Clad Endcap Weld Joints of PHWRs, Materials Evaluation, 1995.
98. Handbook on the Ultrasonic Examination of Welds, The Welding Institute, Cambridge, 1979.
100. P-Scan System for Ultrasonic Weld Inspection, British Journal of NDT, 23 (3), 1981.
103. Considerations on Ultrasonic Testing of Austenitic SS Weld Joints, Doc. V. 704-81, Commission V of IIW, Welding in the World.

Chapter 7

Radiography Testing

The historic discovery of X-rays by Roengten (1895) and radioactivity by Becquerel (1896) with their subsequent and logical application to the examination of material objects provided the starting point for the development and advancement of industrial radiography. This is one of the most widely used NDT methods for the detection of internal defects such as porosity and voids. With proper orientation, planar defects can also be detected with radiography. It is also suitable for detecting changes in material composition, thickness measurement, and locating unwanted or defective components hidden from view in an assembled part. The basic advantage of the use of ionising radiations in NDT arises from the fact that the objects which can be examined can range in size and shapes from micro-miniature electronic parts to mammoth missiles or power plant structures. Ionising radiations, as the name implies are charged particle radiations such as protons, electrons, positrons etc. and electromagnetic radiations such as X-rays and gamma rays. The essential difference between X-rays and gamma rays and the other electromagnetic radiations such as light, ultraviolet and infrared rays from the view point of testing and evaluation is that X and gamma rays are able to penetrate matter which is opaque to light but have a photographic action similar to light.

The basic advantage of the use of ionising radiations in NDT arises from the fact that, ionising radiations can be used for testing a wide variety of materials ranging from light elements such as aluminium, beryllium and magnesium to steel, nickel and other heavy elements. The manufactured forms inspected by these radiations include a wide variety of castings, weldments, composites and assemblies.

7.1 BASIC PRINCIPLE

Radiography is a volumetric NDT method based on differential absorption of penetrating radiation by the component or test piece inspected using: (a) either electromagnetic radiations of very short wave lengths (X-rays or γ-rays), or (b) particle radiations (α, β or neutron). Because of differences in density and variation in thickness of the part or differences in absorption characteristics (causing change in density) caused by variations in composition and presence of defects, different portions of a test piece absorb different amounts of penetrating radiation.

In conventional radiography, an object is irradiated by a beam of X-rays (or γ rays) and the portion of the radiation that is not absorbed by the object impinges on a sheet of film. The unabsorbed radiation exposes the film emulsion, similar to the way light exposes the film in photography (Fig. 7.1). Development of the film produces an image that is a two dimensional shadow picture of the object. Variations in density, thickness or composition of the object being inspected, cause variations in the intensity of unabsorbed radiation and appear as variations in photographic density in the developed film. Evaluation of the radiograph is based on a comparison of the differences in photographic density with known characteristics of the object itself or defects present in the test object.

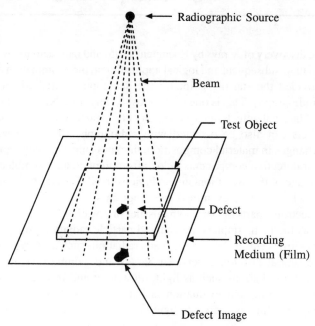

Fig. 7.1   Principle of radiographic inspection

In proton radiography, when a beam of mono-energetic protons is transmitted through the thickness of a material, most of the attenuation occurs after the beam has traversed through 90% of its range. It is possible to detect thickness changes of the order of 0.05% by proton radiography which is an order of magnitude better than with conventional radiographic sources. The advantage of mono-energetic proton radiography for NDT is its excellent thickness discrimination capability. In addition, the low attenuation of the beam over the first 80–90% of its range offers a potential advantage for radiography of biological specimens. The source of protons is often a cyclotron. The proton energy must be matched to specimen thickness. Film and intensifying screens used in proton radiography are similar to those used in conventional X-radiography.

7.2   GEOMETRIC FACTORS IN RADIOGRAPHY

The shadow of an object when exposed to X or γ-rays will naturally show some enlargement. Following conditions are to be fulfilled to produce the sharpest true shadow of the object.

(a) Source size should be as small as can be obtained.
(b) Source should be as far from the object as possible.
(c) The film should be closest to the object.
(d) X-rays shall be directed perpendicular to the recording surface.
(e) Plane of the object and plane of the film to be parallel.

In conventional radiography, the position of a flaw within the volume of a test piece cannot be determined exactly with a single radiograph, since depth parallel to the radiation beam is not recorded. However, techniques like stereoradiography, tomography, triangulation or simply making two or more exposures in different directions can help in locating flaws more exactly within the test-piece volume.

7.3 X-RADIOGRAPHY

In conventional radiography, the source of radiation is X-ray tube consisting of a source of electrons, an accelerating potential and a heavy element target with which the accelerated electrons interact to produce X-rays (Fig. 7.2). Coolidge (1913) built an X-ray tube which used a heated filament to produce electrons. The recent developments are more of electrical and electronics in nature. The replacement of oil insulation by SF_6 gas led to lighter and portable units and development of electronics led to the availability of constant potential units which give stable operating conditions. Replacement of glass tubes by metal ceramics led to an extension of tube life. Modern X-ray generators are available

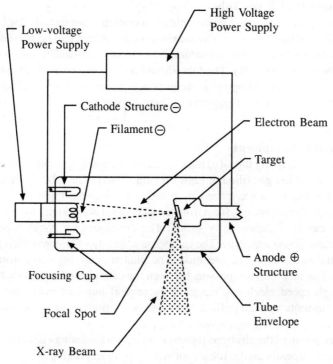

Fig. 7.2 Schematic sketch of X-radiography set up

upto 450 kV and 15 mA current. Also available are X-ray tubes in which voltage can be varied from 5 kV to 450 kV and systems with dual focal spot size and ultra small light weight (15 kg) portable X-ray equipments with an output of 200 kV and 3 mA. Effect of change in wavelength of X-rays with voltage and current is shown in Fig. 7.3 (a) and (b).

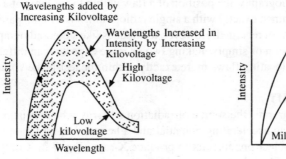

Curves illustrating the effect of a change in kilovoltage on the composition and intensity of an X-ray beam (after ulergy)

Curves illustrating the effect of a change in milliamperage on the intensity of an X-ray beam (after ulergy)

(a)   (b)

Fig. 7.3   Effect of change in wavelength of X-rays with voltage and current

7.3.1   Industrial X-ray Tubes

Industrial X-ray tubes must be capable of operating continuously for indefinite periods at maximum loading. The maximum current that can be passed through an X-ray tube is limited by: (a) saturation limit of the filament and (b) thermal limit of the target assembly. The tube should possess the smallest possible focal area. For maximum radiographic definition, a point source of radiation is the theoretical limit since the penumbra of increasing width occurs as the focal area becomes larger.

7.3.2   X-Ray Equipment

It consists of: (a) X-ray tube, (b) high voltage source and (c) control unit. The X-ray tubes are either gas filled or high vacuum variety. The tubes have a cathode from which electrons are forced by positive ion bombardment. Electrons are generated by thermionic emission from the filament. Tube current and accelerating potential can be independently varied. The envelopes for X-ray tubes are of glass or metallic-ceramic type. The cathode is a tungsten filament which produces the thermal electrons for acceleration. The filament currents range from 1 to 10 amperes. The tube-current, passing between the cathode and the anode by means of the high speed electrons, ranges from several hundred micro amperes for micro focus units upto 20 milliamperes for conventional industrial radiographic units.

The focussing of the electrons (beam) is done by a focussing cup. The sharpness of an image depends on the focal spot size. It is by impinging on the anode that fast moving electrons give rise to X-rays. The relationship for geometric unsharpness is

$$U_g = \frac{F}{D/t}$$

where F is the focal spot size, D the distance from target to object and t the thickness of the object.

7.3.3 Types of X-ray Tubes

There are two types of industrial X-ray tubes, namely (i) bipolar and (ii) unipolar. In bipolar tube, the potential difference with respect to earth on both—anode and the cathode—is equal to one-half of the tube voltage. This is advantageous from the point of view of insulation. The exit window is necessarily situated at the middle of the tube.

Unipolar tubes are not in often use. Only the cathode has a potential difference with respect to earth—the anode already being at the earth potential. These two tubes exist in two forms—with a short anode and a long hollow anode and are air or water cooled. The rod anode tubes make it suitable for the examination of small diameter tubes by single wall single image technique.

Far more is known today about the art of making good radiographs, the factors which control constrast and sensitivity and the limitations of radiography in what it can detect. Various codes have been evolved for the evaluation of radiographs. Sets of reference radiographs showing the appearance of weld and casting defects of different metal thicknesses are commercially available which are extremely valuable for instruction purposes. ASTM E 99 deals with reference radiographs for steel welds.

7.3.4 Focal Spot

The area of the anode which is struck by the electron flux is called the *focal spot* or *target*. It is essential that this area should be sufficiently large, in order to avoid local overheating which might damage the anode and to allow rapid dissipation of heat. The focal loading is the loading in watts/mm^2 on the focal spot (e.g. 20 watt/sq. mm). A relatively higher loading can be applied to small focal spots than to large ones, because the heat is not dissipated from the center in the same way in both the cases. The projection of the focal spot on a surface perpendicular to the axis of the beam of X-rays is termed as the optical focus or focus. This focus has to be as small as possible in order to achieve maximum sharpness in the radiographic image.

One of the methods used for determination of the size of the focal spot is the pinhole imaging technique. Here, a pinhole made in a suitably thick material with high density (lead) and having dimensions one order less than the expected focal spot size is used. The pinhole is aligned parallel to the tube axis and perpendicular to the X-ray beam and a radiographic image of the focal spot is obtained. By scanning this image using a micro densitometer, the focal spot size is obtained.

7.3.5 Target

The target is usually tungsten and is bonded to the copper anode. Other materials are copper, iron and cobalt. The orientation of the target with respect to the electron beam influences the size and shape of the focal spot. Orientations from 0 to 30 degrees are used for various applications. Zero is an angle used for panoramic units. Angle of 20 degrees is commonly selected for directional units.

7.3.6 Rod Anode

The rod anode is another adaptation of the cathode. The special circuit allows the anode to be grounded. This tube, developed for use through small openings, has been replaced by metal-ceramic tube. The target of such an end-grounded tube can be cooled by circulating water in direct contact with the anode.

7.4 GAMMA RAYS

Gamma rays are high energy electromagnetic waves of relatively short wave length that are emitted during the radioactive decay of both naturally occurring and artificially produced unstable isotopes. In all respects other than their origin, gamma- and X-rays are identical. Unlike the broad-spectrum radiation produced by an X-ray tube, gamma ray sources emit one or more discrete wavelengths of radiation, each having its own characteristic photon energy. Naturally occurring radioactive isotopes or elements that can be made radioactive by irradiation are thulium-170, iridium-192, caesium-137 and cobalt-60 which are being used extensively for radiography. Characteristics of these elements are given in Table 7.1. There is a continuous reduction in the intensity of the emitted radiation with time as more and more unstable nuclei transform to stable nuclei. This reduction follows a logarithmic law and each radioactive isotope has a characteristic half-life i.e. amount of time that is taken for the intensity of emitted radiation to get reduced by one-half.

Table 7.1 Characteristics of gamma ray isotopes

	Cobalt-60	Iridium-192	Caesium-137	Thulium-170
Half-life	5.27 yrs	74 days	30.1 yrs	129 days
Energy (MeV)	1.33, 1.17	0.3-0.6	0.66	0.08-0.05
Penetration (Steel thickness)	50-200 mm	12-75 mm	20-100 mm	2.5-10 mm

Another characteristic of gamma ray sources is the source strength which is a measure of the activity of a given source. Source strength is measured in curies (1 curie = 3.7×10^{10} atomic distintegrations/sec) or Becquerel (1 Bq = 1 dis/sec). Specific activity, commonly expressed as curies per gram or curies per cubic centimetre or in Becquerels, is a characteristic of radioactive sources that expresses their degree of concentration. Generally, sources of high specific activity are more desirable because they have lower self-absorption and provide less genometric unsharpness in the radiographs they produce than sources of low specific activity.

7.4.1 Equipment Design

Gamma ray sources are handled in specialised equipment capable of housing the source so as to give a controlled radiation beam as desired. Such an exposure device is called "radiographic camera". The design of gamma radiographic camera has progressed over the years with the objective of ensuring safe operating conditions for radiographers on site. Early models of containers used a simple lead casting for housing the radioactive source and to give radiation protection. The source was manipulated by a long pole to position it over the object to be radiographed. The later models used containers with movable shutters where the source could be stored safely. By removing a shielding component, a beam of radiation would emerge from the beam port.

The more recent development is the use of remote control to wind the source from the shielded position to the exposure point. This is achieved using a flexible source holder with a disconnectable link to a manual wind out cable. The source is moved through an armoured flexible source guide tube with an end stop which is normally fitted into a beam limiting collimator at the weld position. The projector type container has the advantage of remote operation which gives additional safety by positioning the operator to be at a considerable distance away from the source throughout the exposure. The present containers mostly use depleted uranium for radiation shield. This shielding is either in the form of a compact spherical casting with a movable shutter which allows the source to be projected or alternatively a larger casting with an S-tube internal path is used. The 'S' tube design gives full radiation protection with the advantage of no moving parts in the primary shield (Fig. 7.4).

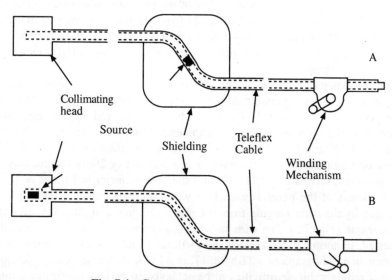

Fig. 7.4   Gamma camera—S tube design

Apart from the classification into manually operated and remotely operated cameras, these units can also be broadly classified depending on their weight, such as (a) manually handled (light weight upto 50 kg), (b) trolley mounted (medium weight 50–500 kg) and (c) fixed (in house-heavy weight over 500 kg).

7.4.2 Advantages and Limitations of Gamma Ray Sources

There are a number of advantages in using a gamma ray source for radiography.

Gamma ray equipment do not require electrical power for operation and therefore are ideally suited for field applications and remote areas. Being compact and considerably lighter than X-ray equipment, they are easily transportable. With the availability of high specific activity isotopes, sources of focal spots as small as 0.6 to 2 mm can be obtained. Further, gamma ray equipment, unlike X-ray units, need minimum maintenance.

The limitations of gamma ray sources include:

(a) The output of a source is limited. If the output is to be increased without increasing the physical size of the source, the specific activity is to be increased. The specific activity is controlled by the neutron flux available in the irradiation positions in a reactor. In the case of X-rays, the output can be increased by increasing the current.

(b) Because of the discrete energies emitted by gama sources, the energy of radiation cannot be matched with the thickness of the specimen as in the case of X-ray units wherein the energy can be varied over a range. This results in radiographs with poor resolution especially in thin section radiography.

(c) Gamma ray sources decay with time.

7.5   PENETRAMETERS

Suitable penetrameters have been designed for evaluation of radiographs for their quality and sensitivity. The quality of the radiographs is always quoted in terms of the amount of detail discernible from the image of the image quality indicators (IQI) of the same material as the specimen to be radiographed. The sensitivity depends on the radiographic technique, the type of IQI used and the specimen thickness.

ASTM penetrameters are plaque and wire type and are very widely used. In UK and other European countries, wire type penetrameters are used. The plaque type penetrameters as per ASTM E-142 have $2T$, $1T$ and $4T$ diameter holes, where T is the thickness of the penetrameter. Minimum diameter of holes is 0.010″, 0.020″ and 0.040″. Sensitivity level is specified as 1-2T, 1-1T, 2-2T where first 1 or 2 indicates that the penetrameter is 1 or 2% of the thickness of the specimen, second 2T or 1T indicates the hole diameter is 2 times or 1 time the thickness of the penetrameter. In a wire type penetrameter, the wires are arranged by diameter ranging from 0.1 mm to 3.2 mm and all wires are of the same length (Fig. 7.5). The wire material is so chosen to match the material to be tested. In normal use, a specification will insist the smallest diameter wire to be seen on a radiograph or a 2T hole, 1T, or 4T hole depending on applications. Typical radiographic sensitivities to be achieved in various applications range from 0.5 to 2% of wall thickness. To assess IQI sensitivity, the radiograph is placed on an illuminated screen of appropriate brightness and the film is suitably masked to eliminate glare emanating from the adjacent regions or any part of the film having particularly low density. The diameter of the smallest wire or drilled hole which can be detected with certainty is taken as a measure of the attained sensitivity.

7.6   INDUSTRIAL X-RAY FILMS

In general, the film consists of an emulsion-gelatin containing a radiation sensitive

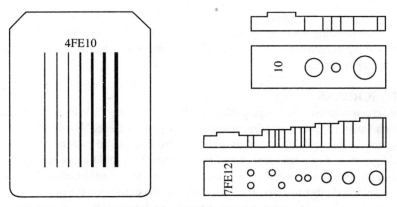

Fig. 7.5   Image quality indicator designs

silver compound- and a flexible transparent blue tinted base. Emulsion on both sides (25 microns) doubles the amount of radiation sensitive silver compound and thus increases the speed. Film with one side emulsion is preferred where highest visibility of the detail is required. Cross sectional view of an industrial X-ray film is shown in Fig. 7.6.

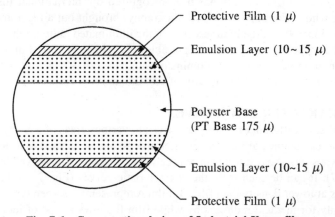

Fig. 7.6   Cross sectional view of Industrial X-ray film

When X- or gamma-rays strike the grains of the sensitive silver compound in the emulsion, a change takes place in the physical structure of the grains. This change is of such a nature that it cannot be detected by ordinary physical methods.

However, when the exposed film is treated with a chemical solution (developer), a reaction causes the formation of black metallic silver. It is this silver suspended in the gelatin on both sides of the base that constitutes the image of the object. The selection of a film for radiography of any particular component depends on the thickness and material of the specimen and on the voltage range of the available X-ray machine. In addition, the choice is affected by the relative importance of high radiographic quality or short exposure time.

If a high quality is the deciding factor, a slower and hence fine grained film should be used. If short exposure times are essential, a faster film (or film-screen combination) can be used. Exposure films can be used with or without lead screens depending upon the thickness and the geometry of the object. Fluorescent intensifying screens must be used in radiography requiring the highest possible photographic speed.

7.7 SCREENS

The screen improves the image quality by filtering out longer wavelength radiations which cause fogging. A companion screen, fitted on the back side of the film, also has an intensifying effect, as it reduces back scattered radiations. For steel weldments, use of a lead foil screen between the film and the source is usually required. The lead screen is not used for light alloy weldments, since with aluminium and other light metals, the softer radiation must reach the film unimpeded to yield an adequate contrast range through the material. A screen on the back side of the film, however, acts positively and is often used.

7.8 FILM VIEWERS

The provision for good film viewing conditions is essential as it is possible to have information on the radiograph which is not seen because of too high a film density or too low illuminator luminance. The importance of relating illuminator luminescence to film density has been recognised by International Institute of Welding whose Commission VA (Radiography) brought out a recommendation (IIS/IIW-335-69) that the luminescence of the illuminated radiograph should not be less than 30 cd/m^2 and whenever possible approximately 100 cd/m^2 or greater. This minimum value requires illuminator luminance of 300 cd/m^2, 3000 cd/m^2 and 30,000 cd/m^2 for a film density of 1.0, 2.0 and 3.0, respectively.

7.9 CHARACTERISTIC CURVE

If a number of different exposures are given to various areas of a X-ray film and the densities obtained at these areas after processing are plotted as a function of log$_{10}$ (exposure), the resulting curve is called a "characteristic curve" of the film (Fig. 7.7). It can be seen from the characteristic curves (Fig. 7.7) that film A saturates at lower density than film B. Film A represents a screen type film used commonly for medical radiography while film B shows a type of industrial X-ray film used directly or with lead screens. These curves also indicate that a low density called "Fog density" is formed on the film even without any exposure to radiation. It consists of optical density of base material (minimum 0.08) and chemical fog of emulsion (minimum 0.04) of the film. A characteristic curve gives information on the speed of the film and the contrast attainable with the film.

7.10 RADIOGRAPHIC DEFECT EVALUATION

Generally, by radiography, we can recognise the nature of a defect and also measure its effective length and width parallel to the plane of the film but the through thickness dimension (height) is less easy to determine. The distance of a defect from surface can be found by stereometric methods. In principle, it is possible to measure the height of the defect from the density of the image on the radiograph using a micro-densitometer. The densities determined from the micro-densitometer trace can be converted into thickness either by absolute calculations using the film characteristics and exposure curves, or by having an appropriate step wedge on the radiography along side of the object and in the case of weldments near the weld.

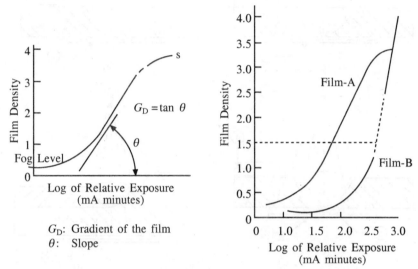

Fig. 7.7 Characteristic curve

It is reported that, for general weld defects occupying 10 to 30% of the thickness, this method can be applied with an accuracy ranging from 3 to 8%. However, this method has not been found to be suitable for planar defects such as cracks. Defects such as porosities, lack of fusion, lack of penetration, voids, inclusions etc. in the welds and hot tears and shrinkage cavities in the castings can be easily detected by radiography. The detectability of cracks by radiography is influenced by the position and size of the crack, the incident angle of X-rays, the distance between the film and the crack, size of the focal spot, and sensitivity of films and screens. Good amount of work has been done on crack detectability and sensitivity. Conventional radiography is being widely used for the inspection of a variety of weldments, castings and complete assemblies in various industries.

7.11 APPLICATIONS
Radiography is widely used in evaluating different type of weld joints and configurations for their integrity.

7.11.1 Butt Welds
Butt joints in the flat plates are usually made with edge preparation of single 'V', double 'V' or square. Inspection techniques for Butt welds with ASTM penetrameter are shown in Fig. 7.8 (a to e). These are applicable for: (1) welds with and without reinforcement (Figs. 7.8a and b), (2) welds with reinforcement and backing strip (Fig. 7.8c), (3) welds with reinforcement and integral backing strip (Fig. 7.8d) and (4) welds with reinforcement and cladded base material (Fig. 7.8e).

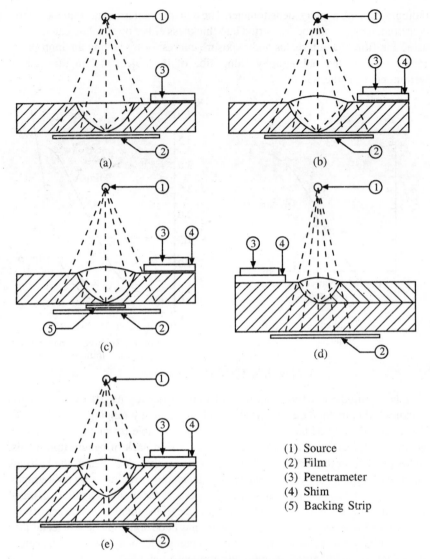

Fig. 7.8   Radiography of butt welds

7.11.2   Fillet Welds

Fillet welds are generally made with square or bevel edge preparation. The exposure set up for different fillet joints are shown in Fig. 7.9.

7.11.3 Fusion Welds on Pipes and Cylindrical Objects

Depending upon the size and accessibility on either side of the pipe, the following techniques are recommended:

Single Wall Penetration: A source inside and film outside given in Fig. 7.10 (a to d) show single wall penetrating setup. Ideal position to locate the source is the centre of the pipe which enables to cover the entire circumferential weld in

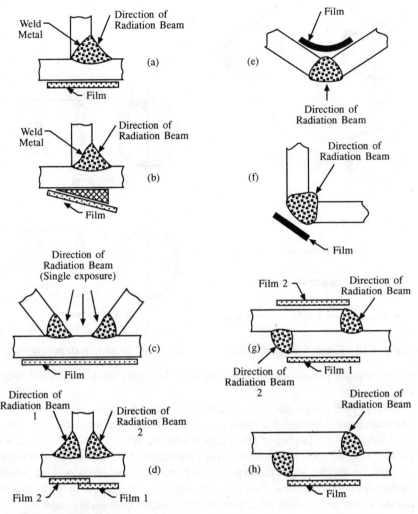

(a) Single-fillet T joint
(b) Single-fillet T joint with equalizing wedge
(c) Two adjacent single-fillet joints radiographed simultaneously
(d) Double-fillet T joint
(e) Corner joint with film positioned at the inside surface
(f) Corner joint with film positioned at the outside surface
(g) and (h) Alternative views for double welded lap joint de surface.

Fig. 7.9   Direction of radiation for various fillet weld configuration

a single panoramic exposure. Butt welds of thick walled pipes are radiographed with source located either in centre or eccentric. To facilitate radiographic inspection of thick walled steam pressure pipe line welds, usually a hole is provided adjacent to the circumferential weld for insertion of radioisotope inside the pipe (Fig. 7.10d).

Double Wall Penetration: Both the film and the source are placed external to the pipe when there is no access to the inside of the pipe (Fig. 7.11). Here the

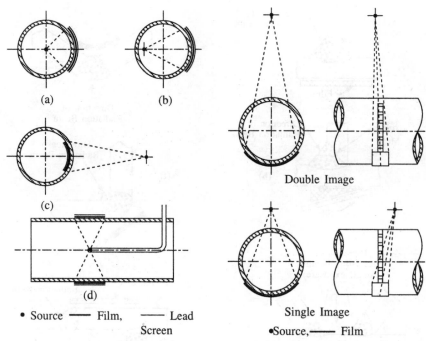

(a)   (b)

(c)

(d)

Double Image

• Source —— Film,   —— Lead
                    Screen

Single Image
•Source,—— Film

Fig. 7.10   Single wall penetration   **Fig. 7.11   Double wall penetration**

radiation beam passes through both the walls butt only the bottom weld image is evaluated.

Double Wall Single Image: This technique is used for pipes with OD > 89 mm. The source is either placed on the top of the weld (superpositioned) technique or it is slightly offset. Degree of offset depends on the SFD (Source-Film Distance) chosen. The radiation source is placed at a minimum SFD compatible with source size and the wall thickness of the pipe. The film is wrapped on the welded portion further from the radiation source. Overlapping of the images is avoided by placing the source offset by about 10 degrees from the plane through the weld.

Double Wall Double Image: The technique is specially suited for smaller pipes upto 89 mm diameter. The source is placed offset to the weld, the inclination being 10 to 15 degrees to avoid the overlap of top and bottom weld images. Minimum two exposures are taken (the second after rotating the weld through 90 degrees). Both top and bottom images are recorded on film with suitable separation.

Fusion butt welds of the transmission pipe line can be speedily radiographed with X-ray machine or high activity gamma sources, mounted on a crawler which moves inside the pipe at a preset speed (Fig. 7.12). Figure 7.13 shows the effect of direction of radiation beam on the appearance of defects. Figure 7.14 shows typical radiographs of weld defects.

7.12   ADVANCES IN RADIOGRAPHY

7.12.1   High Resolution Radiography

High resolution X-radiography has been developed to offer an edge over

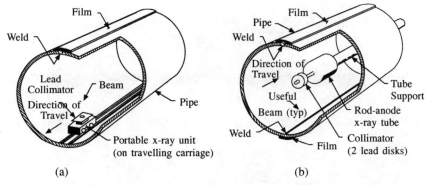

Fig. 7.12 Pipe crawler for radiography of transmission lines

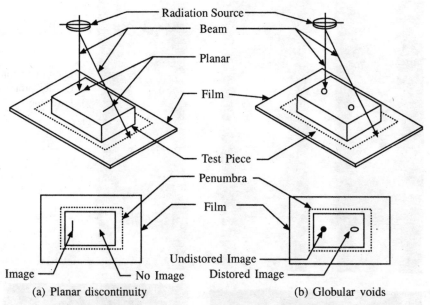

(a) Planar discontinuity   (b) Globular voids

Fig. 7.13 Effect of direction of radiation on appearance of defects

conventional radiography for better definition of defects and detectability of small defects like microcracks in jobs having thin sections and complex geometries. This is more so in the present context of the use of high technology manufacturing processes like laser welding and electron beam welding which has led to drastic reduction in component sizes and have consequently necessitated detection of smaller defects.

Advancements in electron-optical systems, vacuum technology and computer controlled parameter optimisation and monitoring techniques have made X-ray generators of very fine focus and smaller sizes of anode tubes available for industrial radiography. Advantages of such systems compared to conventional radiographic systems are:

(a) Fine focal spots (15 microns) give advantages like higher resolution, higher contrast and posibility of large magnifications.

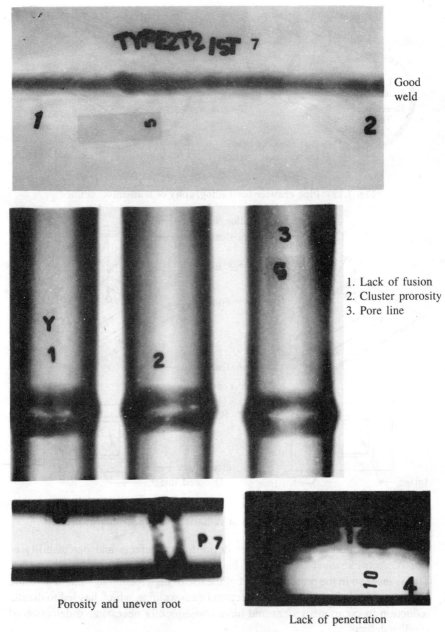

Good
weld

1. Lack of fusion
2. Cluster prorosity
3. Pore line

Porosity and uneven root

Lack of penetration

Fig. 7.14 Positive prints (Radiographs) of typical weld defects

(b) Rod anode X-ray heads are available in small sizes (diameter 6 mm onwards and lengths between 100 and 1000 mm) which facilitate panoramic radiography of smaller diameter pipe welds and radiography of complex joints like tube to tube sheet weld joints.

(c) High resolution of the defect of the order of 25 microns using direct enlargement is possible which facilitates radiography of thin objects and use of large film to object distances.

(d) Specially shaped anodes give a variety of X-ray emission modes for panoramic, radial backward or forward throw of X-rays and directional throw of X-rays for varied applications.

(e) Easy adaptability for on-line fluoroscopy.

Main limitations of this technique are the maximum voltage (max. 225 kV) and maximum current (3 mA) which restrict thickness of objects to be radiographed to 3 mm of steel equivalent. The equipment is not portable like conventional X-ray equipment and has restricted use for in-service applications.

Typical radiography study of tube-to-tubesheet welds of steam generators: The usefulness of microfocal radiography for evaluation of critical tube-to-tubesheet weld joints has been described to bring out the potential of the test method. In the steam generator of the Prototype Fast Breeder Reactor (PFBR), steam is generated by the transfer of heat from secondary sodium to water. Due to the inherent dangers of sodium-water reaction, the integrity of weld joints separating sodium and water/steam is of paramount importance. This is particularly true and very important for the tube-to-tubesheet joints. Use of projective magnification by microfocal radiography for the quality evaluation and optimisation of the welding parameters of such small tube-to-tubesheet welds of the steam generator of PFBR was found to be effective.

Weld joint configuration: Typical configurations of the tube-to-tubesheet welds are shown in Fig. 7.15. The first three configurations (a, b and c) involve a fillet weld to the face side and are not desirable because of the following reasons:

(1) The existence of crevice between the tube and tubesheet may lead to failures by crevice corrosion and stress corrosion cracking.

(2) The weld configuration is not amenable for NDT inspection.

The disadvantages mentioned above are overcome by using the configuration shown in Fig. 7.15d, which envisages a machined nipple from the tubesheet side to which the tube is butt-welded. This design has been considered acceptable for the PFBR steam generator. The machined nipple section has a length of about 30 mm to which the tube (18 to 23 m long) is butt-welded. Due to restricted access from outside, the welding is carried out by pulsed TIG welding utilising a rotating electrode placed on the bore side. For the PFBR steam generator evaporator, the tube (material: 2.25 Cr-1 Mo ferritic steel) to be welded has an outer diameter of 17.2 mm and a wall thickness of 2.3 mm. Because of the small bore and wall thickness, autogenous welding (without filler wire addition) has been adopted. The Welding is carried out in the 5G position with the arc starting at the bottom of the tube. As the weld pool will be subjected to differing gravity effects, different current values are used, along with control of inside and outside gas pressures as the weld progresses. Provision exists for programming four levels of current for different durations.

Weld inspection: As indicated above, the tube-to-tubesheet weld joint is the most critical joint in the steam generator assembly, as it separates sodium from water. Hence, it has to be inspected thoroughly with high reliability. In the actual steam generator (evaporator) configuration, six tubes surround the central tube

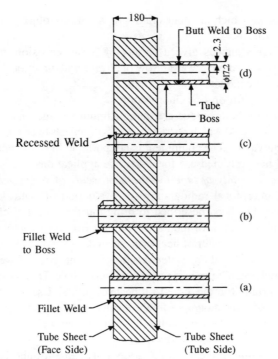

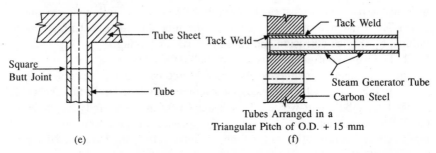

Fig. 7.15 Typical weld configurations of tube-to-tubesheet joints

arranged in a triangular pitch pattern as shown in Fig. 7.16. The maximum radial distance between the centre of one tube to another is 31.75 mm. Visual examination and dye penetrant testing reveal the external features such as concavity, convexity, undercut or other surface defects. However, the detection of internal defects requires the use of other NDT techniques. Due to the typical joint configuration, conventional ultrasonic testing or X-radiography is ruled out because of the problems of access. Hence, gamma radiography using a very small thulium source (size 0.1 mm) or microfocal radiography using a rod anode tube are the possible choices.

Choice of inspection based on standard requirements: One of the main defects that has been encountered in the initial welds was microporosity. Standards have been established for acceptable porosity in the weld. According to this standard,

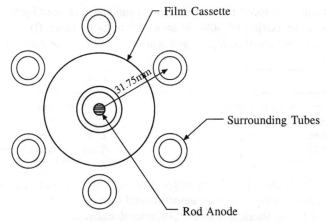

**Fig. 7.16 Radiographic test arrangement for inspection
of tube-to-tubesheet weld joint**

(1) the total pore count in the entire weld must be such that the sum of the diameters of all the pores visible should be less than 2.7 mm. (2) local concentration of pores in a 3.0 mm circle anywhere in the weld must be such that the sum of their diameters should be less than 0.6 mm and (3) any single pore with a diameter greater than 0.46 mm is not permissible.

Since both gamma radiography and microfocal radiography could be used, a theoretical comparison was made on the possible geometric and actual unsharpness and the critical size of the flaw detectable when a projective magnification of 3X (limited by the pitch distance of 31.75 mm) is used. The following formulae have been used

$$U_g = S (M - 1) \tag{1}$$

$$U_t = (U_g^2 + U_f^2)^{1/2} \tag{2}$$

$$d = U_t/M \tag{3}$$

where U_g is the geometric unsharpness; U_t the resultant total unsharpness; U_f the film unsharpness assumed to be a maximum of 0.05 mm in the energy range 80–100kV; d is the true unsharpness related to the image detail size or the critical size over and above which the flaws are detectable (mm) and M is the magnification and S is the source size in mm.

Thulium source: Currently a 0.1 mm, 1110 GBq source is commercially available.

So using $S = 0.1$ mm, $M = 3$ and $U_f = 0.05$, we have from equations (1), (2) and (3):
Geometric unsharpness $U_g = 0.2$ mm
Resultant unsharpness $U_t = 0.2062$ mm
Thus the critical size of the flaw detectable, $d > 0.0687$ mm

Microfocal radiography: The microfocal radiography unit used for this application is a 160 kV Andrex model MX-3. The focal spot size as quoted by the manufacturers is about 15 microns (case I) and, the measured focal spot at 90 kV with an optimisation of 60%, is about 40 microns (case II). Using these parameters, the values of S, U_g, U_t and d are given below for these two cases.

Case I	Case II
$S = 0.015$ mm (quoted by manufacturer)	$S = 0.040$ mm
$U_g = 0.03$ mm	$U_g = 0.08$ mm
$U_t = 0.0583$ mm	$U_t = 0.0943$ mm
Thus, $d > 0.0194$ mm	Thus, $d > 0.03145$ mm

From case II it can be seen that microfocal radiography with a rod anode gives a much higher sensitivity for flaw detection and lower geometrical unsharpness as compared to the thulium source. The microfocal radiography technique is thus better suited for the detection of microporosity of the order of 50 microns or more as stipulated in the standard. Hence, microfocal radiography was adopted for the examination of these welds.

Microfocal Radiography of Evaporator Welds

Choice of rod anode configuration: The microfocal radiography unit used for the investigation is of rod anode type with a maximum voltage of 160 kV and current of 250 μA. The optimisation of the current can be carried out either by microprocessor or manually. Due to the small inner diameter of the tube (12.6 mm), rod anodes of length 350 mm and with diameter of the order of 10 mm were selected. Different configurations of the rod anodes are possible, namely (1) radial panoramic with X-ray emission angles ($-15°$) $\times$ ($+15°$) $\times$ $360°$; (b) backward throw with X-ray emission angles ($-5°$) $\times$ ($-60°$) $\times$ $360°$; and (c) forward throw in which the beam emerges from the front as a cone with an apex angle of $30°$.

In the present study, both the radial panoramic and the backward throw configurations were tried. It was observed that the weld widths attainable ranged from 3 to 5 mm. The welds were not uniform and they were also wavy in nature. With the very small source-to-object distance of 6.3 mm, it was seen that when a radial panoramic beam was used, the X-ray beam could not cover the weld width completely. It was then decided to use the backward throw configuration. Since the X-rays were emitted in the backward direction, the probe had to be slightly offset with respect to the weld centre. This resulted in an apparent increase in the source-to-object distance, thus covering the entire weld.

Weld Radiography: Radiography of the weld was carried out using a projective magnification of 3X. As indicated earlier, the magnification is limited by the pitch of the surrounding tubes. Due to the geometry of the tubes, a circular split holder was designed to hold the film in position. This holder, made of aluminium, has a lead backing (0. 1 mm thick) for minimising scattered radiation. Special wire type penetrameters with 10 wires and diameters ranging from 120 to 14 microns (supplied by M/s. Andrex Radiation Products, Denmark) were used. The penetrameters were placed both on the source side and on the film side and radiographs were taken. An ultra-fine-grain, slow-speed film (Agfa D2) was used. The radiographic parameters employed are given in Table 7.2.

Table 7.2   Radiographic Parameters employed

Voltage	90 kV
Exposure	120 μA min
Wall thickness of the tube	2.3 mm
Technique employed	Single-wall Single-image
Source to object distance	6.35 mm
Probe used	Backward throw with a beam angle $-5° \times -55° \times 360°$
Projective magnification	3X
Film used	Agfa D2
Penetrameter	Wire type
Processing conditions	Manual, Standard
Density on radiograph	2 to 2.3
Sensitivity achieved	A 32 micron wire could be resolved corresponding to 1.39% of the wall thickness

Results on trial welds have shown that it is possible to resolve a 32 micron-diameter steel wire placed on the source side. This corresponds to about 1.39% of the wall thickness of the tube. The same level of sensitivity was obtained when penetrameter was placed on the film side also. This is because of the size of microfocal spot and small wall thickness. This result is of significance, as in field conditions, with a tubesheet of about 180 mm thick, placement of penetrameter on the source side and also ensuring that it is in contact with the tube wall, would be difficult.

Radiographs taken during the development stage of the orbital welding method indicated the following features: (1) gas porosity; (2) wavy nature of the weld joint; (3) uneven weld reinforcement; and (4) weld ripple

The welding parameters used for initial welds are indicated in Table 7.3. Based on the observations from micofocal radiography, suitable corrective actions were taken for altering the welding parameters. Subsequent radiographic examinations (Table 7.4) have revealed a reduction in the porosity to acceptable levels, improved weld joint and uniform weld reinforcement.

Table 7.3   Initial welding parameters

Parameters	Level I	Level II	Level III	Level IV
Weld Current	80A	76A	71A	68A
Duration	10s	20s	22s	8s
Background current	30A			
Pulse timing	Peak current: 0.6 s		Background current: 0.9 s	
Down slope time	8s			
Nature of current ǫ	Pulsed			
Fixture rotation speed	2 rpm			

Table 7.4   Final welding parameters

Parameters	Level I	Level II	Level III	Level IV
Weld Current	95A	90A	85A	80A
Duration	15s	15s	15s	15s
Background current	15A			
Pulse timing	Peak current - 0.4s		Background current - 0.4s	
Down slope time	10s			
Nature of current	Pulsed			
Fixture rotation speed	2.2 rpm			

Figure 7.17 shows a positive print of typical radiograph obtained with the original welding parameters indicating the microporosity and the 50 micron steel penetrameter wire. Figure 7.18 shows the radiograph of a joint which was welded using modified parameters. No microporosity is observed in the radiograph.

Fig. 7.17   Typical positive prints of radiographs of welds with welding parameters as per Table 7.3

Root concavity is observed which was found to be within the acceptable limits. Thus, microfocal radiography has helped in the optimisation of welding parameters through successive trials and also ensured the quality of this critical joint.

Fig. 7.18   Typical positive print of radiographs of welds made with welding parameters as per Table 7.4

7.12.2   High Energy Radiography

Radiography using X-ray systems of 1 MeV or more is commonly termed as high energy radiography. The basic principles of this technique are similar to those of conventional radiography. Its advantages are: (a) Examination of thicker sections economically due to the greater penetration of the high energy photons, (b) Possibilities of large distance to thickness ratios (D/T) with correspondingly low geometrical distortion and (c) Short exposure times and high production rates.

The wide thickness latitude, good contrast and reduced amount of high angle scatter reaching the film results in radiography with excellent penetrameter sensitivity and good resolution. A number of systems such as synchrotron, betatron etc. are available for high energy radiography of which the Electron Linear Accelerator (LINAC) is the most popular one (Fig. 7.19).

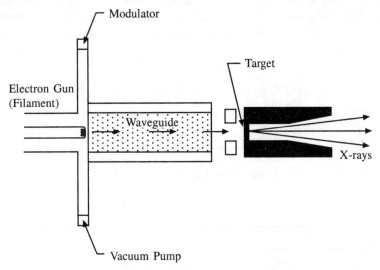

Fig. 7.19   Electron linear accelerator

7.12.3   Electron Linear Accelerator (LINAC)

LINAC accelerates electrons by radio-frequency voltages that are applied such that the electrons reach an acceleration point in the field at a precise time. The accelerator guide consists of a series of cavities which causes gaps when the radio-Frequency power is applied. The cavities have holes in each end which allow electrons to pass to the next cavity. When an electron is injected at the proper time, it gains energy as it is accelerated across these gaps. Proper phasing of the radio-frequency power is essential for accelerators.

Recent developments in LINAC include portable machines with energies upto 16 MeV and radiation output upto 10,000 rads/min at one metre from the target. Increased operating frequencies upto 9300 MHz permit light weight X-ray head. In the newer configuration of portable sets, it is possible to operate the accelerator and the collimator away from radio-frequency source using a flexible waveguide. Total weight of X-ray head is thus reduced, permitting easy positioning for inspection of welded pipe lines, valves and other components with limited accessibility. Radiography of steel upto 500 mm (20 inches) is possible with LINAC which produce better radiographs than any other high energy equipment for steel thicker than 100 mm.

7.12.4   Real Time Radiography

Real time Radiography or Fluoroscopy differs from conventional radiography in that the X-ray image is observed on a fluorescent screen rather than recorded on a film. Fluoroscopy has the advantages of high speed and low cost of inspection. Present day real time systems use image intensifiers, video camera and monitor. The image intensifier tube converts photons to electrons, accelerates the electrons and then reconverts them to light (Fig. 7.20) Intensifiers typically operate in the range of 30–10,000 light amplification factors. Improvements in electronic gain, fluorescent and photo cathode layer efficiency and electron optics have made modern X-ray image intensifiers very useful in medical and industrial applications. Modern tubes are available with 10 to 40 cm input diameters and trifield configuration.

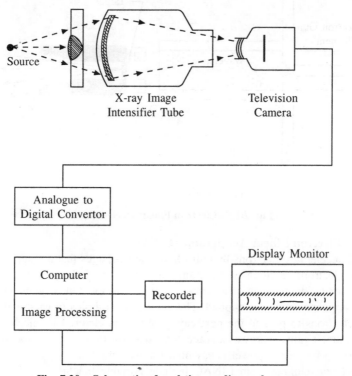

Fig. 7.20   Schematic of real time radiography system

A typical 21 cm tube performs with resolution of 40 line pairs per mm and gain of the order of 14,000. The overall geometric distortion at the centre is less than 2%. The use of microfocal units in conjunction with image intensifying system greatly enhances the versatility and sensitivity of the real time radiographic set up. The inherent unsharpness of the fluorescent screens would be compensated by the focal spot size (<100 microns) of the microfocal units.

With X-ray energies greater than 400 kV and with gamma rays, a computer aided real time radiography system can match the performance of film radiography. If a slightly poorer sensitivity can be accepted, a conventional minifocus X-ray set with 0.3/0.4 mm focal spot size can be used with some projective magnification and computer digital image processing. If high flaw sensitivity is not needed, the advantage of computerised image processing coupled with an equipment with

X-ray intensifier and a television camera with a digital output would reduce operating costs and provide high inspection speed. An advantage of real time microfocal radiography is that of zooming or projection magnification by dynamically positioning the object with the manipulators between the X-ray tube and the image receptor. The use of real time radiography is finding increasing applications in industries where speed in testing is a primary consideration. Direct examination of the welds in real time saves films and the associated processing time and is found to be cost effective in the long run. With the advent of image processing systems, the sensitivity that can be achieved is comparable to film sensitivity. Figures 7.21 and 7.22 show typical radiograph of a weld joint. Figure 7.21 gives the raw image wherein penetrameter wires are not clearly seen. After contrast stretching and image enhancement (Fig. 7.22), the lack of penetration can be seen and the wire penetrameters can be identified thereby increasing the sensitivity. On-line monitoring of welding is another possibility by real time radiography.

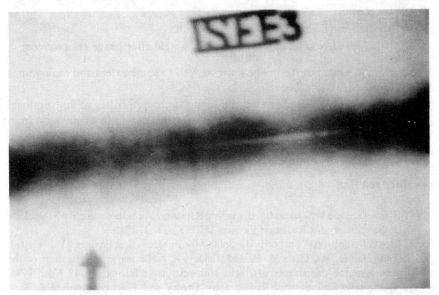

Fig. 7.21   Positive print of a radiograph of a weld before image enhancement

7.12.5   Image Processing

Any image on a film or a screen can be scanned with a closed circuit television camera with a digital output and stored on a magnetic tape or disk as a number of pixels. A pixel array of 512×512 elements with 256 brightness levels for each pixel is quite common and can be handled through a personnel computer. Once stored as digital pixel data, the image is available for computer enhancement techniques such as contrast stretching, edge enhancement, special filtering, differentiation, averaging, pattern recognition etc. The versatility of image processing is that this can be performed in real time as well as on film images. This technique suffers from the following limitations:

Fig. 7.22   Positive print of a radiograph of a weld after image enhancement

1. Enhancement of the image noise as well to some extent and radiographs are inherently noisy.
2. The limited dynamic range and contrast characteristics of conventional TV cameras result in a loss of image quality during its acquisition from the film/screen.

Further reading

7. Baldev Raj and Venkataraman, B. Ionising Radiations for Non-destructive Evaluation, Indian Society for Radiation Physics, ISRP(K) TD-1, 1989.
8. Bernd Rohloft, NDT methods, The South African Mechanical Engineer, Vol. 4, 1994.
16. Dutli James, W., Gerhold. H. and Tenney, A preliminary Investigation of the Radiographic Visualisation of Cracks, Non-destructive Testing, Vol. 12, No.2, 1994.
29. Halmshaw, R. Industrial Radiography Theory and Practice, Applied Science Publishers, London, 1982.
30. Halmshaw, R. and Hunt. C.A. Can Cracks be found by Radiography, British Journal of NDT, 1975.
49. Kohutek, T.L. Fundamentas for a procedure for Non-destructive determination of position, shape of flaws in Welds by Radiometric Measurements.
54. Milewski, J.O. and Hmelo et. al, Using Synchrotron X-ray Micro Tomography to detect defects, Welding Journal, 73(2), 1994.
55. Milewski, J. V., Hmelo, A.B. and Amico, D. Characterizing Laser Fusion Welded Aluminium using Synchrotron X-ray Microtomography, The Minerals, Metals and Materials Society, USA, 1993.
94. Yokota, O. and Ishii, Y. Crack Detectability by Radiography, International Journal of NDT, Sep. 1979.
99. Specifications for Image Quality Indicators for Industrial Radiography, BS 3971, 1980.

Chapter 8

Acoustic Emission Technique

Acoustic Emission Technique (AET) with potential for many important applications has already become an important non-destructive testing technique. Its origin lies in the phenomenon of rapid release of energy within a material in the form of a transient elastic wave resulting from dynamic changes like deformation, crack initiation and propagation, leakage etc. It is a real time technique which can detect initiation and growth of cracks, plastic deformation, fatigue failure, leaks etc. which are not amenable for detection by ultrasonics and other NDT methods, due to access considerations and very small sizes of the early stage cracks.

AET is used during in-service inspection of installed welded vessels and for on-line weld monitoring during fabrication. It is used as a helpful complimentary technique for inspection of critical areas in important installations. During in-service inspection and hydrotest of welded vessels used in petrochemical, nuclear and allied industries, welded zones are generally weaker, particularly the nozzle areas. Many defets that come to light through AE inspection/hydro test are most likely to be detected in the welded and surrounding regions and AET to this extent is very useful in monitoring of welds in vessels when employed under such conditions.

Principle of Acoustic Emission Testing

Acoustic emission inspection detects and analyses minute AE signals generated by growing discontinuities in material under a stimulus such as stress, temperature etc. Proper analysis of these signals can provide information concerning the detection and location of discontinuities and the structural integrity. Depending on the nature of energy release, two types of AE are observed. These are: (1) Continuous and (2) Burst. Continuous emission is characterised by low amplitude emissions. The amplitude varies with AE activity. In metal and alloys, this type of emission occurs during plastic deformation by dislocation movement, diffusion controlled phase transformations and fluid leakage. Burst emissions are characterized by short duration (10 microseconds to a few milliseconds) and high amplitude pulses due to discrete release of strain energy. This type of emission occurs during diffusionless phase transformations, crack initiation and propagation, stress corrosion cracking etc.

Technique

It is difficult to use a single all-encompassing parameter to describe an experimental result uniquely. Hence a number of AE parameters are used for interpreting the experimental results. Some of the parameters are used to identify the change in source of AE during the progress of a test, while others are used to eliminate background noise.

Figure 8.1 shows a typical AE signal and the various parameters used for interpretation. 'Ringdown counts' is the number of times the signal crosses a threshold level set for eliminating background noise. This could be used independently or as the cumulative counts with respect to time, load or any other parameter. Count rate is another parameter commonly used.

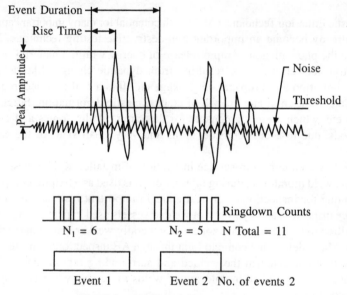

Fig. 8.1   AE Signal Parameters

The most common ways in which AE signals can be processed are:

1. Counting: Ringdown counts, Ringdown count rates, Events.
2. Energy analysis: used for both continuous and burst type emissions.
3. Amplitude analysis: used to characterise emissions from different processes.
4. Frequency analysis: used to identify different types of failures.
5. Advanced signal analysis concepts such as pattern recognition, spectral analysis, maximum entropy etc.

AET is capable of detecting growing flaws at least an order of magnitude smaller than those detectable by any other known NDT method. AET is also capable of locating one or more discontinuities while they are growing. When the discontinuity approaches critical size, the AE count rate increases markedly, thus giving a warning for impending instability and failure of the component.

8.1   ON-LINE MONITORING OF WELDS BY ACOUSTIC EMISSION
AET can be adopted for simultaneous detection of defects as the welding progresses in real time. The defects so found can be immediately rectified thus avoiding the

completion of defective weld and then carrying out conventional NDT techniques to find out the defects and repairing the weld, resulting in loss of time and finance. AET has been successfully used for on-line monitoring of welds prepared by TIG, submerged arc, electroslag welding etc. However, non-slag forming welding methods are most suitable for AE monitoring.

The main problem of AE monitoring of welding process is elimination of unwanted signals generated during welding. The unwanted signals may be generated due to welding process like metal transfer, slag cracking and detachment and noise caused by operator and electrical interference due to high frequency starter pulses. But these noises can be eliminated by proper signal conditioning and processing techniques. Limitations of these techniques include interpretation of wrong signals and extensive calibration for different applications. The defects that can be detected, located and quantitatively evaluated by AE monitoring during welding are: (1) weld cracking associated with phase transformation, (2) nucleation and growth of cracks during welding and subsequent cooling e.g., delayed cracking, (3) porosity and slag inclusions, (4) microfissuring, (5) hot and cold cracking and (6) reheat cracks.

Once these defects are located, these regions are further probed using other NDT techniques for in-depth analysis. AE occurs only under the influence of a normal or applied stimulus due to constraints, temperature gradient, phase transformation etc. that cause deformation and crack initiation and propagation. This indicates that AE source is the site of dynamic change in a material to the stimulus generated during welding process, which responds to the stimulus by releasing part of the energy in the form of elastic stress waves. This dynamic nature of AET makes it highly potential technique for monitoring of welding process. The above said sources may be present in welding during weld bead solidification and further cooling.

One of the important factors to be considered is the calibration of AE system. This is carried out after adopting the system to the welding procedure to make sure that the system collects the signal properly and locates the source of AE correctly. Simulation sources are used for this particular purpose.

8.2 EXPERIMENTAL SETUP

A typical experimental set up used for AE monitoring during resistance spot welding is shown in Fig. 8.2. With necessary modifications, this can be applied even to any other welding process. Currently with the advancement of microprocessor technology and availability of sophisticated instrumentation, the advantage of considering many signal parameters for analysis is being increasingly recognised.

Both on-line and off-line data processing are followed. AE instrumentation consists of signal detection, data acquisition and signal processing and analysis units. Piezoelectric transducers having high sensitivity and ruggedness are widely used for detecting AE signals. Resonant and non-resonant type of transducers are used with narrow and wide band instrumentations, respectivily.

Preamplifier that follows the transducer is generally followed with a selectable gain post-amplifier so that the signal is brought to a level where data acquisiton can be carried out. Flaw location can also be carried out with sensor array.

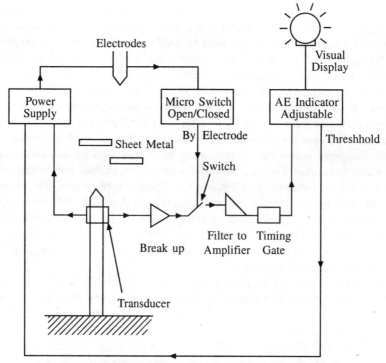

Fig. 8.2   Experimental setup during spot welding

Processing and analysis like audio monitoring and parameter distribution can be incorporated into the system. For source location, two or more sensors are allowed to be excited by the source and the arrival sequence and the difference in time of arrival are measured and from this data, source location is arrived at.

8.3   ADVANTAGES OF AET FOR WELD MONITORING

In addition to AET's superiority over RT and UT, the other advantages are:

1. AET is particularly useful for high technology industries like nuclear, aerospace etc., where defect free welds are a must for high reliability.
2. AET is best and economical since defects are found during welding and immediate repair of weld and also feed back for changing the process parameters are possible based on AE results.
3. In resistance spot welding, weld quality can be immediately known by AE monitoring without going in for many samples being destructively tested.
4. In very big offshore structures where several metres of welds are made, total ultrasonic testing is costly. First AE monitoring during welding is carried out and only defect indications identified by AET are further probed by UT.
5. This method is particularly sensitive for detection of cracks which are the most serious flaws in welds.
6. In most cases, AE monitoring of welding is cheaper and simple to apply compared to other NDT methods.

The two ways of monitoring the integrity of welded structure are: (1) proof testing initially and then periodically at regular intervals and monitoring AE generated during these tests and (2) Continuous monitoring of structures by AET. The success of the structural integrity monitoring using AET depends on the calibration of the test set up and the methods used for processing and analysing the signals.

Many simulation experiments are carried out by introducing flaws into the structure and monitoring AE response during growth of these flaws. Some of the conclusions obtained are: (1) Flaw growth was successfully detected in time to prevent the failure. (2) Good correlation was obtained between the crack growth measurement by pitch-catch ultrasonic method and the AE generated. (3) The sensitivity of AET can be judged by the fact that flaw growth as small as 25 μm can be detected with transducers spaced at 1.25 meters apart in a particular test. (4) Fluid leaks can also be detected. Figure 8.3 gives the statistical location map for defects on a cylindrical portion of a reactor vessel during a hydrotest. Most of the defects were small and were located either in or adjacent to weld area or at the nozzle to vessel interface.

8.4 WELDING NOISE

Unwanted signals (noises) during welding can be eliminated by proper signal conditioning and processing techniques. Electromagnetic interference (EMI) consists of noise conduction or radiation. The EMI can be eliminated by providing better shielding to sensor, preamplifier and main amplifier in high conductivity metal cases. Use of differential sensor also reduces the EMI.

Thermal expansion/contraction and warpage may give noise from uncleaned surfaces due to cracking of mill scale etc. This can be eliminated by cleaning or

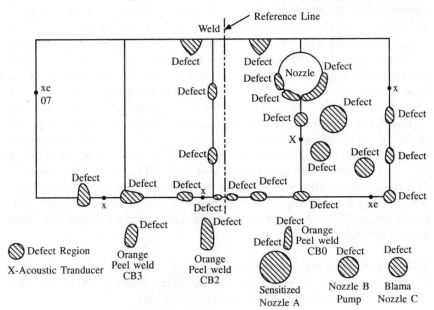

Fig. 8.3   Statistical location map

descaling the plates being welded. Generally, during the welding process, in order to avoid noise due to electrically floating condition of the component being welded, it is normally considered to remove the AE instrument ground from mains and connect it along with a blocking capacitor to the structure under test. But, it is better to use a battery operated AE system which is grounded to the surface of the structure. Isolation transformer between the instrument and the power supply also helps in reducing the noise. It is desirable to see that the sensors, pre-amplifiers, main system etc. have the same ground. Arc welding gives weld spatter and fracturing of slag. One should be careful to identify these noise sources and eliminate them from analysing.

8.5   APPLICATIONS OF AET FOR MONITORING WELDING PROCESS

AET has become recently a code approved technique. ASTM standard E749 deals with AE monitoring during continuous welding and ASTM E751 on AE monitoring during resistance spot welding.

8.5.1   TIG Welding

It has been reported that good relation between AE generated and weld crack length could be obtained during TIG welding of stainless steel. Detection of formation of cracks and lack of penetration during TIG welding are possible with high degree of success. However, defects like porosity or pin holes which produce relatively weak AE signals may be difficult to detect unless these are accompanied by cracking/deformation.

8.5.2   Submerged Arc Welding (SAW)

Submerged Arc Welding (SAW) is a versatile process which is used for continuous welding, running up to a few metres. Figure 8.4 shows a typical arrangement for AE monitoring where a moving sensor configuration with sensor position fixed relative to the weld bead is shown. One of the major problems in SAW process is the trapping of slag. This is related with the bead surface of the weld. The AE rate increases drastically as the bead formation changes from a normal bead to what is called a rope bead. The normal bead presents a smooth surface that prevents slag from being trapped. The rope bead has edge and pockets along its side which can trap slag during the next weld pass thus causes a slag inclusion. The high rate of AE generation in the case of rope bead can be explained as follows: The glassy cover over a normal bead lifts away smoothly as it cools and solidifies whereas glassy cover from poorly (rope) formed bead with partially trapped slag fractures extensively as it separates from the weld bead surfaces. The real time detection of this can reduce the rework-time from days to minutes.

8.5.3   Electroslag Welding (ESW)

During in-process weld monitoring of electroslag welding (ESW), the AET successfully identified excessive flux and shallow flux.

Typical AET set up for ESW monitoring is shown in Fig. 8.5. A differential

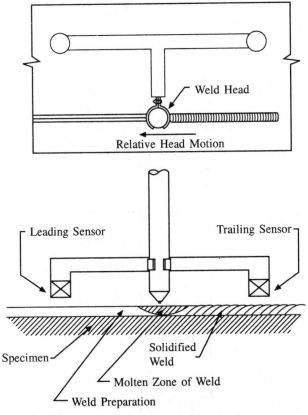

Fig. 8.4   Moving sensor configuration

type transducer is mounted on a wave guide with a magnetic base. This arrangement allows the transducer to remain cool, provides very high contact pressure to the rough steel surface and eliminates the necessity for a viscous couplant. Literature suggests that AET can be used for controlling unmeasurable parameters like flux additions and for detecting weld discontinuity formations.

8.5.4 Electron Beam Welding
AE monitoring during electron beam welding (EBW), provides with discontinuity detection and location. Crack detection and location, detection of incomplete penetration and detection of burst/void and mismatch are possible. AE parameters can be used for process control. EBW used for turbine engine part fabrication is an excellent candidate for monitoring in real time and using AET to achieve effective process control during the weld pass.

The EBW process is similar to other welding techniques except for the fact that this is done in an evacuated chamber to avoid any contamination. The sources of AE in EBW are also the same as those occur in other welding processes. Hence, the real time discontinuity detection and characterisation of welds is the major advantage of the use of AET in the case of EBW. In many cases, EBW has to be carried out in a number of revolutions and a multiple pass weld may be

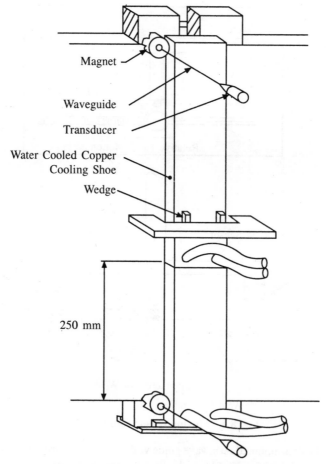

Magnet

Waveguide

Transducer

Water Cooled Copper
Cooling Shoe

Wedge

250 mm

Fig. 8.5   AE setup for electroslag welding

required. In such cases, it is desirable to use a sensing method that avoids the problem of sensor electrical leads getting tangled. Experience has been obtained for controlling the welding process using rolling dry contact differential type sensors. Use of differential sensor minimises the radio frequency interference.

In EBW of nickel base alloys, it has been found that cracking during cooling process produces high amplitude AE bursts which can easily be distinguished from a background of much lower amplitude. In the case of EBW, the AE energy (rms voltage) is related to the nugget size, depth of penetration and overall volume of the weld and can be used as a criterion for control of welding parameters. When the beam current focus position and feed rate are held constant, a reduction in the detected AE energy indicates incomplete penetration or under fill or a weld cavity.

Crack initiation and propagation, excessive porosity, metal expulsion and inclusions generate burst type emission. Use of sensor with two resonance frequency bands: One in the range of 140 to 200 kHz and the other above 300 kHz could detect the two types of situations: (a) incomplete penetration or under fill or weld cavity and (b) crack initiation and propagation, metal expulsion and inclusion. Figure 8.6 shows the AE system for electron beam weld monitoring. To make the best use of the two types of AE, the signal is fed into both channels of an independent channel controller. Suitable plug-in filters are used for dual frequency configuration.

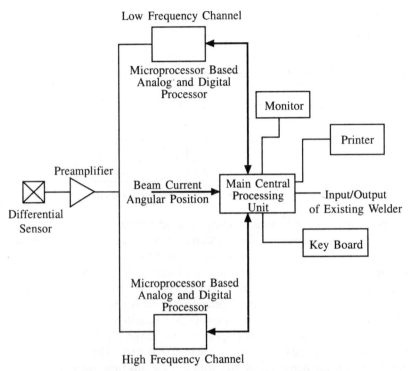

Fig. 8.6 AE system during electron beam welding

8.5.5 Laser Spot Welding

Figure 8.7 shows the experimental setup used for real time monitoring of the laser welding of insulated copper wires. Whenever a weld is made, AE is generated by the fusion of the material. The mechanical stress signal is then detected by a differential PZT sensor whose output is amplified and filtered. The AE generated during a particular time period (Controlled by the laser intensity) is only counted and analysed. Figure 8.7 shows the laser intensity and the gate for the AE collection. It can be seen from Fig. 8.7 that there is almost a linear relationship between the shear strength of the weld and the AE counts. The AE envelope is an indication for the weld quality. A go/no go signal can be generated using a comparator to compare the magnitude of the AE envelope to a variable threshold externally adjusted and is indicative of an acceptable weld.

8.5.6 Resistance Spot Welding (RSW)

The AE generated can be related to the weld quality parameters such as strength and size of the nugget, the amount of expulsion and the amount of cracking.

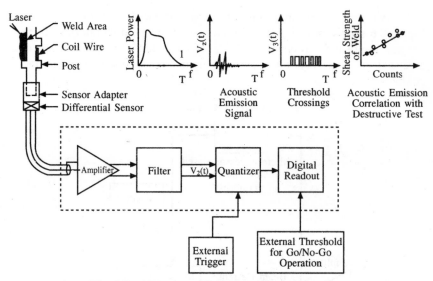

Fig. 8.7   AE system for laser welding evaluation

Therefore, in-process AE monitoring can be used both as an examination method and as a means for providing feedback control. The various stages in the RSW are: set down of the electrodes, squeeze, current flow, forging, hold time and lift off. Various types of AE signals are produced during each of these stages. Using time and amplitude or energy discrimination or both, the AE response corresponding to each stage can be separately detected and analysed. AE during nugget formation and expansion can be used to correlate with the strength of the weld. The sensors normally used have a frequency response in the range 100 kHz to 1 MHz. The sensor is normally fixed to the lower (grounded) electrode. The instrument should have provision for detection of AE within a certain time interval or energy/amplitude range. ASTM standard E751 describes the procedure for the measurement of the AE response associated with selected stages of the resistance spot welding process. This standard also provides guidelines for feed back control by utilizing the measured AE response signals during spot welding process.

8.6   AET FOR STRUCTURAL INTEGRITY MONITORING

Degradation of ageing plants/components is caused by corrosion, erosion, wear, fatigue, creep etc. The successful operation of the structures/components during the entire life can be achieved by pre- and in-service inspection of critical components of the structures to predict the failure in advance before any catastrophe occurs. Acoustic emission technique is a potential non-destructive testing tool for assessing the structural integrity of critical components like pressure vessels, pipelines etc. in nuclear, petrochemical and chemical industries. Using this technique, on-line monitoring of critical components and structures can give advance warning before occurrence of any catastrophe due to material degradation under service conditions. A few case studies on the application of AET for monitoring structural integrity in critical components/weld joints are presented.

8.6.1   Typical AE Monitoring During Hydrotesting of Waste Stripper

Acoustic Emission monitoring during hydrotesting of a waste stripper of a heavy water plant was carried out. In the waste stripper, waste liquid depleted in deuterium is received from bottom of the tower. Hydrogen sulphide dissloved in the waste liquid is stripped off by direct injection of primary steam in the stripper, to bring down the hydrogen sulphide content upto permissible limit. AE monitoring of two regions of the vessel namely the weld joint between the shell and the skirt; and the gas outlet nozzle and the flange (pad) joints at the top of the vessel, was done. The objective of the work was to detect and locate any active defects, which are the sources of acoustic activity, during hydrotesting. Sixteen channel acoustic emission equipment was used for this work. Eleven resonant sensors (150 kHz frequency) and one broadband sensor were mounted at these two regions. Calibration of the sensors was done with the help of pencil break simulation. Based on the level of background noise, the response of the sensors to the pencil break signals and the attenuation of the signal (the inter sensor spacing), the gain and threshold were optimised, to ensure that the signals due to crack initiation/ propagation are detected reliably. Hydrotest of the vessel was carried out at a maximum pressure of 26.4 kg/cm^2, with periodic holds at different pressures. The reloading cycle was immediately carried out following the hydrotest, from 22.5 to 26.4 kg/cm^2. Figure 8.8 shows the AE activity obtained during the final pressure cycle and during repressuring cycle of the two regions of the vessel. During hydrotesting, with increase in pressure cycle, the extent of acoustic activity increased and AE was generated in newer areas. There are no concentrated active zones which would indicate any crack growth phenomenon. In the repressurising step, both the regions (shell to skirt weld region and top flange and nozzle weld region) where emissions observed in the previous pressurisation cycles are not generated again and resulted in much reduced activity. These results indicated that the AE signals generated during hydrotesting are due to microyielding of the vessel and/or surface oxide detachment and not by any crack growth phenomenon at the monitored location.

8.6.2   AE Monitoring during Hydrotesting of Horton Sphere

Acoustic Emission monitoring during hydrotesting of Horton sphere in a petrochemical industry was carried out. For AE monitoring during proof testing, the sensors were used in different groups and in different configurations to cover the whole structure. In group I, twelve sensors of 150 kHz resonant frequency each were used to cover the whole sphere in triangular location mode. Two probes were placed at the bottom and top (near the flanges) of the sphere. The other probes were placed on the sphere surface in two circumferential rows with five probes in each row. These two circumferential rows were at 9.5 m distance along the surface of the sphere from top and bottom points of the sphere respectively. Based on the response of the sensors to simulated pencil break source, the inter-sensor distance of 9.5 m was optimized. In group II, three sensors of the same frequency were mounted in triangular location mode in the region where defect was suspected by ultrasonic testing earlier. In group III, one broad band sensor was mounted near the suspected region. All the sensors were connected to the acoustic emission testing system kept away from the sphere. By this, the entire

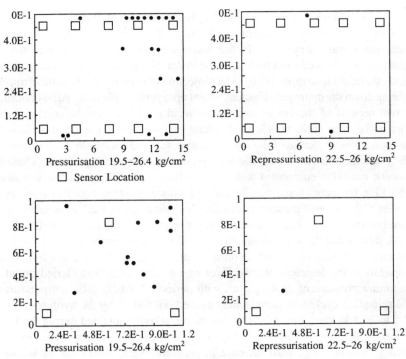

Fig. 8.8   AE monitoring during hydrotesting of a waste stripper

vessel could be covered to locate any sources of AE from discontinuities or crack growth from any part of the vessel.

The hydrotest of the vessel was carried out to a pressure of $22 kg/cm^2$, with periodic holds at different pressures. The reloading cycle was immediately carried out following the hydrotest from 20 to 22 kg/cm^2. Figure 8.9 shows the AE activity obtained during the final pressure cycle of the sphere for the sensors of group I. During the hydrotest it was observed that acoustic emission signals were generated only during the pressure rise. With increase in pressure, AE signals were generated in the newer areas and the araes where AE occurred in the previous pressure steps, do not generate AE in the subsequent pressure steps. Subsequent inspection of the vessel and simulation study by pencil break were done after the hydrotest. This indicated that the AE signals were generated from the regions of the vessel which were in contact with the concrete pillars and also the regions where decohesion and/or fracture of oxide sacle or paint layer occurred. The results obtained from the broad band sensor were analysed in terms of the spectral energy, which increased with pressure rise and was predominantly concentrated in the low frequency band upto 200 kHz. This was attributed to micro-yielding taking place in the sphere. This was also confirmed from the fact that, during the repressurization stage (20–22 kg/cm^2), the energy of the signals was at the background level.

8.6.3   On-Line Monitoring of a chemical Vessel using AET

In another case study, on-line AE monitoring has been used to monitor the

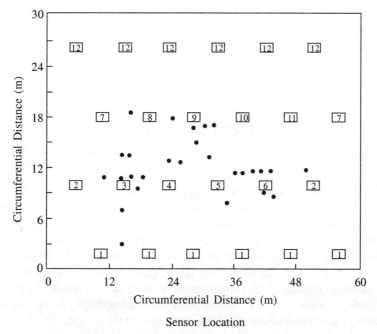

Sensor Location

Fig. 8.9   Locations of AE sensors on a Horton sphere

integrity of carbon dioxide absorber unit in a fertiliser industry. During periodic inspection of the vessel it was observed that the vessel had suffered severe chemical corrosion. Cracks were also detected in the fillet welds of the cleats of the internal support structure. It was proposed to carry out acoustic emission monitoring to assess the status of the detected cracks as also to detect any nucleating cracks in the welds of the cleats. AE monitoring was carried out continuously for a period of several months and it was observed that propagation of the defects had occurred at some locations. Subsequently using ultrasonic technique, it was confirmed that none of the defects observed earlier had extended into the surface of the vessel. Based on the recommendations made from the acoustic emission results, the vessel was put into service.

Further reading

8. Bernd Rohloft, NDT methods, The South African Mechanical Engineer, Vol. 4, 1994.

27. Goswami, G.L. An Introduction to Acoustic Emission Technology for In Process Inspection of Welds, BARC Report 1216, Commission J, Doc V, 806, 1987.

52. McElory, J.W. AE Inspection of Buried Pipelines, Symposium on AE Monitoring of Pressurised Systems, ASTM, SPP 697, 1979.

89. Votava, E. and Jax. P. Inspection of Nuclear Reactors by Means of Acoustic Emission during Hydrotest, Symposium on Acoustic Emission Monitoring of Pressurized Systems, ASTM, STP-697, 1979.

90. Wadley, H.N.G., Scruby, C.B., and Speake, J.H. Acoustic Emission for Physical Examination of Metals, International Metals Review, No. 249, 1980.

Chapter 9

Leak Testing

The ever growing technological developments along with the need for more reliable and safer products and systems, particularly while handling hazardous fluids and gases, have created a tremendous need for manufacturing the pressure vessels and pipelines with very minute leakage rates. This need has thrust on the technologists to develop the most sensitive and reliable methods of leak testing.

Leak testing is used to determine the rate at which a liquid or gas will penetrate from inside to outside of the component or vice-versa, as a result of a pressure difference between the two regions. Leak testing methods can be classified according to the pressure and fluid (gas or liquid) in the system. The commonly used methods are: (i) Acoustic leak detection, (ii) Bubble testing, (iii) Flow detection (iv) Specific gas detectors, (v) Quantity loss determination etc. Leak testing is performed by creating vacuum inside the component or by pressurising the component and applying the tracer on the other side to indicate the location and quantity of the leak. The major factors that determine the choice of the leak testing methods are the physical charecteristics of the system, the tracer fluid, the size of the anticipated leak and the reason for the testing in different ways i.e. whether to locate or detect the leak or measure the leak rate. Leak testing can be employed on a variety of components like heat exchangers, steam generators, pressure vessels etc.

9.1 PRESSURE TESTS

9.1.1 Methods of Pressure Leak Detection

As leak is the passage of fluid from one side to the other side of the boundary, the method of leak detection employs this fluid at certain pressure and detects its leakage to other side by some means. If the vessel under test is filled with fluid at a pressure higher than the atmospheric pressure, then the method is called Pressure Method. If the vessel is evacuated below the atmospheric pressure, then the test involved is called Vacuum Method. It is inconvenient under certain circumstances to carryout vacuum tests due to the size, location or condition of the plant. Under these conditions, pressure test becomes imperative.

9.1.2 Types of Pressure Tests

The pressure tests are classified into three groups, namely, (i) Pressure method, (ii) Bubble leak method and (iii) Ultrasonic leak detection method.

(i) Pressure Method: The component or the plant is pressurised to a known pressure and then sealed noting the time. After a time, the fall in pressure will be noted, keeping the volume constant. This gives the rate of leak in torr litre/sec. Depending on the leak tightness required and the sensitivity of the differential pressure gauge, the time allowed for reading the pressure drop varies. It should be noted that the sensitivity depends on the volume of the component also. The pressure drop reading should be taken when the temperature is the same as it was at the time of pressurisation.

(ii) Bubble leak Method: When one fluid immiscible in another fluid gets trapped into that fluid, a bubble is formed. Most common examples are air bubbles in water and soap bubbles in air. The easy formation of bubbles with liquids of smaller surface tension is taken due advantage of in selection of liquids for these types of tests to increare the sensitivity. It should be remembered that the bubbles in this method are continuously supplied by gas (generally hydrogen) and as such if this supply is at a higher rate then the bubble formation is also quicker. It should also be noted that the flow rate is proportional to square of the pressure. The degree of leak tightness is estimated by the bubble formation using proper combination of pressure, gas and liquid.

(iii) Ultrasonic Leak Detection: In this method, use is made of the fact that any gas at high pressure leaking out into the atmosphere produces disturbances in the air. These are nothing but a composition of waves at different frequencies. It is observed that a fair amount of wave intensities are produced in the ultrasonic range of about 40 kHz. The detector comprises of the probe or a receiving transducer which picks up the ultrasound and converts it into an electrical signal, a pre-amplifier and an amplifier to amplify the low signal, a converter circuit and a means of display system to indicate the amplified output.

The sensitivity of the system depends on the pressure of the gas used, the distance of the leak from the probe and the sensitivity of the circuit. These units will be calibrated with some standard leak. The application of the method is on (1) Pipe lines carrying chemicals, (2) Air-conditioning units, (3) Pressurised cables, (4) Boilers, (5) Gas cylinders etc.

9.2 HALOGEN, HYDROGEN AND SF$_6$ (SULPHUR HEXA-FLUORIDE) DETECTORS

9.2.1 Halogen Leak Detectors

In closed loop refrigeration systems, there is a need for detection of leakage of freon like gasses. Halogen detectors meet this requirements. A platinum surface heated from 1073 to 1173 K is particularly sensitive to halogens or gases and vapours of compounds containing halogen and liberates more positive ions in their presence. This is due to the alkaline element impurities present in the platinum metal which is utilised by constructing a diode with a platinum spiral as an anode surrounded by a collector electrode. The platinum spiral is heated electrically and kept at a positive potential with respect to the collector. The positive ions emitted by this spiral are collected and this collector current is amplified and measured (Fig. 9.1). This detector is used in two modes: Sniffer mode—which sniffs the pressurised halogen comming out through the leak and the detector detects the presence and rate of leak. In the other mode, the halogen detector is connected to a vacuum system which also evacuates the job under test. Halogen and halogenated compound gases are sprayed over suspected regions. Halogen sprayed over the job enters through the leak in to the system and gets detected. The sensitivity of a well designed detector is about 10^{-6} torr lit/sec (std cc/sec). The major advantage of this detector is its ready applicability to various types of refrigeration systems with adequate sensitivity. Other advantages are the simple construction, ruggedness, protability and low cost and also can be operated by unskilled personnel.

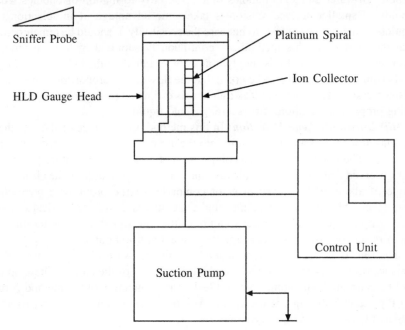

Fig. 9.1   Halogen leak detector.

9.2.2   SF$_6$ Detector

SF$_6$ is a highly electronegative gas with a large electron capture cross section. It is also safe to handle, inert chemically and non-toxic in nature. The acutual sensitive element is an electron capture detector employing a disc containing tritium as an anode cum beta emitter and a stainless steel mesh at a negative potential with respect to the tritium source. The beta particles (electrons) continuously emanating from the tritium disc produce a large amount of ionisation in the region and the standing current is in the order of 10^{-9} amps. When the detector cell volume contains some electronegative components like SF$_6$, freon or oxygen, the electrons are captured and there is a reduction in the standing current. This method is simple and the equipment inexpensive and portable (Fig. 9.2). The sensitivity is limited by the background current due to the atmospheric oxygen.

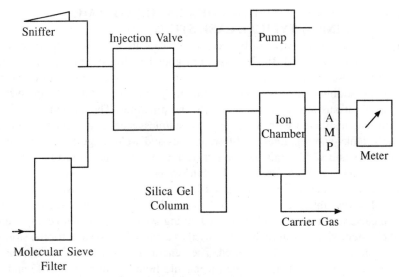

Fig. 9.2 SF₆ leak detector

9.2.3   Thermal Conductivity Leak Detector

This utilises the altered thermal conductivity of the envionment when a suitable search gas like hydrogen or helium from the leak is encountered. The heat is carried away from the thermistor. Thermistors are temperature dependant resistors with very large temperature coefficient. Usually two identical thermistors are employed, one of them suitably isolated from the search gas entering the system and the other is mounted in the path of sniffed air sample. Both the thermistors are electrically heated and form the two arms of a measuring bridge circuit. When the search gas coming out of the leak from a pressurised job is sampled by the sniffer, the bridge is unbalanced and the unbalanced voltage is amplified and indicated. The sensitivity of this detector is of the order of 10^{-5} std cc/sec. The advantages of these detectors are the simplicity of their construction, low cost, imunity to the ambient temperature variations and the small size. The disadvantages are the limited sensitivity and the hazards associated with the search gas.

9.2.4   Mass Spectrometer Leak Detector

Another leak testing method is the mass spectrometer helium leak detection (MSLD) which is useful in the detection and accurate quantification of minute leakage rates, (10^{-13} std. cc/sec). The selection of an appropriate leak testing method mainly depends upon the nature and the type of the component and the maximum allowable leakage rate. The mass spectrometer helium leak testing under vacuum can provide accurate information on the size of the leak in terms of the leakage rates. Helium leak testing of large sized components such as pipelines and pressure vessels particularly under vacuum, requires a vacuum of 10^{-1} Pa or better in the component, so that the MSLD operation does not get distrubed, as it needs a vacuum of 10^{-2} Pa.

9.3   HELIUM LEAK TESTING OF A LARGE VOLUME PIPELINE: A TYPICAL CASE STUDY

Liquid sodium is an universally accepted coolant used for removal of heat in Fast Breeder Reactors (FBR) because of its good heat transfer property. It is also a poor moderator. There are many systems incorporated in the reactor to handle the liquid sodium, such as, primary sodium system, secondary sodium system etc. with various tanks, pressure vessels and pipelines. The secondary sodium system is constructed with AISI type 316 stainless steel material consisting of vessels, tanks and pipelines of different sizes and weld lengths totalling about 700 metres and weld joints numbering over 1300. It is interposed between the active primary sodium circuit and steam-water circuit. This system has two identical and independent loops. Each loop is designed to transfer 25 MW of thermal power. Intermediate heat exchanger (IHX), expansion and surge tanks, steam generator modules and associated piping system are the main components of the system. Sodium storage tank is used as a part of the system for the storage whenever sodium has to be emptied. The general arrangement of the system is shown in Figure 9.3. It is designed to handle liquid sodium at 773 K and all welds are to be 100% radiographed and helium leak tested under vacuum to a leak tightness of 10^{-8} std. cc/sec for local leaks and 10^{-7} std. cc/sec for global leaks. These components are to be manufactured with utmost care with stringent quality control measures as any micro-leak could develop into a large leak and the consequences are severe. Hence, it becomes essential that all high temperature sodium systems should have high degree of leak tightness, thereby demanding the use of helium leak testing under vacuum.

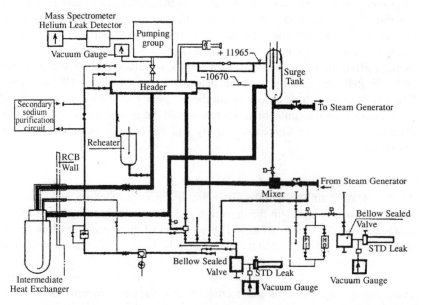

Fig. 9.3   Helium leak testing set up

Sequence of Leak Testing: The comprehensive programme of the leak testing was planned by taking into account all the complexities of the piping system.

The following steps are considered essential and according to which the test sequence is planned: (1) to test wherever possible, in small spools of piping with resonable numbers of weld joints in each spool, (2) avoid welding of major tanks and vessels prior to helium leak testing (HLT) of weld joints in the piping system and (3) to test individually the large volume vessels and tanks and after satisfactory testing, include these with terminal welds and test the terminal joints with the vacuum jacket method and clear the system completely.

Testing of Major Tanks and Vessels: All the major vessels/tanks are helium leak tested under vacuum at shop and ensured leak tightness as required by the specification. The testing details of sodium storage tank are given below and the other vessels/tanks are also tested in a similar way.

Testing of Large Sized Storage Tank: The storage tank of the secondary sodium system is about 3500 mm in diameter and 3500 mm in height, fabricated using 14 mm thick AISI 316 type stainless steel material, with a storage capacity of about 24 cubic metres of sodium at 432 K. Figure 9.4 illustrates the general assembly of the tank with the test set-up. The large volume of the tank forbids the direct use of any standard leak detector to test the tank under vacuum. Large capacity high vacuum pumping system with a capacity of 2000 m^3 per hour at 10 Pa needs to be employed to evacuate the tank to a vacuum of 5×10^{-2} Pa or better. A standard leak and a vacuum gauge are connected to the port available at the far away point from the pump with a bellow sealed valve. The 400 mm dia.

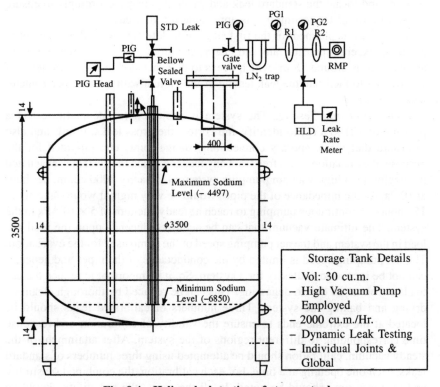

Fig. 9.4   Helium leak testing of stroage tank

manhole is used to connect the pumping system with a 2500 mm long pipe of 160 mm dia. The tank is positioned in a pit of 2500 mm deep and the pumping system is positioned at a higher level to have the pumping from top. It may take about 80 hours of continuous pumping to reach an equilibrium state of vacuum of 5×10^{-3} Pa in the system. The combined sensitivity and response time are obtained with the auxiliary vacuum pump running serially. This is necessary because the degassing rate would be very high due to the large surface area. Care should be taken with respect to any difference in actual calibration of the equipment without any additional pumping and the system calibration with the auxiliary pump on. This correction is to be applied for all the leakage indications noted during the testing. All the weld joints can be suitably tested by jacketing each weld joint with a polythene hood. After completion of testing of each weld joint, a global leak test is conducted by enclosing the tank with a polythene envelope and filling the same with helium. The observations are made after an hour for global leak and that should be within the acceptable limits.

Testing of Secondary Sodium Piping System: Testing of large volume piping systems like secondary sodium piping system should be systematically planned in advance so that all the weld joints are tested and cleared with least time. It would be ideal to follow the test sequence discussed earlier for the leak testing of this system. As large number of weld joints are involved in various lines at different elevations, it is appropriate to sub-divide the pipe lines into different sections and locate the standard leak and vacuum gauges accordingly to ensure the sensitivity of the testing that is applicable for all areas.

The system is planned for the first stage of leak testing with all the pipelines and tanks except expansion tank and steam generators. The total volume involved at this stage is around 18 m^3 which needs to be evacuated to a vacuum level of 1×10^{-2} Pa to facilitate the leak testing of the system with a mass spectrometer leak detector.

Evacuation and Testing: The system is subjected to pneumatic test at a pressure of 101 kPa (g) to identify and correct the gross leaks, if any, and also to ensure that the temporary connections, flange joints etc. provided for the purpose of evacuation, were free from any leakage. Then the system is evacuated by employing a high vacuum pumping system of capacity 2000 cu. m. per hour at 10 Pa. As the impedance of the pipes would be very high, it would take about 150 hours of continuous pumping to reach a steady vacuum of 5×10^{-3} Pa in the system. The ultimate vacuum that can be achieved depends upon the total gas load in the system and the net pumping speed of the pump used for the evacuation. The net pumping speed is limited by the conductance of the pipes and hence, it can not be increased endlessly for a system. So, it is important to reduce the gas loads encountered due to degassing. This can be reduced by thorough cleaning, drying and baking the system. Three numbers of calibrated leaks should be located at the extreme ends to ensure the validity of calibration and response time corresponding to different regions of the system. After attainment of the steady vacuum, calibration should be attempted using three numbers of standard leaks; each one opening at a time. For each calibration, the combined sensitivity and response time should be noted. In all the cases, the sensitivity should be within the acceptable limit.

The testing of the weld joints should be started from the nearest point from the pumping unit. A polythene jacket is provided on each joint and helium gas filled into it and observed for a minimum of half an hour more than the response time achieved for each of the areas. Every time a helium hood of a particular joint is filled with helium and prepared for testing, the previous helium hood is removed and flushed with compressed air. Only one or two weld joints are tested at a time. Any leak noticed, is marked and identified for rectification. Thus, all the weld joints are helium leak tested sequentially.

After completion of the leak testing of the weld joints in the piping system, the large volume tanks which would have already been helium leak tested earlier are connected to the piping system with the terminal joints. Each joint is leak tested by suitable vacuum jacket and cleared. It may be noted that the knowledge of vacuum technology, pumping system, geometry and intricate nature of the components, relative placement of vacuum pumps and detectors and their quantity and assigned locations for standard leaks based on the component etc. would go a long way to overcome the problems generally encountered in helium leak testing of large sized pipelines and vessels. It is suggested that design review shall be made to consider the test requirements and incorporate all the possible provisions for smooth and efficient helium leak testing.

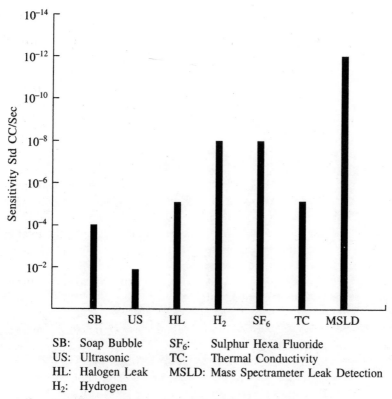

SB: Soap Bubble SF_6:   Sulphur Hexa Fluoride
US: Ultrasonic   TC: Thermal Conductivity
HL: Halogen Leak   MSLD: Mass Spectrameter Leak Detection
H_2: Hydrogen

Fig. 9.5 Leak detection methods and their sensitivity

The various leak testing methods described above and their test sensitivity are given in Fig. 9.5. It is observed from the figure that conventional methods like soap bubble and ultrasonic give lower sensitivity whereas MSLD gives the highest sensitivity.

Further reading

68. Palaniappan, M. and Subbratnam, R. Leak testing, pressure testing and field experience: Course on welding metallurgy, technology and quality assurance, IIW, Kalpakkam, 1996.

Chapter 10

Thermography Testing

All objects around us emit electromagnetic radiations. At ambient temperature and above, these are predominantly infrared radiations (IR). IR are invisible to eye. But with the aid of a suitable detector, IR can be converted into a visible image. Variation in the temperature of the surface of the object can be visualized from the thermal image of an object. This means that deviations from normal temperature can be detected from a distance. It is this advantage that the technique exploits for ever increasing applications in a number of industries.

10.1 BASIC PRINCIPLE

Thermography makes use of the infrared spectral band of the electromagnetic radiation. The infrared band is further subdivided into four smaller bands, the boundaries of which are arbitrarily chosen. They include the near infrared (0.75–3 μm), the middle infrared (3–6 μm), the far infrared (6–15 μm) and the extreme infrared (15–100 μm). The most commonly used band for commercial infrared imaging is between 0.75–15 μm.

The properties of infrared radiations are similar to those of other electromagnetic radiations such as visible light except that their transmission and absorption behavior is different from that of visible light. Infrared radiations travel in straight lines outward from the source. They can propagate in vacuum and in certain liquids, solids and gases. They can be optically focused and directed by lenses or mirrors or dispersed by prisms. IR can also be transmitted through certain materials which are opaque to light. The intensity of the spectrum of the emitted IR is dependent upon the absolute temperature of the body. The basic factors affecting the thermal measurements include (a) emissivity, (b) surroundings and (c) atmosphere.

(a) Emissivity: This is defined as the ratio of the radiance of a body at a given temperature to the corresponding radiance of a black body at the same temperature. For the 'black body', the emissivity factor is 1.0. Actual objects are seldom "black". Normally, various materials and treated surfaces exhibit emissivities ranging from 0.1 to 0.95. Emissivity is a critical parameter for quantitative measurement of the temperature.

(b) Surroundings: It is important to have the object surroundings free from thermal radiation sources, otherwise the radiation from these sources would also be reflected by the object under examination leading to erroneous values.

(c) Atmosphere: The effects of atmosphere are of importance when the object

is far away. The atmosphere not only attenuates the radiation from the target but also alters the spectral characteristics. However, these effects are negligible in the cases where the object under investigation is located quite close and the atmosphere is uncontaminated with vapours, smoke, fog, hot gases etc. Occasionally, one may need to make some critical measurements on an object in presence of hot air/gases as in the case of furnaces. In such cases, suitable filters such as high temperature gas filters are used along with the appropriate correction factors to take into account the ambient temperature and attenuation by these filters. In case where the objects are situated at a large distance as in the case of airborne thermography, atmospheric absorption plays a very important role. The atmospheric absorption is quite a complex process and in these cases, mathematical modelling is resorted to for estimating the temperatures.

10.2   DETECTORS AND EQUIPMENT

The detection system for infrared imaging can be a contact (surface) system such as a cholesterol liquid crystal or a non-contact tele-system such as a thermographic camera. Surface systems tend to be less costly and simple and can have high resolution. Camera systems are more expensive. However, theremal imaging with tele-camera systems has wider engineering applications.

The block diagram of a non-contact thermography system is shown in Fig. 10.1. It basically consists of an infrared scanner, monitor, control unit and a calculator for field applications. The output can also be stored in a modified video casette recorder which can be analyzed later using a personal computer

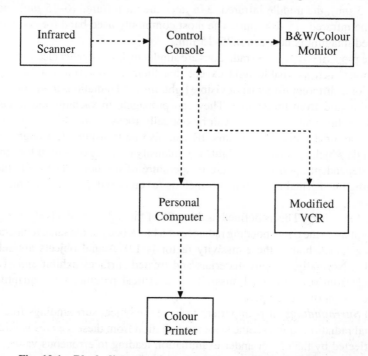

Fig. 10.1   Block diagram of a non-contact thermography system

with image processing facilities. The infrared scanner essentially consists of an optical system, scanning mechanism, infrared detector and associated electronics. The optical system collimates the incoming infrared radiation into the detector. The commonly used materials for mirrors and prisms in the optical system are germanium, silicon, sapphire, barium fluoride and arsenic trisulphide. The scanning mechanism scans the surface within the field of view. It consists of two octagonal prisms rotating perpendicular to each other at a high speed. The heart of the thermography system is the infrared detector. There are different modes for acquiring a thermal image.

1. Image Converters—Here the thermal image is first converted into electron image through the use of converters. The electron image is then converted into an optical image.
2. Pyricon Based Devices—These are normal vidicon tubes with infrared sensitive face plates (sulphate triglycine).
3. Mechanical scanning devices—Here the image is scanned with a moving mirror across a fixed and cooled detector (mercury cadmium telluride or indium antimonide). This is the type of system which is used extensively in the field of NDT.

The advent of personal computers has revolutionized the field of thermography. Thermograms can be subjected to image processing and enhancement to obtain minute details not otherwise visible. Software options for image processing include contrast stretching, spatial filtering, thermal chopping, relief presentation etc.

10.3 TECHNIQUES

Thermography can be classified basically into two categories: (a) passive and (b) active. In passive technique, the natural heat distribution is measured over the surface of a hot structure. This is generally used in temperature monitoring. In an active technique, heating or cooling is induced or applied to the part or the complete surface and the movement and redistribution of temperature profile across the test surface is measured. This is generally used in non-destructive evaluation.

10.4 APPLICATIONS

In the petroleum industry, this technique finds applications in the monitoring of stack temperature, maintenance of plant equipment such as reaction towers, refining furnaces, ducts and piping, detection of corrosion in oil tank shell, measurement of oil levels etc. Thermal imaging has been extensively applied for condition monitoring of furnace tubes, gas and fluid transfer lines, evaluation of heat resistant linings in refractory furnaces etc. This technique is ideally suited for the wear determination of refractories in blast furnaces, hot blast stoves and steel stoves and the inspection of rotary kiln lining and estimation of temperature within the kiln.

Thermographic inspection of an entire electrical power systems can be performed. Stator lamination insulation, core insulation, slip ring temperature measurement etc. of turbogenerators are also made using thermography. Apart from these important applications, this technique can also be applied for:

(1) Location of loose contacts on busbar joints of switchyard, switchgear etc.
(2) Location of improper jointing of lugs in cable joints
(3) Finding irregularities in distribution boards
(4) Detection of hot spots in isolators due to presence of dirt or moisture which could lead to corona.
(5) Checking the adequacy of insulation.

Thermal imaging is also employed for on-line quality assessment of welding process. It is possible to identify arc misalignment, lack of penetration etc. using infrared thermography during welding. These details are given in Chapter 15 on Intelligent Welding. Typical thermal imaging pictures of good weld and bad weld are also given in Chapter 15.

Further reading

8. Bernd Rohloft, NDT methods, The South African Mechanical Engineer, Vol. 4, 1994.
19. Farlay, J.M., Thomson, J.L. and Dikstra, B.J. Non-destructive Testing to Avoid Weld Failure, International Conference on Weld Failures, London, Edited by Harrison. J.D. The Welding Institute. 1988.
31. Halmshaw, R. Nondestructive Testing, Metallurgy and Materials Science Services, Edward Arnold, London, 1992.

Chapter 11

In-Situ Metallography

In-service inspection (ISI) of components especially in power plants is necessary for damage assessment, life prediction and extension. Periodic in-service inspection by means of non-destructive testing to gain information on damage assessment is carried out as a routine and mandatory procedure. ISI of the components is aimed to minimize unforseen breakdowns and accidents and thus the safety and reliability of the operation is assured. Most of the inspection procedures give only gross information about loss of material thickness and defects associated with the material. However, the microstructural degradation suffered by the component under the hostile environment cannot be determined by the conventional non-destructive evaluation methods. However, by adopting *in-situ* metallography techniques, the microstructural degradation such as grain growth, grain boundary oxidation, precipitation, creep damage and graphitisation can be evaluated since the microstructure exhibits the damages experienced by the component under the actual operating conditions. In-situ metallography is a well established NDE technique for evaluation of microstructural damages and it is also finding extensive applications in condition monitoring and life assessment problems.

In-situ metallography (field metallography) is related to microstructural evaluation of plant structural components during service. Regular metallography consists of preparing a section of a material in laboratory by usual grinding, polishing and etching sequence for revealing microstructure and then examining the same under an optical microscope in the laboratory. In the *in-situ* metallography, instead of sectioning a component for metallographic examination, the surface of it is metallographically prepared '*in-situ*' by using portable grinding, polishing and electro-polishing units and it is a nondestructive method. Microstructure can be examined on the prepared spot using a protable microscope or can be registered on a replicating tape which on processing in the laboratory will reveal the microstructure.

In the context of welding, insitu metallography is indispensible to ensure quality welding. During welding, there is fusion of the two parts of the material (similar/dissimilar) being joined. The fused mass and the adjacent regions of the parts undergo thermal cycle with heating to different temperatures and cooling back to room temperature at different cooling rates. Many times preheating and post-weld heat treatment are employed for ensuring stress free weld joints. In the weld and interface regions, there would be dilution and alteration in the chemistry of the parts leading to formation of different microstructural features, particularly undesirable phases like intermetallics are formed during dissimilar joints. In order to ensure that the weld joint has the required microstructural features which in turn decide the mechanical propertiic and in-service performance of the joint, it would be necessary to carry out in-situ metallography of weld joints. Also, in weld joint operating at higher temperatures, the microstructural changes taking place in service, should not degrade the properties. For example, delta ferrite in austenitic stainless steel weldments may get converted to sigma phase, an embritling phase. In-situ metallography of such welds as part of in-service inspection provides a method for detection of formation of sigma phase. It is clear that *in-situ* metallography plays a significant role in assessing welded joints.

NDT techniques like ultrasonics are very much influenced by microstructural characteristics of a material. Nondestructive testing in conjunction with metallography is extensively used in quality evaluation of components not only during stages of manufacturing and installation, but also in-service and during maintenance. The major advantage of metallographic examination is that, it can provide valuable information regarding the origin and nature of flaws and thus plays a key role in failure investigation. It also helps in determining whether indications obtained from NDT methods such as ultrasonic and magnetic particle testing are due to metallurgical structure or due to flaws present in the component being tested. Indications of magnetic particle examinations are re-checked by *in-situ* metallographic examination to find out ghost indications due to variations in chemistry and heat treated conditions of the welds. Some times, it becomes impractical to adopt satisfactory quality control techniques and therefore process is controlled by using combination of metallographiic examination and statistical techniques.

This chapter discusses an approach to the selection of system and sites for field (*in-situ*) metallography, the procedure for obtaining a replica, and the significance of microstructural characteristics of typical power plant material for damage assessment.

11.1 SELECTION CRITERIA OF SITES FOR *IN-SITU* METALLOGRAPHY

The criteria for selection of systems and sites for field metallography are based on the expected damage mechanism(s), which in turn is (are) governed by the type of materials used in fabrication of the components and service conditions. Replica locations are also selected on the basis of problematic sites identified from known experience.

For example, in components fabricated from plain carbon steels operating at temperature above 673K, or Cr-Mo steels above 753K, the primary mechanism expected is graphitzation. This type of damage usually occurs in the portion of HAZ, nearest to the unaffected base metal. Therefore, when graphitization is of concern, sites for replication should be located primarily at the interface of weldment/base metal.

In the case of Cr-Mo steels and austenitic steels, the expected damage mechanism is creep—the time dependent deformation of materials. Creep is governed by operating stresses in addition to the temperature and time factors. Thus, when creep is the damage mechanism of concern, sites for replication should be selected from the more highly stressed locations in components and system operating at the highest temperature.

In weldments, creep damage usually occurs first in the HAZ, or weld metal very close to the weld fusion line, where the microstructures are most susceptible to creep damage. Experience suggests that longitudinal welds in high temperature system deserve special attention. In the case of circumferential welds, it is important to determine the most likely location around the weld where high tensile stresses occur.

11.2 REPLICATION PROCESS

Replication process results in the production of a "hard copy" or "finger print" i.e., replica of the microstructural features for subsequent metallurgical evaluation involving following steps:

1. Grinding and polishing the surface to be examined. Polishing is performed by either mechanical methods or electropolishing to produce a 0.20 μm finish. Electropolishing can be accomplished much faster than mechanical polishing, but its successful application is more sensitive to the temperature of the metal surface.

2. Etching the polished surface with an appropriate etchant (e.g. 2–5% nital, i.e. nitric acid in alcohol in the case of carbon and low alloy steels) to develop the microstructural features.

3. Firmly applying a thin (50 μm) cellulose acetate film that has been wetted and softened with a mild solvent (acetone) immediately prior to application. An alternate method is to spray the polished and etched surface with a strong solvent, e.g., acetone, and immediately apply the film. Keeping the film free of extraneous foreign particles is more difficult with this technique. In either case, it is the softening by the solvent that allows the film to capture the metallurgical features in a reverse topography, with depressions becoming protrusions. The film is allowed to dry and is then removed.

4. Removing the film and attaching the dried film to a flat surface (usually a microscopic glass slide) for microscopic observations. It is important to keep the film flat to enable viewing at high magnification, upto 1000X using an optical microscope for metallurgical evaluation.

The metallurgical features recorded on the replica are much more distinguishable when the replica is either blackened at the back side prior to attaching the replica to the glass slide or applying a thin film of gold on the front side by vapour deposition. After etching the polished surface (step 2), the microstructural features can be directly observed using a portable optical microscope and recorded with the camera attached to the microscope. Photography is possible only when sufficient access is available for vibration free mounting of the microscope assembly. Replica provides valid images of the microstructures when produced by skilled personnel.

11.3 SIGNIFICANCE OF MICROSTRUCTURAL OBSERVATIONS

The significance of creep and fatigue damage and cracks are commonly assessed at a magnification of 200X. Microcracks usually form by the coalescence of aligned cavities indicating advnaced creep damage. Macrocracks develop by the growth of microcracks. From a practical stand point, the changes in base metal are not as important as in the HAZ and weld metal because the last two undergo significant creep damage well before any creep related problems develop in the base metal. For the evaluation of microstructures of various materials, ASM-Metals Handbook, Vol. No. 8 on 'Metallography, structures and phase diagrams' may be referred to.

Microstructural features are very useful in assessing microstructural degradation, damage assessment and life prediction. Periodic measurements made during inservice inspection help in knowing any unanticipated degradation in components, thus avoiding premature failures. Many a time, after an accident, like accidental increase in temperature and pressure, fire accident etc., it is necessary to confirm that the metallurgical conditions of the components are not altered and the component is acceptable. This can be successfully verified using *in-situ* metallography.

11.4   DECISION MAKING

Personnel responsible for the availabiltiy and reliability of plants and industries depend on metallurgists to provide appropriate recommendations based on the microstructural characteristics revealed by *in-situ* metallography. Decisions like repair, replace or use as-is with future monitoring at a given periodicity are taken.

11.5   APPLICATIONS

Metallographic examination is used for the following applications:

1. Pre-service quality assessment.
2. Evaluation of material condition.
3. Condition monitoring of components
4. Failure analysis.
5. Assessment of creep damage, temper embrittlement etc.

11.6   TYPICAL CASE STUDIES

Case 1: Inspection of a Nitrogen Gas Reheater Shell

A nitrogen gas reheater heat exchanger shell suffered damage since there was insufficient gas flow into it. Consequently, temperature of the heaters and reheaters increased considerably thus damaging the insulation and the outer aluminium sheet on the vessel. The damage was seen in the form of melting of this aluminium sheet at some locations of the pipeline.

The shell was examined metallographically at the unaffected portion and the affected portion at the base metal. Figure 11.1 shows the microstructure at the unaffected portion of the base metal. The heat affected region on the shell in the base metal showed grain growth and in many places grain boundary oxidation (Fig. 11.2). This was revealed by the existence of thick etching of grain boundaries. The grain size in these locations was about 150–200 microns and the normal

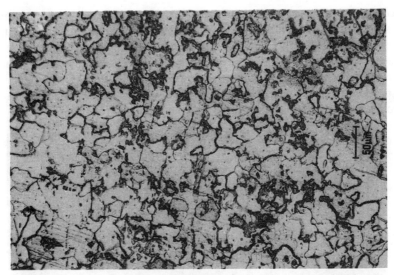

Fig. 11.1   Microstructure at the unaffected portion of the base metal

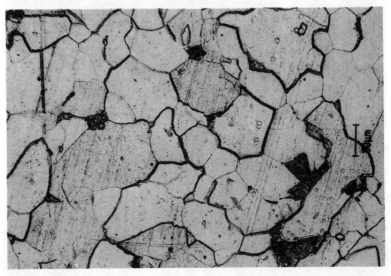

Fig. 11.2   Grain growth and grain boundry oxidation at the heat affected zone

grain size was about 30–55 microns in the unaffected portion. From the above microstructure, it was found out that there is a three fold increase in the grain size and hence considerable softening. The grain boundary oxidation leads to lack of toughness. It was recommended to take into account the reduced mechanical properties while deciding on the continued use of the component.

Case 2: In-Service Inspection of Super Heater Pipelines

In a thermal power station which was under operation for the past thirty years, *in-situ* metallography was carried out on several locations on the primary and secondary superheaters. The pipelines which carry steam at temperature and pressure of about 673 K and 42 kg/sq cm respectively was taken up for examination. These pipelines were 267 mm in diameter. When the temperature of steam exceeds the normal level, it passes through a 755 mm dia. attemperator shell to bring down its temperature. Hence, the attemperator shell was also taken up for inspection. The secondary superheater pipelines depicted normal ferrite/pearlite microstructure which is shown in Fig. 11.3.

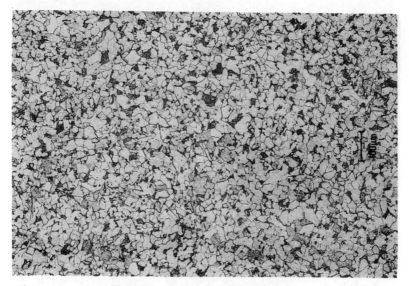

Fig. 11.3   Ferrite-pearlite structure

Fig. 11.4   Decarburisation region in the superheater

In the primary superheater pipeline, small amount of decarburisation was found in one of the locations as shown in Fig. 11.4. Microstructural degradation in the form of graphitisation was found on the attemperator shell. The graphite flakes were found to be randomly distributed which results in loss of strength of the component. Graphitisation is a microstructural change that occurs in carbon or low alloy steels that are subjected to moderate temperatures for long periods of time. Graphitisation results from decomposition of pearlite into ferrite and carbon (graphite) and can embrittle the steel parts, especially when the graphite particles form along a continuous zone through a load carrying member. Graphite particles that are randomly distributed cause only moderate loss of strength. Hence it is necessary to periodically monitor to check for the formation of graphite if any.

Further reading

6. BaldevRaj, Jayakumar, T. and Thavasimuthu, M. Practical Non-destructive Testing, Narosa Publishing House, New Delhi, 1997.
8. Bernd Rohloft, NDT methods, The South African Mechanical Engineer, Vol. 4, 1994.
19. Farlay, J.M., Thomson, J.L. and Dikstra, B.J. Non-destructive Testing to Avoid Weld Failure, International Conference on Weld Failures, London, Edited by Harrison, J.D. The Welding Institute. 1988.
39. Ivan Dickson, J. Failure Analysis Techniques and Applications Conference Proceedings, The Materials Information Society (ASM), 1992. 39.
71. Rakesh Kaul, Muralidharan, N.G., Kasiviswanathan, K.V., Jayakumar, T. and BaldevRaj, Weld Related Failures—A few case studies, Proceedings of National Conference on Failure Analysis for Safety and Reliability in Process Equipments, FAIL 95, Ooty, Sept. 95.

Chapter 12

Residual Stress Analysis in Weldments

Residual stresses are self equlibrating stresses existing in mateials or components under uniform temperature conditions. When two pieces of plates/pipes are jointed together by welding, localised residual stresses coupled with shrinkage are generated in the vicinity of the weld. The presence of these residual stresses can be determental to the strength of the joint. Tensile residual stresses are generally determental, increasing the susceptibility of a weld to fatigue damage, stress corrosion cracking and fracture. During welding, temperature conditions range from melting point of the material to room temperature. Mechanical and thermal properties of the material are temperature dependent and thus change with temperature during the welding process. The material stress-strain behavior is elastic-plastic and temperature dependent. Thermal stresses are produced in the material during the process of heating and cooling. When the material is cooled to room temperature, the locked in stresses present in the material are retained as residual stresses.

Since the residual stresses are self-equilibrating stresses, resultant force and moment generated by them must be zero. The residual stresses can generally be classified into residual stresses of 1st, 2nd and 3rd kind (Fig. 12.1). Residual stresses of the 1st kind (Macro stresses) are nearly homogeneous across large areas say, several grains of a material and are in equilibrium over the bulk of the material. Residual stresses of the 2nd kind (microstresses) are nearly homogeneous across microscopic areas, say one grain, or part of a grain and are equilibrated across a sufficient number of grains.

Residual stresses of 3rd kind (Sub-micro stresses) are homogeneous across submicroscopic areas of a material, say by some atomic distances within a grain and are equilibrated across small parts of a grain. Usually, superposition of residual stresses of the 1st, 2nd and 3rd kind determines total residual stress acting at a particular point of a material or a component.

12.1 DIFFERENT SOURCES OF WELDING STRESSES

12.1.1 Shrinkage Residual Stresses

An important source of residual stresses which is present in fusion welded joints is the shrinkage of hot zone, which is impeded by colder zones which shrink by a very little amount. In a single pass fusion welded plate, the longitudinal and transverse residual stress distributions along the weld line (y-axis) and along a

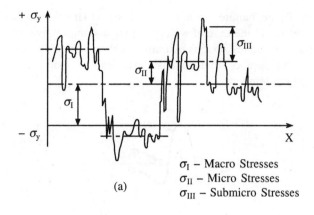

σ_I – Macro Stresses
σ_{II} – Micro Stresses
σ_{III} – Submicro Stresses

(a)

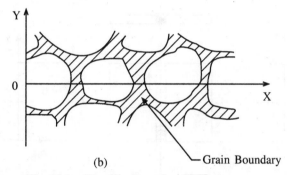

(b)　Grain Boundary

Fig. 12.1　Classification of residual stresses

line perpendicular to the weld line (X-axis) are shown in Fig. 12.2. The longitudinal residual stresses, that is the stress component parallel to the weld line, are tensile stresses within the weld and in the heat affected zone. These are maintained in equilibrium by compressive longitudinal stresses in zones farther away from the weld (X-axis). If the weld line is sufficiently long (Y-axis), the tensile longitudinal stresses in the centre of the weld have constant value over a certain distance. Towards the ends of the weld line, they reduce to zero. This longitudinal stress distribution along the weld is responsible for the distribution of transverse strains represented schematically on the far left (Fig. 12.2). These are equal to zero at the ends of the weld line and increase towards middle. This means that the transverse strains are hindered along the length of the weld and thus even if no external force or restraint impedes the transverse shrinkage, residual stresses must arise transverse to the weld line. The distribution of these transverse residual stresses is schematically represented in Fig 12.2. Their magnitude is consistently smaller than that of the longitudinal stresses.

12.1.2　Transformation Residual Stresses

Transformation associated with a change in volume can give rise to residual stresses if parts of the weld and of the heat affected zone which reach a high temperature pass through a phase transition during the course of cooling while less heated regions do not pass through such a phase change. The transformation of austenite to ferrite, bainite or martensite is known to involve an increase in the volume. Therefore, in the case of welding of steel, compressive stresses would arise in the transformed region if phase transformation is the only stress generating process and if it takes place simultaneously in the entire region which has reached a sufficiently high temperature.

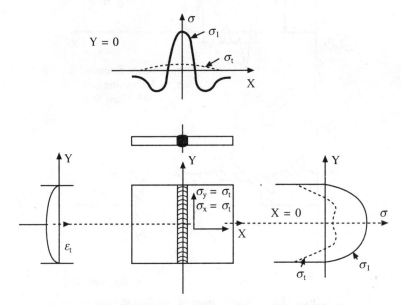

Fig. 12.2   Distribution of longitudinal and transverse residual stresses

12.2   RESIDUAL STRESS DISTRIBUTION IN PIPES

In the case of welded pipes, residual stress distribution is largely affected by the material, pipe diameter, pipe thickness, heat input and size of the weld bead compared to the thickness of the pipe. Many pipes that are used in the pressure vessel and piping industry are schedule 80 pipes. For this size of pipes, the conventional girth welds generally lead to high tensile residual stresses on the inside surface of the pipe. The weld induced inner surface residual stresses can be at the level of the yield stress of the material. Thicker pipes generally have less residual stress (tensile or compressive) on the inner surface of the pipe than the pipes that of schedule 80 or lower schedules. The high tensile stresses in the inner surface of the pipes have been associated with cracking in welded pipes and are of concern to the industries. Intergranular stress corrosion cracking is influenced by the presence of high tensile stresses. Various methods have been developed including heat-sink welding, last pass heat-sink welding, back-lay welding and induction heating to reduce stresses.

Today, welding is the most widely used joining process in the industry. Failures in welded structures still occur and are substantially damaging in economic terms. One of the important points as to why there are still uncertainties in the performance of a welded structure is related to the uncertainties regarding the knowledge of residual stresses.

12.3 RESIDUAL STESS RELIEVING METHODS

Residual stresses are often removed partly (or fully) by various stress relief methods as they are harmful in many industrial applications. Plastic flow is a requisite for the relief of residual stresses. Often, the appropriateness and the adequacy of a stress relief operation are considered before making the choice. This means that the residual stress measurements are often needed after the stress relief operations to ensure adequacy of the stress relief methodology. The common methods for relieving residual stresses are as follows:

(i) Post-weld thermal treatments (annealing)
(ii) Vibration
(iii) Mechanical
(iv) Shot peening
(v) Ultrasonics

12.4 RESIDUAL STRESS MEASURING METHODS/TECHNIQUES

12.4.1 Classification of Methods for Measuring Residual Stresses

Measurement of residual stresses can be generally classified into the following categories:

(i) Mechanical or stress relaxation methods.
(ii) X-ray and neutron diffraction methods.
(iii) Methods using stress sensitive properties.

Several variations are available in each category of these methods.

12.4.2 Mechanical Methods

The mechanical methods are based on the fact that removal of part of an internally stressed body results in a stress redistribution in both the removed portion and the remainder of the body. This redistribution is accompanied by a change in strain distribution whose magnitudes are related to the magnitudes of the stresses. Measurement of strain distribution is complicated, since the residual stresses are generally triaxial in nature. In many cases, however, measurement of the strains in one direction either longitudinal or transverse is sufficient.

Strain gauges are normally used for measuring the changes in the strain distribution. Detailed configuration of a commercial linear strain gauge is shown in Fig. 12.3. Strain release during stress relaxation can also be determined by the use of grid systems, brittle coatings or photo elastic coatings instead of strain gauges. An inherent disadvantage of stress relaxation methods is that they can at the most be semi nondestructive. Important methods presently available in the category of mechanical and stress relaxation methods are:

(i) Dissection method
(ii) Hole drilling method
(iii) Brittle coating method
(iv) Photo elasticity method

12.5 DIFFRACTION METHODS

Diffraction methods are based on the phenomenon that when a metal is under stress, applied or residual, the resultant elastic strain causes the atomic planes in

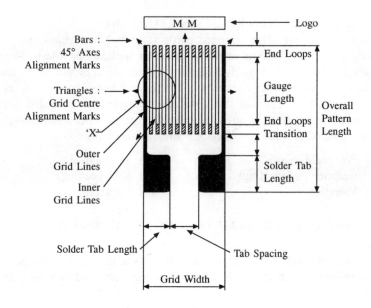

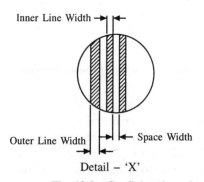

Fig. 12.3   Configuration of a linear strain gauge.

the metallic crystal structure to change their spacing. Diffraction methods measure this interplanar spacing to arrive at the stresses present in the crystalline material. The method is made possible by the fact that wavelength of the electromagnetic radiations used for investigations is of the same order of magnitude as the atomic spacings in metallic crystals (a few Angstroms). The two important diffraction methods are: (i) X-ray diffraction method and (ii) Neutron diffraction method

12.5.1   X-Ray Diffraction Method

This is a very commonly used method. With the help of portable equipments, it is possible to make use of the technique on large objects and carry out the measurements in field and quickly. It can be used for quantitative analysis of macro and micro residual stresses separately.

Principle of diffraction: A monochromatic X-ray beam of sufficient intensity is made to incident in the direction AB on the atomic planes as shown in

Fig. 12.4. The reflected beams from successive planes of atoms are observed in the direction BC. Bragg's law defines the condition for diffraction by the following equation:

$$n\lambda = 2d \sin \theta \qquad (12.1)$$

Where λ is the wavelength of incident X-rays; θ the angle between incident or reflected beams and surface reflecting planes; d the interplanar spacing and n the order of reflection ($n = 1, 2, 3 \dots$).

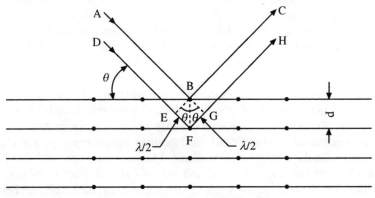

Fig. 12.4   Principle of diffraction

Equation (12.1) shows that, if the wavelength of X-rays is knwon, the interplanar spacing d can be determined by measuring the angle θ. The first order stresses or macro stresses which are the needed types of residual stresses shift the X-ray diffraction peaks. Measurement of the peak shift is the first requirement in such methods. The techniques generally used for residual stress measurement are: (i) single exposure method, (ii) double exposure method and (iii) $\sin^2 \psi$ method.

Some typical case studies are:

Residual stress measurements in ferritic steel tube welds using X-ray diffraction technique: X-ray diffraction (XRD) technique has been used to measure the residual stresses before and after post weld heat treatment, in autogenous butt weld joints in 2.25 Cr-1 Mo steel tubes. The tubes are used in the steam generator assemblies of fast breeder reactors.

Hot liquid sodium flows in the shell region (outside the tubes) and water inside the tubes. A leak in the tube will lead to the generation of hydrogen due to the reaction of sodium with water with dangerous consequences. Tube to tube sheet weld joints are the weakest regions were a leakage path can be formed with relative ease. Apart from the requirement in the quality control procedures that the weld joints should be free from unacceptable defects that may lead to leak paths, it is also considered essential to use a NDT technique to assess the residual stress (RS) pattern and to evaluate the post weld heat treatment (PWHT) to be used for removing the residual stresses whose presence, otherwise, may lead to the failure of the tube to tube sheet weld joint.

The typical dimensions of the tubes and the tube sheets of various steam generator modules in the case of a fast breeder reactor are as follows: (a) Evaporator:

tube outside diameter 16 mm, tube wall thickness 2 mm, and tube sheet thickness 150 mm, (b) Superheater: tube outside diameter 21.3, tube wall thickness 2.9 mm, and tube sheet thickness 135 mm, (c) Reheater: tube outside diameter 35 mm, tube wall thickness 2.5 mm, and tube sheet thickness 80 mm. The weld joints are prepared from the bore side of the tubes by internal bore welding technique from the tube sheet side by TIG process. The joint is square butt. The welding of the full thickness is done in a single pass without adding filler metal. Preheat is done at 523K. Pre purging and post purging are done to avoid oxidation. Pulse current is varied from 95A to 80A. Rotation is done at a rate of 2.2 revolutions per minute.

The weld joints in the 2.25 Cr-1 Mo steel tubes are individually post weld heat treated by split type external, and rod type internal electric heaters at 988 K (715C) for 30 min. The joints are then subjected to micro focal rod anode X-radiography, and helium leak testing under vacuum. For the purpose of the investigation, the tube sheet constraint was simulated using a special set up (refer Fig. 7.14). A total of 9 tube to tube weld specimens have been prepared each about 200 mm long, six with preheat and 3 without preheat. For the experiments, the tube to tube joints thus obtained were trimmed to get a length of 140 mm with the weld joint at the centre. The selection of the tube specimens was made after carrying out visual and microfocal radiography ensuring that weld joints satisfied the requirements for steam generators of fast breeder reactors in terms of weld penetration, weld width and internal defects like porosities.

The equipment used for the measurement of the residual stresses is a portable X-ray stress analyzer (Rigaku Strainflex MSF) and multiplex method was used for the stress measurements. The conditions used for XRD measurements are given in the Table 12.1. The ψ angles used were 0, 10, 20 and 30 degrees.

Table 12.1   X-ray diffraction conditions

Characteristic X-ray	Cr K_α
Diffraction plane	{211}
Diffraction angle (degrees)	156.5
Filter	Vanadium
Tube voltage	30 kV
Tube current	8 mA
Irradiated area	2×2 mm
X-ray fixed time	5 sec

Figure 12.5 shows the residual stress (RS) variations across a weld joint prepared with pre heat. The variations on both the outside surface and the inside surface are shown. The tensile stress maximum occurs at the weld centre line both on the outside and the inside surface. On the inside surface, the zero crossing of RS from tensile to compressive occurs about 2 cm away from the weld center line, as compared to 1 cm on the outside surface. The maximum compressive stress level on the inside furface is also much higher than that on the outside surface. The asymmetry in the variation of RS both on the outside and the inside surfaces is attributed to the restraint offered by the tube sheet block on one side where the compressive stresses were found to be higher.

Variation of stress distribution at different depths below the top surface is also shown in Fig. 12.5. These measurements were done after removing 50 to 150 micron layers on the outside surface. Surface removal was done by electropolishing only at the point of measurement so as to avoid any stress relaxation due to layer removal. It is seen that, within a depth of only 150 microns, the stresses approach zero values. This shows that the RS is restricted only to a thin layer at the top.

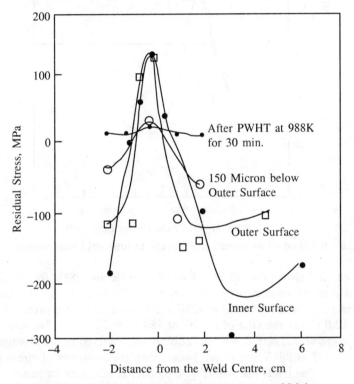

Fig. 12.5　Residual stress variations across a weld joint

Figure 12.6 shows the RS variation for a tube joint obtained without preheat. The maximum tensile stresses on the outside (curve A) and the inside surfaces (curve B) are again similar. The value of tensile stress on the outside surface is similar but compressive stress is much higher in tubes without pre heat as compared to the tubes with pre heat. However, the compressive stress levels on the inside surface are lower in tubes without pre heat. From the stress magnitude point of view, significant difference was observed in the tubes with pre heat and without pre heat except that the zero crossing of RS in the tube without pre heat takes place 1.0 cm away on inside surface and 0.5 cm away on outside surface which is lesser than that in the tubes with pre heat. This indicates that stress is concentrated in smaller area in the tubes without pre heat. Similar trends as above were seen in all the nine tubes examined (with or without pre heat). Comparison of the RS data on weld joints with and without pre heat, specially for the tensile stress, shows that pre heat is not necessary.

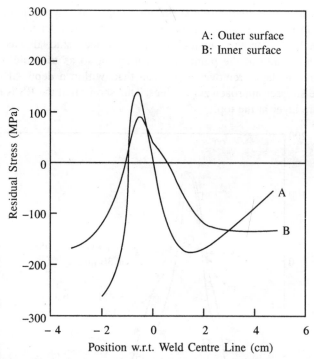

Fig. 12.6 **Residual stress variation for a tube to tube weld joint without preheat**

Figure 12.7 shows the effect of PWHT at 923K and 988K for 30 minutes. There is a significant decrease in the overall RS. The stress in the weld centre is, however, still tensile for PWHT at 923K and reaches zero stress in case of 988K. Figure 12.8 shows the effet of PWHT at 988K for 2.5 hours. The stresses are now compressive. There is not much difference observed in the average stress value (PWHT at 988K for 30 min) other than redistribution of stress pattern which means that PWHT at 988K for 30 minutes is sufficient for stress reliving. Figures 12.7 and 12.8 show that PWHT for stress relieving as conceived in the fabrication procedure for the steam generator tube to tube sheet weld joint of the prototype fast breeder reactor, is appropriate.

X-Ray Diffraction based Residual Stress Analysis of Repair of Cr-Mo Steel weldments: Premature failure of weldments is often reported in the industry. Once failure occurs, the common practice now a days is either to replace the whole component or repair the failed region by welding. Since repairing is more economical, the process of repair welding assumes technological significance.

Experimental Details: Specimens of 12 mm thick normalized and tempered 9 Cr-1 Mo plates (dimension: 200 mm × 50 mm × 12 mm) were used for the study. A groove of 3 mm depth was made to simulate the crack on which the repair-welding was done. Specimens marked as A, B, C and D (9 Cr-1 Mo) steel and E, F, G and H (2.25 Cr-1 Mo) steel were prepared using conventional (Specimen A & E), Half bead (specimen B and F) and Butter bead-temper bead repair welding methods. In the case of butter bead-temper bead method of repair,

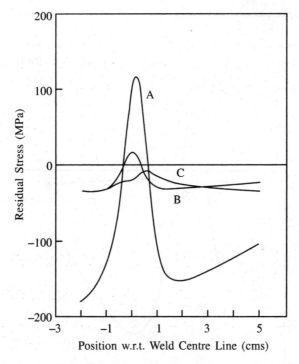

Fig. 12.7 Effect of PWHT-Line A as-welded; Line B at 923 K and Line C at 988K

to give more heat input in the second layer, two approaches were analyzed. One way is to increase the electrode current while depositing the second layer. Specimens C and G were made by increasing the current value of the same diameter electrode (current was increased from 100 amps to 150 amps). The other way of doing this was increasing the electrode diameter which automatically requires an increase in the electrode current. Specimens D and H were prepared by altering the electrode dia. from 3.15 mm to 4 mm. In all these methods, the initial layer was deposited using 2.25 Cr-1 Mo steel electrode of 3.15 mm diameter.

Residual Stress Measurements: In this study, the d vs $\sin^2 \psi$ method was used for estimation of the residual stresses. The equipment used was a portable X-ray stress analyzer (Rigaku Strainflex MSF). This instrument has a back reflection type goniometer with a 2 theta scan range of 140 to 170 degrees. The spot size of the X-ray beam was 3 mm dia. This was achieved by masking the specimen with a lead sheet of 0.25 mm thickness having a 3 mm dia. hole. The conditions of X-ray diffraction are as follows: The ψ angles used were 0, 10, 20, and 30 degrees. The diffraction plane used for stress measurement was {311} and X-ray used was CoK_α. In the analysis, residual stress perpendicular to the weld interface was measured, along a line across the weld line. All the measurement areas were electrolytically polished prior to stress measurements to expose fresh surface required for getting good signal to noise ratio.

Figure 12.9 shows the typical residual stress distribution of all the four specimens of 9 Cr-1 Mo repair welds. Comparative analysis of the stress distribution observed

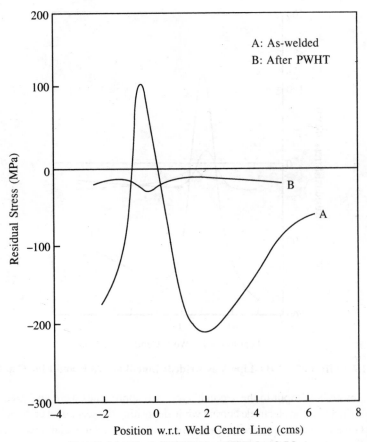

Fig. 12.8   Effect of PWHT at 988K for 2.5 hrs

in all the four specimens indicates that all the four repair methods generate equally high residual stresses at the weld center after the repair. All the specimens showed almost similar stress distribution except for a small difference in the nature of stress distribution pattern. At the weld center, as shown in Fig. 12.9, specimen A had 264 MPa tensile stress whereas all other specimens showed tensile residual stress of 300 MPa. The only major difference in the residual stress distribution of all the four specimens is the residual stress value observed in the HAZ region, 5 mm away from the weld center line. Residual stress values in the HAZ region are found to be continuously reducing from specimen A to D, (In the HAZ region, specimens A, B, C and D had residual stresses of 124 MPa. tensile, 108 MPa tensile, 80 MPa tensile and 44 MPa compressive) respectively. Particularly specimen D showed a considerably large drop in the residual stress in the HAZ as comparaed to other specimens. This continuous reduction of residual stress from specimen A to D is attributed to the increase in the heat input for different methods for repair welding. The lower value of residual stress in the case of specimen D indicates that, in butter bead-temper bead methods, it is advantageous to use electrodes of higher diameter for second pass to get lower residual stresses in the HAZ region.

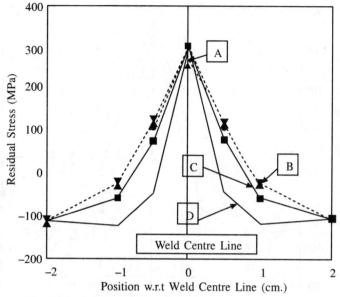

Fig. 12.9 **Residual stress distribution in 9Cr-1 Mo steel.**

In case of 2.25 Cr-1 Mo steel repair welds also, all the specimens showed similar stress distribution (E, F, G, H) and residual stresses observed at the weld centre (Fig. 12.10) were highly tensile (around 270 MPa). In this case also, it was observed that repair carried out by butter bead-temper bead method showed lower residual stresses as compared to other methods. However, in this case, other than at weld center, nowhere else tensile residual stresses were observed; also, maximum compressive stresses observed in this case were too high (– 300 MPa) as compared to 9 Cr-1 Mo (–120 MPa). This indicates that, use of any repair method is safe with respect to generation of residual stresses in the HAZ is concerned. However, butter bead-temper bead method will generate lower stresses as compared to other methods. Also, (1) Butter bead-temper bead method is found to generate lowest residual stresses in the HAZ. (2) In the case of 9 Cr-1 Mo steel, it was observed that for butter bead-temper bead method, it is better to use an electrode of higher diameter, during second pass rather than to increase the electrode current, as only the former method gives compressive residual stress in the HAZ. (3) Micro-hardness profile shows that butter bead-temper bead method is superior to other methods. This observation is in accordance with the results obtained from residual stress distribution of all the specimens.

12.5.2 Neutron Diffraction Method

Neutron diffraction method is similar to X-ray diffraction method with a difference that its penetration in most of the materials is upto several orders of magnitude greater than that found with X-rays. Neutron beams from reactors have wavelength of the order of 0.1 nm - similar to that of an X-ray beam. Unlike X-rays, neutrons interact only weakly with matter thus penetrating several centimeters in most materials. The penetration depth may be varied by changing the energy of the

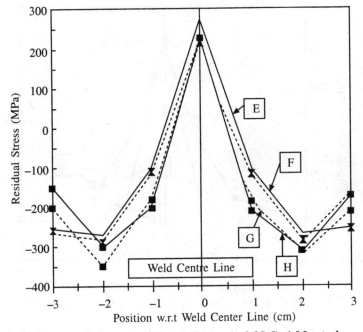

Fig. 12.10   Residual stress distribution in 2.25 Cr-1 Mo steel

neutrons using suitable filters. Because of the ability of the neutrons to penetrate inside the bulk materials, it is an important method for internal stress measurement. This important advantage is also driving the development of reference standards for ultrasonic methods calibrated with the help of neutron diffraction method. However, this application requires improvements in the precision attainable with neutron diffraction method. Neutron sources are relatively weak when compared to conventional X-rays and coarse collimation has been used to increase intensity at the expense of the resolution. Neutron beams of sufficient intensity are only available at the site of reactors or accelerators.

12.6   ULTRASONIC METHODS
Ultrasonic methods for evaluating residual stresses are based on the changes in the velocity of ultrasonic waves due to stress. Several methods using ultrasonic waves of various types such as longitudinal, transverse and surface, have been tried with varying degrees of success. All the methods utilise the deviation in the behaviour of the metal from the linearity of Hook's law of elasticity.

$$\sigma_0 = E\varepsilon \qquad (12.2)$$

where σ_0 is the stress within the elastic limit; ε the strain and E the second order elastic constant (or Young's modulus in isotropic materials).

By including the higher order strains

$$\sigma = E\varepsilon + F\varepsilon^2 + G\varepsilon^3 \qquad (12.3)$$

where F is the third order anharmonic constant, G the fourth order, and so on.

For the measurement of macrostresses, it is enough, if we consider the effect upto second order strain.

12.6.1   Pulse-Echo-Overlap Method

The pulse-echo-overlap method is a versatile and relatively simple method that gives accurate measurement of ultrasonic velocity in materials. The accuracy arises from the fact that the method is capable of measuring the transit time accurately from any cycle of one echo to the corresponding cycle of the next echo. The method is able to handle diffraction (beam spreading) and phase corrections properly. The principle of measurement in this method is to make two successive back echo signals of interest to overlap on the oscilloscope by driving the X-axis with a carrier frequency whose period is the travel time between the signals of interest. Then one signal appears on one sweep of the oscilloscope and the other signal appears on the next sweep. The time resolution of the order of 0.1 nsec. is possible to achieve.

The use of shear (transverse) rather than longitudinal ultrasonic waves introduces the possibility of another methods of velocity measurements. In a stressed part of the weldment, a transverse wave will in general split into two polarised components with different velocities. The residual stress present can thus be related to the difference in the velocities of these two polarised components. Individual measurement of velocities of the two perpendicular components is the most popular approach for the use of transverse wave birefringence in quantitative analysis of residual stresses in weldments.

The use of surface Rayleigh waves in weldments offers the possibility of measurement of surface residual stresses which are not possible using bulk waves. Moreover, longitudinal and transverse bulk waves average the stress present over the thickness through which they propagate. There are several ways of generating Rayleigh waves in weld surfaces. However, special purpose non-contact electro magnetic acoustic transducers (EMATs) are preferred for this purpose. Except the transducer for generating and detecting surface wave signals, the other instrumentation requirements are the same as discussed earlier for accurate velocity measurements.

12.7   BARKHAUSEN NOISE ANALYSIS

This technique, applicable to ferromagnetic metals and alloys, depends on the Brakhausen effect which takes place when a magnetic field is swept in a ferromagnetic specimen along a hysteresis loop. Two types of high frequency signals are thereby generated. One—the Magnetic Barkhausen Noise (MBN) is due to irreversible change in magnetic moments during the hysteresis. The second, the Magnetomechanical Acoustic Eission (MAE) is due to elastic deformations associated with magentic domain activities during irreversible changes in magnetisation. MBN signals are acquired by a sensor coil. MAE signals are acquired by a piezoelectric transducer. Both MBN and MAE signals are strong functions of microstructure and stress (deformation) conditions. Several practical applications are therefore possible from MBN and MAE analysis. One of them is the determination of the residual stresses.

12.7.1 Applications and Limitations

The disadvantages of the Brakhausen noise technique are its surface specificness, less spatial resolution, and unreliability. Surface specificness is not a problem in many cases because it has already been pointed out earlier that it is the surface residual stresses that are often more important. The less spatial resolution comes due to the necessity of the use of a sensor coil whose size cannot be reduced very much. The reliability of the technique is being improved by extensive studies with respect to various types of microstructures which also influence the nature of the signals apart from the stress condition inside the specimen. It is hoped that use of the MBN signal will find widespread application in weld joints in those cases where high spatial resolution is not important. The method is simple, cheap and quick.

Evaluation of Post-Weld Heat Treatment in 2.25 Cr-1 Mo Steel Tube to Tube Sheet Weld Joint: 2.25 Cr-1 Mo ferritic steel is used extensively as a structural material in steam generating systems of power plants. At elevated temperatures, the performance of weldments is considered to be the life limiting factor. As welded components normally have regions of base metal, weld and heat affected zone (HAZ) with large variations in microstructure, hardness and residual stresses, post weld heat treatment (PWHT) is carried out to remove the residual stresses, thereby, obtaining a more or less uniform hardness in the composite weldment. As already indicated, when a ferromagnetic material is subjected to a varying magnetic field, the discrete changes in flux density induces voltage pulses in the pick up coil. This phenomenon called MBN is attributed to the discrete movement of magnetic domain walls overcoming the obstacles in their path during magnetization. Hence, variation in microstructure or hardness significantly affects the MBN activity. It has been observed that, there is an inverse relationship between MBN and hardness. Since, the microstructure and hardness values are significantly different before and after PWHT in weld and HAZ regions, it is possible to use MBN technique to evaluate the effectiveness of the PWHT. Therefore, an example is given to demonstrate the viability of the MBN technique for the evaluation of PWHT of 2.25 Cr–1 Mo steel tube to tube sheet butt weld joint.

Experimental Procedure: For the investigation, the tube sheet constraint was simulated using a carbon steel block, tack welded to the tube. An indigenously developed PC based MBN analysis system has been used in this work. The tubes were subjected to a continuously varying magnetic field sweep cycle with a period of 30 s/cycle in an electromagnetic yoke. The current signal from a sweep controller circuit is fed to a bipolar high current generator to generate a triangular field. The applied magnetic field was measured at the centre of the yoke using a Hall probe (Walker Scientific Inc.) connected to Gaussmeter (Walker Scientific Inc. MG-50), in the absence of the sample. The applied magnetic field was varied between ±12000 A/m. This field corresponds to a current of ±0.7 A. The applied magnetic field was calibrated with respect to the current and is found to vary linearly with the current. The MBN signal was acquired by an in-house made 2 mm diameter ferrite cored surface probe having 4,000 turns. The probe design was optimised for a better signal to noise ratio. The MBN signal in amplified to 68 dB. The RMS voltage of the MBN signal is measured using a RMS meter having a time constant of 0.25 s. The output voltage signals of al¹ ɨhe parameters were conditioned suitably for PC based data acquisition. The applied current and the RMS voltage of the MBN are acquired for half of the magnetization cycle i.e. from negative maximum of the field to positive maximum of the field. The parameters were acquired by a PC-AT through a 16 channel, 12 bit resolution A/D converter card having a maximum sampling rate of 100 kHz and by using a data acquisition software.

MBN measurements were made at the weld centre, and 5, 15 and 25 mm from the weld centre on both sides of the weldment. The measurement positions were selected in such a way so as to cover weld, HAZ and base metal regions (Fig. 12.11). The microhardness profile in the weldment of this steel before and after PWHT has been well established. However, the macrohardness values were measured at the positions selected in this study using a Vicker's hardness tester with a load of 5 kg for the purpose of correlating with MBN data. After the measurements in the 'as welded condition', the tubes were post weld heat treated at 973 K for 1 h followed by air cooling. The measurements were repeated at the same locations after removing the oxide layer. It is well known that the irreversible movement of magnetic domain walls contributes maximum to magnetization process and hence, to the generation of MBN as compared to domain nucleation and rotation processes in any ferromagnetic material. It is also known that, an increase in hardness, which arises from an increase in lattice strain (i.e. dislocation density) during welding, significantly increases the resistance to domain wall movement and hence, reduces the MBN activity. Reported microhardness profile and the microstructural variations in the weldment in this steel clearly showed a maximum hardness in the weld region and a rapid fall in the hardness as the distance from the fusion boundary increases. PWHT considerably reduced the hardness of the fusion zone and HAZ. Studies on the influence of stress on the MBN showed that the stress dependence of MBN is more complicated as it is also sensitive to microstructure. The MBN behaviour with respect to stress is different for materials with different microstructures. In some cases, MBN increases with increase in tensile stress, while in some other cases, MBN initially increases with tensile stress upto a certain maximum and then decreases with further increase in stress. The residual stress measurements made using X-ray diffraction

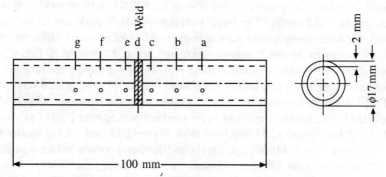

Fig. 12.11   Schematic diagram of weld joint indicating positions of MBN measurements

(XRD) measurements on the tube to tube sheet weld joint used in this study showed that the weld region shows the maximum tensile stress and the HAZ region shows the maximum compressive stress in the as-welded condition (Fig. 12.7). The MBN measurements at various locations do not correlate with residual stress values obtained by XRD measurements. This can be attributed to different microstructures in weld, HAZ and base metal regions. Moreover, the XRD measurements give information from only surface layer, whereas the MBN gives information about the subsurface much deeper than X-rays. However, the macrohardness values would represent the subsurface features like MBN. Hence, the MBN is correlated with the hardness values.

The microstructure in the HAZ of this steel consists of coarse-grain bainite near the fusion boundary, fine-grain bainite at the intermediate region and an intercritical region composed of tempered ferrite and transformed austenite towards the base metal side. With the MBN probe used in this study, it is not possible to distinguish the different microstructures within the HAZ in this weld joint. However, the probe size used in the present study is small enough to obtain the average effect from the HAZ and it can be clearly distinguished from the weld and the base metal regions.

Figure 12.12(a) shows the typical variation in the RMS voltage of the MBN signal as a function of applied magnetic field at different locations of the weld joint in the 'as-welded condition'. Figure 12.12(b) shows the same after PWHT. Figure 12.13 shows the MBN peak height at different locations before and after the PWHT for three different weld joints. It is clear from Fig. 12.12(a) that there is maximum MBN peak height at both ends (parent metal region) and there is a gradual reduction in the peak height as the probe is moved towards the weld centre. The weld region shows the minimum MBN peak height. The difference in the peak height and peak position at the two ends (positions a & g in Fig. 12.12a) is attributed to the difference in the heat transfer during welding due to the presence of thick carbon steel support block on one side and the free end on the other side. The carbon steel block acts as a heat sink on one side and the free end is subjected to slow cooling, thus introducing different thermal ageing conditions. Variations in MBN peak heights were observed in this material for the rod specimens, thermally aged for different durations and is attributed to variation in lath/grain size and precipitation of different carbides. In the 'as-welded' condition, a systematic variation in the MBN can be observed on both sides of the weld centre. The large variation in MBN peak height indicates significant differences in the hardness in the weld, HAZ and base metal regions. This is supported by the hardness measurements as evident from Fig. 12.14 which shows the hardness values at these regions for the same three tube joints, before and after PWHT. It can be seen from Fig. 12.13 that, after PWHT, the MBN peak height becomes more or less same at all the locations. This is also supported by the narrow variations in the hardness values after PWHT as shown in Fig. 12.14. Figure 12.15 (derived from Figs. 12.13 and 12.14) shows the relationship between MBN peak height and hardness values before and after PWHT obtained from different locations for all the three tube joints. It is seen from Fig. 12.15 that the hardness and MBN values cluster into a distinct region after PWHT. This clustering can be used to verify the effectiveness of PWHT by specifying a minimum amplitude of the MBN signal. In the 'as-welded condition', it can be observed that an inverse linear relationship exists between MBN and hardness. There is a large increase in the MBN peak height in the weld and HAZ regions after PWHT as compared to the base metal regions. This is attributed to the removal of residual stresses and reduction in dislocation density in the weld and HAZ during PWHT. A small increase in MBN peak height in the base material region after PWHT (Fig. 12.13) is attributed to the effect of tempering which enhances the domain wall movement. A two peak behaviour in the MBN, indicated by slope change in the RMS plot at about 3000 A/m, can be observed at the base metal regions in the 'as-welded condition' and at all the regions after the PWHT (Figs. 12.12(a) and (b)).

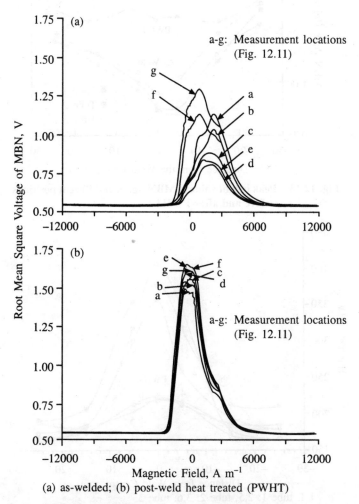

(a) as-welded; (b) post-weld heat treated (PWHT)

Fig. 12.12 Variation in RMS voltage of MBN signal as a function of applied magnetic field: (a) as-weld condition and (b) after PWHT

Similar observation has been found in the rod samples of this material tempered at 973 K for different durations. This has been attributed to the tempering associated with the dissociation of martensite or bainite transforming into ferrite and the precipitation of different types of carbides such as Fe_3C, $M_{23}C_6$ etc. The peak height and the peak position strongly depend on the number of moving domain walls and the mean free path of the domain wall displacement which inturn depends on the microstructure.

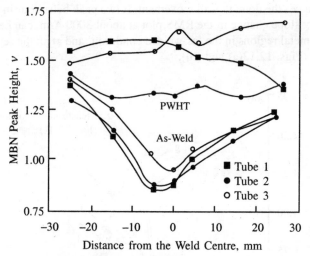

Fig. 12.13   Peak height value of MBN signal at different positions before and after PWHT

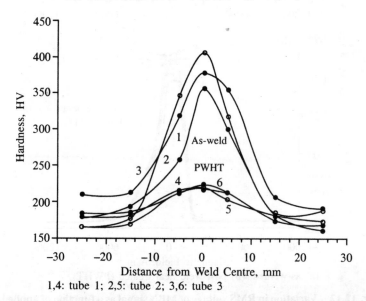

1,4: tube 1; 2,5: tube 2; 3,6: tube 3

Fig. 12.14   Hardness values at various positions before and after PWHT

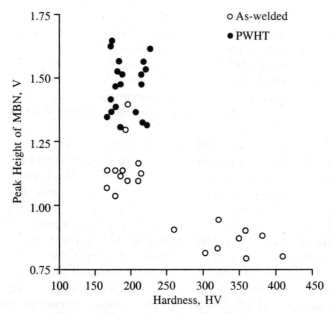

Fig. 12.15   Relationship between MBN peak height and hardness values

It is inferred that the MBN peak height values in the weld and HAZ regions significantly differ before and after PWHT and found to be complementary to the hardness values. It is possible to evolve an acceptance criterion based on MBN peak height values to ensure the effetiveness of PWHT. This study clearly establishes that the MBN peak height analysis can be used as field NDT technique for the assessment of PWHT in ferritic steel weldments. This assessment is faster than the microhardness measurements, since, the MBN analysis does not require special surface preparation. This technique can be very useful for the assessment of PWHT even under restricted access conditions.

12.8   TYPICAL CASE STUDIES

12.8.1   Evaluation of Residual Stresses in Weldments using NDT techniques

A few examples of residual stress measurements in various weld joints have been described.

Ultrasonic measurements: Ultrasonic technique of evaluating residual stresses is based on the measurement of changes in the velocity of ultrasonic waves due to stress and by establishing the acoustoelastic constant for the material. For precise ultrasonic transit time measurements, pulse-echo-overlap technique is employed. Following are the basic steps involved in the residual stress measurements using ultrasonics: (i) Determination of acoustoelastic constant (AEC) of the material, (ii) Ultrasonic transit time measurements across the weld joint and (iii) Estimation of residual stresses using AEC.

Ultrasonic measurements were carried out across 15 mm and 47 mm single

"V" weld joints of AISI type 304 stainless steel using a 2 MHz longitudinal wave transducer. At each position, on an average, five measurements were carried out. Relative changes in the velocities were converted into respective residual stress values by using AEC. Finally, semidestructive hole-drilling strain gauge technique was carried out on these weld joints, at the same positions where ultrasonic measurements were made. Measurements were also carried out on 8 mm and 15 mm joints of carbon steel, before and after the PWHT at 873 K for 2 hr.

XRD Measurements: Residual stress measurements were carried out across the 8 mm and 15 mm thick carbon steel weld joints and on Al-SS explosive weld using a portable X-ray analyzer (Rigaku Strainflex MSF). This is a back reflection type diffractometer with 2θ scan range from 140 to 170 degree. In the case of mild steel welds, Cr target was used. For Al-SS explosive welds, two different targets (Cu and V) were used to get diffraction planes with good peak intensity.

Magnetomechanical Acoustic Emission (MAE) Technique: The MAE measurements were carried out on mild steel weld joints before and after PWHT. A magnetic yoke has been used to magnetize a portion of the weld joint locally. AET-5000 acoustic emission system with a piezoelectric transducer having a resonant frequency of 175 kHz along with necessary accessories was used to capture the MAE signals. The yoke was moved in steps of 5 mm and the rms voltage of the MAE signals was recorded at each position.

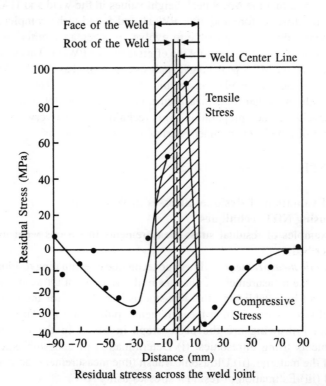

Residual streess across the weld joint

Fig. 12.16   Ultrasonic method

Results and Discussion: Figure 12.16 shows the residual stress measurements made using ultrasonic technique in 15 mm thich AISI type 304 stainless steel weldment. Stresses at the weld are tensile in nature and change over to compressive at the HAZ. The stresses again become tensile further away i.e. in the parent metal region. The results of the ultrasonic technique have been supplemented by hole drilling strain guage technique (Fig. 12.17). A similar trend was also observed in the case of 47 mm thick SS weldment except at the weld centre line, where ultrasonic technique could not be used due to intense scattering taking place due to the textured weld structure. Similarity in the stress distribution pattern was observed for both the methods. However, the absolute values could not be compared since the strain gauge method gives only the subsurface stress distribution, whereas the ultrasonic method give the stress distribution averaged over the thickness of the plate.

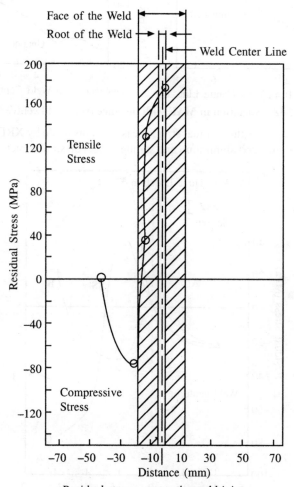

Residual streess across the weld joint

Fig. 12.17   Hole drilling method

Figure 12.18 shows the variation in MAE before and after PWHT. The MAE results have also shown good correlation with respect to the effect of annealing. Similar results were also obtained for ultrasonic and XRD techniques on the same weld joints showing the effect of PWHT on relieving of residual stresses. The XRD and the ultrasonic results showed that the trends in the surface stress variations can be different from those occurring in the thickness direction. All the three techniques can be used to monitor the effect of stress relief annealing.

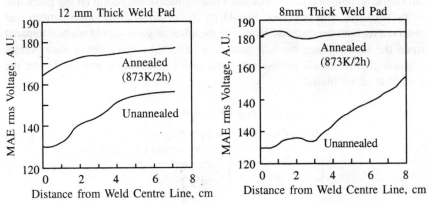

Fig. 12.18   Variation in MAE with distance from weld centre line

Figure 12.19 shows the residual stress measurements made by XRD technique on a explosively welded aluminium and stainless steel dissimilar metal weldment

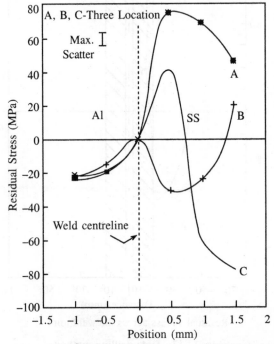

Fig. 12.19   Residual stress measurements by XRD technique

at three locations (B at the centre of the specimen and A and C are located on two sides of B). Magnitude and the nature of the residual stresses observed in both aluminium and stainless steel phases at the interface are similar. The explosive energy applied for welding is found to influence the region within 10 mm on both sides of the weld interface. Beyond 10 mm, the residual stresses were found to be equal to the residual stresses originally present in the plate prior to the explosive welding.

Further reading

20. Furner. PandKuntny, M. Residual Stress Measurements in Welded Aluminium Alloys, Proceedings of Vth Balton Landing Conference, ANS 1978.
57. Moorthy, V., Vaidyanathan. S., Jayakumar, T. and BaldevRaj, Evaluation of Post Weld Heattreatment in 2.25 Cr-1 Mo Steel Tube to Tube Sheet Welded Joints using Magnetic Barkausan Noise Measurements, Material Science and Technology, Vol. 13, July, 1997.
61. Murugan, S., Kumar, P. V., BaldevRaj and Bose. M.S.C. Residual Stress Analysis in Weldments-Theoretical Approach, Indian Welding Journal, Vol. 29, No. 4, Oct. 1996. Commission V, DOC 1014–93.
63. Nichols. R.W., Residual Stresses in Welded Construction and their Effects, International Conference, The Welding Institute, Vol. 12, London, Nov. 1977.
64. Noyar, I.C. and Cohen, J.B. Residual Stress Measurements by Diffraction and Interpretation, Springer-Veriag, New York, 1987.
65. Palanichamy, P., Joseph, A., SanjayRai, Jayakumar, T., Bhattacharya, D.K. and Kasiviswanathan, K.V. Non-destructive Measurement of Residual Stress in Carbon Steel Weld Joints, Indian Welding Journal, Vol. 27, No. 4, Oct. 1994.
77. Sanjay Rai, Sujith, S., Jayakumar, T. X-Ray Diffraction based Residual Stress Analysis of Repair Welds, Proceedings of the 14th World Conference on NDT, Oxford Press, New Delhi, 1996.

Chapter 13

Automation and Robots in NDT

The major limitations of manual non-destructive testing are reliability and repeatability in the test results. The techniques used are more operator dependant and hence the results obtained by various operators (agencies) can be varying. As the demand for more and more quality materials especially by nuclear, space and aerospace industries has increased in the past few decades, the need for more reliable and repeatable operator independent examination has become a necessity. To meet these demands, automation and robotics play a crucial role in the evaluation of materials for quality products. Automation considerably reduces the time required for inspection thereby reducing the cost of inspection.

The first servo-controlled industrial robot was developed in the USA in 1961. It is obvious and natural that when an industrial robot is observed in operation on a production line, it is nearly impossible not to compare the robot's motion with that of a human operator. The mystique that has been created about the industrial robot comes from the robot's ability to move an object from one point to another in any number of complex paths, while at the same time reorienting the direction of the object as it moves. This "manipulative" capability allows the robot to perform many complex operative tasks which otherwise could only be performed by humans (some times with difficulty). It is also true that some of the operations can be done by robots alone and not by human beings, for example, in hostile environmental conditions, locations with access constraints etc.

Robot is a re-programmable multi functional manipulator designed to move material parts, tools or specialised devices through variable programmed motion for the performance of a variety of tasks. We can classify industrial robots into four categories:

(1) manual manipulator that performs sequence of tasks which are fixed or preset.
(2) playback robots that repeat fixed instructions.
(3) numerically controlled robots that carry out tasks through numerically loaded information.
(4) intelligent robots that perform through their own recognition capabilities.

Although industrial robots are available in a wide variety of configurations, the state-of-the-art robots consist of four basic elements: (a) a manipulator or motion system (b) a control system, (c) a sensor or feedback system and (d) a power supply. The manipulator is the basic mechanical element of the robot and is responsible for performing the work. The control system is the robot's brain and is responsible for directing the movement of the manipulator. The sensor is the external feedback system which allows the robot to react to its external environment. The power supply is the energy source for the robot. The most fundamental objective of an industrial robot is to move an object through three-dimensional space. This motion is mechanically accomplished by the manipulator. The manipulator consists of a mechanical "arm" and a "wrist", both of which are mounted on a support stand. A mounting surface is provided at the end of the wrist for attaching the tool ("end effector") with which the robot performs its jobs. The end effector is in the form of a gripper device for grasping and manipulating a part. There are several ways in which a manipulator can be constructed in order to move a part through space. As in the human arm, motion is achieved through a series of mechanical linkages and joints. The basic configuration of the mechanical arm is best described in terms of its coordinate system. There are four different coordinate systems being used to move a part from one point to another point.

The simplest is the rectangular or cartesian coordinate system (Fig. 13.1). In this system, all motions are translational that is straight along one of three perpendicular axes. The three axes along which the arm can be moved are

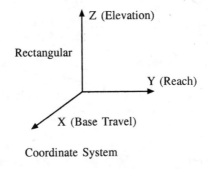

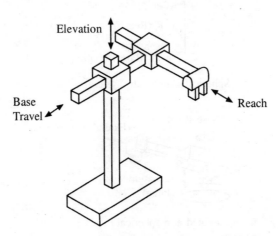

Fig. 13.1   Typical rectangle cartesian coordinate system

known as "degrees of freedom". In general, the number of degrees of freedom or articulation of a robot specifies the number of different ways in which the end effector can move. Such a motion can either be translational (straight movement along an exis) or rotational (rotation about an axis).

The three rotational systems in use are: (a) cylindrical, (b) spherical and (c) jointed-arm spherical (Figs. 13.2(a), (b) and (c)). The cylindrical coordinate

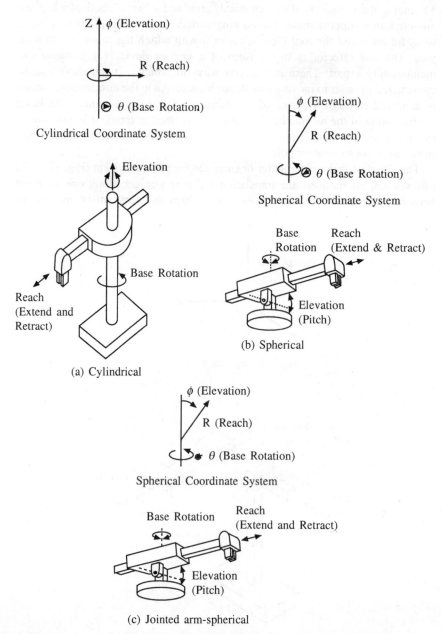

Fig. 13.2   Typical rotational system

system provides three basic degrees of freedom, including two translational and one rotational motion. Robots with spherical coordinate system allow one translational motion and two rotational motions. The jointed arm system also provides three degrees of freedom, all of them rotational. Thus, the simplest robots tend to rely more on translational movements, while complex robots typically use more rotational motions.

13.1 MANIPULATOR ARM OPERATION

The manipulator arm is basically a series of mechanical linkages and joints that move in a specified sequence. The function of the arm in to bring the end effector to a specified point in space. This motion is accomplished by hydraulic, electric or pneumatic drive systems. The arm mechanisms are driven by several actuators which may be pneumatic or hydraulic cylinders, hydraulic rotary actuators or electric motors. These actuators either drive the links directly or they indirectly drive them through gears, chains or ball screws. In the case of hydraulic or pneumatic drives, valves mounted on the manipulator control the flow of air or oil to the actuators.

Hydraulically driven robots have the advantage of mechanical simplicity, strength and high speed. Electrically actuated robots, most of which are driven by DC servo motors, are generally not as fast or as strong as hydraulic robots, but they tend to be more accurate and can repeat sequence of operations with higher precision. Pneumatically driven robots are generally used for small "pick and place" type of operations. In addition to actuators, each link of the manipulator arm has a feed-back device which keeps the controller informed of its position. The type of feedback mechanism can range from a simple limit switch actuated by the manipulator arm to various position measuring devices such as encoders, resolvers and potentiometers. The type depends upon several factors such as the type of movement and the desired resolution. These feed-back devices are the internal sensors used by the robot controller to gather information by which to generate signals to move the end effector through space. End effectors are installed on the mounting surface of the wrist. This is the tooling used to perform the robot's task. Most end effectors are designed for a specific application.

13.2 CONTROL SYSTEM

The control unit is the "brain" of the robot. The basic function of the controller is to direct the motion of the end effector so that it is both positioned and oriented correctly in space. The controller stores the required sequence of motions of the manipulator arm and the end effector in a memory. It directs the manipulator through the programmed sequence of motions. At the same time, it interacts with the manipulator and other machines connected with robot through a series of feed back devices to ensure that the correct motions are being followed.

Robot control is one of the most rapidly changing areas of robot technology. Improvements in microelectronics capabilities, cost reductions, improved robot performance, higher level programme languages etc. are all having an impact on the evolution of robot control technology.

13.3   MEMORY

The robot memory (or data storage) is an integral component of the controller. It stores the program and then gives commands to the robot through the controller. The most common form of computer memory device is RAM (Random Access Memory). The RAM chip is a temporary storage device for information. It holds all data entered into memory until power is removed or until new information replaces the existing data. The ROM (Read Only Memory) is a chip which permanently contains data in memory. It can not be replaced or erased by new data. The PROM (Programmable Read Only Memory) is a chip which can be programmed by the user and then like ROM, PROM also will permanently holds that data. Other storage devices commonly used include magnetic tape, magnetic disks and floopy disks.

13.4   APPLICATIONS OF ROBOTS

The plants in which industrial robots are currently used are generally large and for sophisticated operations. In addition to automobile and foundry industries, other large and small equipment manufacturers are current users of robots. Robots are found in both mass production and batch operations and most companies which use robots also tend to use other advanced production tools such as computer aided design, computer aided numerical control and computer aided testing.

13.4.1   Robots in Non-destructive Evaluation

Tracing back the history of evolution and development of NDT techniques for the past few decades, it can be said that, in the earlier stages (primitive stages), more operator (human) dependent techniques like Ultrasonics, Radiography, Eddy-current, Penetrant Inspection etc. were used for non destructively evaluating a material or a component. Due to limitations of equipment capabilities and accessories, these techniques had their own inherent limitations and deficiencies in the earlier stages. These earlier problems were overcome by the advancement of electronics by which more sophisticated equipments have come into the market. Due to the increase in demand from industries like nuclear, space and chemical for quality products, the necesity to overcome the operator dependency has become essential. For more reliable and repeatable inspection, manipulators and robots have come into existence and the demand for these devices for pre-service and in-service inspections is growing faster.

Since ultrasonics is the most commonly used technique for inspection of welded components both during fabrication and also during service, tremendous growth has taken place in the development of automatic or semi-automatic testing systems in this field.

13.4.2   Developments of Ultrasonic Scanners/Manipulators for Inspection of Welded Components

An operator-independent system would consist of a scanning device which could be used on various pipe genometries by operators with minimal training. Once installed, the device would consistently scan the weld region and transmit all the necessary positional and ultrasonic data to a central processing unit for monitoring and/or storage. Such a controlled system removes the shortcoming of differences in manual scanning skills in the accumulation of data. All parts of the system should be reliable both in recording and/or displaying data and in the physical sense of being rugged and always available for use.

The data displayed offers high resolution and the precision necessary to accurately detect and size the smallest flaw. The storage of all the data is done in an easy-to-use format such as magnetic tape, floopy disc or the like. This permanent storage could be recalled at any time in the future to compare subsequent examination results with base-line data. The system allows all forms of data manipulation desired to fully characterize the nature of indication and measure the size of a flaw. (Example: B scan system explained Sec. 6.8, in Chapter 6.)

13.4.3   Internal Rotary Inspection System (IRIS)

Heat exchangers contain many tubes, all of which are subjected to corrosion during their service life. The wall-thickness determines whether a tube is fit for further service or not. Although the general thinning of the tube wall indicates the overall corrosion damage, it is not a reliable indicator of the condition of the tube. A few deep pits, where the wall is very thin, could make it unfit for further service even though there is otherwise relatively little corrosion. To find such pits and measure the wall thickness requires an instrument that can measure the wall thickness over the whole surface of the tube with good spatial resolution.

Internal rotary inspection system (IRIS, Manufactured by M/s Pan American Industries, USA) is designed to measure the wall thickness of corroded heat exchanger tubes. IRIS employs the conventional pulse echo technique for measuring the wall thickness, but uses a novel method for displaying the measurements. All of the measurements during a scan around the circumference of the tube are displayed on an oscilloscope screen. The image produced is a stationary rectilinear picture of the circumferential cross section of the tube.

Figure 13.3 shows the probe manipulator head utilized for measuring the wall thickness of the heat exchanger tubes. The transducer is supported on a probe body which fits into and is centered in the heat exchanger tube.

The ultrasonic pulses are emitted along a path parallel to the probe axis. These pulses are reflected by a 45° mirror so that they are directed normal to the tube wall. Reflections from the inner and the outer walls follow this same path back to the transducer. The mirror is supported on a water driven turbine that spins on an axis parallel to the probe axis. As the mirror turns, the point of impingement of successive ultrasonic pulses is advanced along the circumference of the tube wall, so that the whole circumference of the tube is covered with each revolution of the mirror.

With pulse repetition frequency of 10 kHz and the mirror rotating at 1800 rpm and by moving the probe from one end of the tube to the other, the entire tube volume will be covered by the beam. Figure 13.4 shows the display that is generated. The lower half of the figure is a stylized drawing of the picture that would be produced by the arbitrary circumferential section shown at the right of the drawing. An uncorroded tube produces a vertical rectangular pattern on the

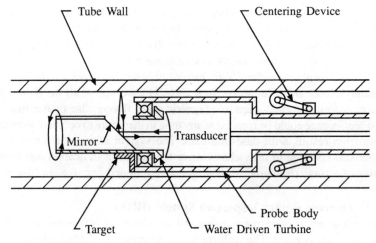

Fig. 13.3   Typical cross section of IRIS inspection head

oscilloscope screen. The width of this pattern is the measure of the wall-thickness. Its vertical height corresponds to the circumference.

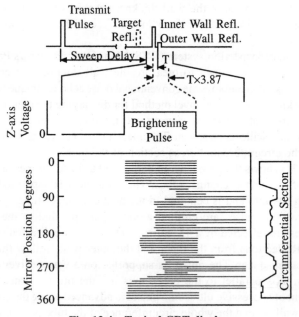

Fig. 13.4   Typical CRT display

Inspection of Heat Exchanger/Steam Generator Tubes: Studies conducted on heat exchanger tubes having baffle plates with uniform gap between tubes and the plate, tubes where baffle plates make a contact on the OD of the tubes at some points and tubes having defects at the point under the baffle plate clearly proved that IRIS can be used as an alternate/complimentary method to eddy current testing since presence of baffle plate poses lot of problems for eddy current testing due to poor signal to noise ratio. The studies indicated that, whenever there exits an uniform gap between the baffle plate and the tube, the presence of baffle plate is not seen in the B-scan picture and only the cross section of the tube is seen. If the tube comes into contact with the plate due to sagging/deformation thereby eliminating the gap between the tube and the baffle plate, the place of contact of the baffle plate is seen clearly by IRIS (Fig. 13.5). Figures 13.6 to 13.8 show the B-scan pictures of the tubes with the defect under the baffle plate. It is evident from Fig. 13.8 that the presence of baffle plate is seen by IRIS, if the defect is through-and-through type and the location of the baffle plate signal with respect to that from the tube OD of the adjacent region of the tube wall can well be correlated to the gap between the baffle plate and the tube.

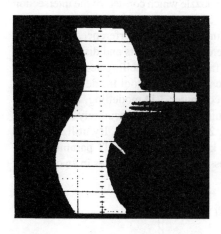

Fig. 13. 5   Baffle plate and tube in contact

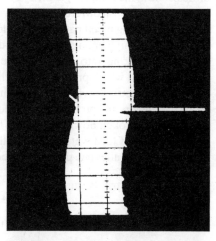

Fig. 13.6   10% WT defect under baffle plate

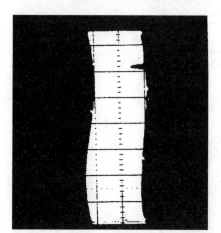

Fig. 13.7   20% WT defect under baffle plate

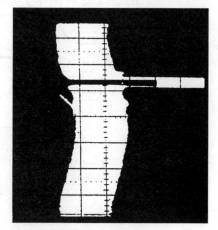

Fig. 13.8   Through-and-through defect under baffle plate

It is also reported that IRIS is successfully used in detecting weld concavity in tubes. It is best used for trend analysis of corroded tubes for failure prediction and life extension of heat exchangers/steam generators.

13.4.4 Automated Ultrasonic Testing of Feed Water Nozzle of Boiling Water Nuclear Reactor

The objective of this inspection program is to ensure that even if thermal fatigue cracks are initiated in the feed water nozzle, their growth will be limited to avoid threat to the integrity of the reactor vessel. Two vital methods of inspection available to detect defects in nozzles: Ultrasonic inspection and Liquid penetrant inspection.

Determination of ultrasonic inspection parameters for nozzles is particularly difficult due to the complex geometry of the nozzle which consists of the intersection of two cylinders of different diameters. Sufficient sensitivity of inspection is hampered by long metal paths with cladding associated interferences. Sensitivity of UT must be high enough to reliably detect small defects and distinguish false indications. Taking into account these facts, 3-D modelling techniques have been developed which provide an excellent calculation tool for dealing with the complex geometries involved. Through computer 3-D modelling, the optimum probe parameters and probe scanning requirements can be accurately determined. The model is broken down into zones 1, 2 and 3 (Fig. 13.9). By utilizing a full scale mock up of feed water nozzle with known defects, the UT parameters can be calculated. To alleviate personnel access restrictions to nozzles in an operating

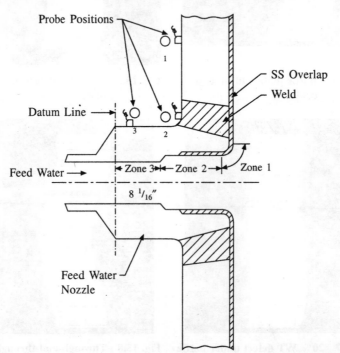

Fig. 13.9 Critical regions of feed water nozzle for automated Ultrasonic testing

plant such as clearance and high radiation levels, remote operated scanning mechanisms have been developed and used.

Because of the wide variance of inspection parameters in a typical nozzle geometry, phased array approach has proved to be a fast and reliable inspection system that avoids frequent probe changes. With the phased-array technique, the skew angle with the associated angle of incidence is sequentially changed and controlled electronically in selected ranges and increments to have optimum coverage of the inner radius zone (Fig. 13.10). The ultrasonic raw data for each angle within the array scan program is digitally stored.

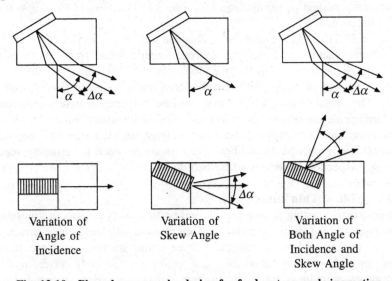

Variation of Angle of Incidence

Variation of Skew Angle

Variation of Both Angle of Incidence and Skew Angle

Fig. 13.10   Phased array probe design for feed water nozzle inspection

The manipulator/scanner has to be mounted on circumferential tracks and can carry different inspection modules, consisting of manipulator arms and search units for inspection of different zones. The modules are designed for fast assembly and removal to minimize radiation exposure. Since the manipulator/scanner is completely remote controlled, once the modules have been attached, exposure to radiation is further reduced to a minimum.

On-going developments include integrating fully the UT and manipulator systems, making the software more user friendly and enhancing the report generation capabilities.

13.4.5   In-service Inspection of Reactor Pressure Vessels

Increasing the plant operational availability requires more vigorous in-service inspection during all the necessary stages. Consequently, higher degrees of automation of inspection equipments and reduction in radiation exposure of inspection personnel are most important. Recent developments have led into a higher automated ultrasonic inspection system comprising of an improved large scale manipulator and new, thoroughly computerized ultrasonic data acquisition, processing and evaluation equipment.

Ultrasonic inspection of nuclear Reactor Pressure Vessel's (RPV) cylindrical parts, nozzles and bottom head is performed from the inside using central mast manipulator. Actually, these are large-scale heavy weight robots centered along the RPV cylindrical axis and carrying as well as positioning the ultrasonic probe system along RPV's inner surface of the inspection volume to be covered. The improved central mast manipulator in combination with phased array probe system can perform inspection effectively and also carry out repair work on RPV or on its core internals. During design, particular attention has been paid for substantially reducing dwell time in the plant, decreasing radiation exposure of personnel, perfecting manipulator functioning and improved ease of operation and maintenance.

Figure 13.11 shows the carriage mechanism used for in-service inspection in fast breeder reactors for inspection of circumferential seams of the main vessel. The carriage mechanism carrying the ultrasonic and eddy-current probes has to move in the gap of about (300 mm) between the main vessel and the safety vessel. The carriage has X, Y and Z axis movements that are remotely controlled. The carriage mechanism has provisions for carrying out visual inspection, surface cleaning equipments to remove scales and foreign materials and to apply couplant for ultrasonic inspection. In addition, facilities are provided for grinding, repair welding, inspection of welds and for helium leak tests.

13.4.6   NDT of Thin Tubes

Non-destructive testing is extensively used on thousands of smooth thin tubes, seamless or welded, drawn or rolled products made of stainless steel or zirconium alloy by nuclear and other industries. Three testing methods used are: multi-frequency eddy currents, ultrasonics and metrology. The eddy current test for preliminary soundness testing combined with a metrology system permits continuous measurement of the average diameter and the ovality. Ultrasonic testing is a complimentary way for detection of additional flaws coupled with a simultaneous thickness measurement system. Supply and selection are automatic on these facilities with simultaneous sorting into several categories depending on tube quality. All data resulting form these tests are collected for each tube by means of a data centralizing system.

The multi frequency eddy current testing method is based on the simultaneous operation of several frequencies, induced into the tube by a circling type coil. The equipment is designed to systematically test each tube at three frequencies 10, 100 and 500 kHz.

The ultrasonic test equipment comprises of four main parts: (a) driving mechanism, (b) tank, (c) electronics and (d) data processing system (Fig. 13.12). The ultrasonic system is meant for the detection of flaws in the tube. The ultrasonic waves explore the whole tube. This tube is given a relative helicoidal movement in relation to the transducers. These transducers (4 Nos.) are positioned in pairs in order to free themselves from the orientation of the flaw. A fifth transducer is used to measure the tube thickness continuously. In the driving mechanism, the helicoidal movement is provided by a set of three tilting drive rollers in a row. The tubes flow past one by one. They are positioned before testing on a slope

Specifications

- In service inspection requirement — As per ASMC-Section
- Size/Number/PCD of openings in roof slab for access to inspection area — 290 × 590 mm/.8 Nos./S 14300 mm
- Gap between vessels — 300 ± 30 mm (in cylindrical region) 320 ± 30 mm (in knuckle region)
- Radiation field (Gamma) — ≤ 1.0 Sv/hr (5 days after reactor shutdown)
- Carriage movement — X, Y & Z Axes
- Mode of control — Remote
- Accuracy of location — ± 1 mm W.r.t. Desired inspection location
- Type of inspection required — Visual & ultrasonic
- Visual inspection requirement — Capability to resolve 0.1 mm scratch line on the vessel surface
- Ultrasonic inspection requirement — Capability to detect defects of size 0.6 mm (deep) × 5 mm (Length)
- Surface cleaning requirement — Capability to remove scales, surface discolouration, foreign materials & couplant used for UT.
- Additional requirements — Capability to grind, reweld, inspect & helium leak test. An area of size 150 (l) × 50 (b) × 40 (d) mm
- Time of inspection — During fuel handling
- Duration of inspection — <10 days
- Frequency of inspection — (a) Prior to commissioning (b) Once in 3 years thereafter

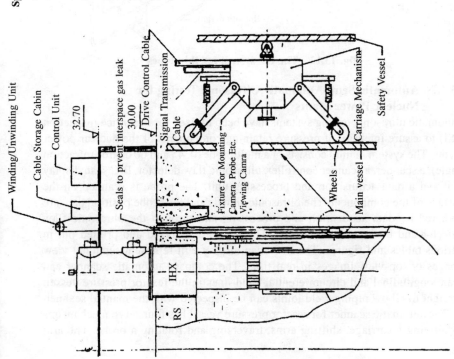

Fig. 13.11   Carriage mechanism for ISI of pressure vessel.

and are automatically brought onto the rollers by slotted pulse type rotors. The tubes are driven by rubber or plastic rollers and these rollers are driven by friction by a single shaft assembly. The rotation speed is adjusted by a DC motor. The tubes are tested by immersion method. Automatic ejection occurs after a control signal is received from the electronic unit into bins that are different according to whether the tubes are to be accepted or rejected. The flaw detection is achieved by four transmitter-receiver plug-in units whose frequency varies continuously between 0.5 and 15 MHz. Four dual-channel selectors are connected to them, permitting both continuous recording of the four channels and automatic selection for any echo exceeding a pre-set threshold.

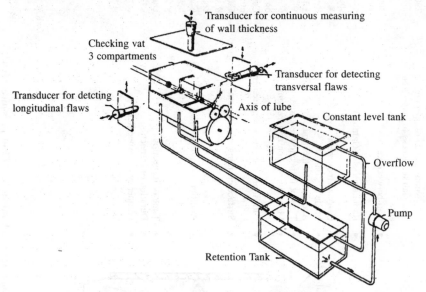

Fig. 13.12   The UT system for thin tubes

13.4.7   Automatic/Semi-Automatic Ultrasonic Testing for Nuclear Power Plants

Automatic ultrasonic testing systems have been utilized for in service inspection (ISI) to assure integrity of pressure retaining components of the nuclear power plants. The system mainly consists of a multiprobe (0, 45 and 60 degree refraction angle), a scanner, a scanner controller, ultrasonic flaw detector, B/C scan display unit and a data acquisition and processing unit. The probe is scanned on the surface of the component. The ultrasonic signals and the probe position data are gathered by data acquisition and processing and through the ultrasonic flaw detector and the scanner controller. The data are analyzed and printed out in various tables and figures. The B/C scan display will represent sectional view images or top-view images in real time. The compact automatic scanner can scan longitudinal and circumferential weld lines in the reactor pressure vessel. Straight to elbow piping weld joints can be inspected with the manual scanner.

The automatic scanner for reactor pressure vessel has four servo mechanisms for driving a carriage, shifting arms, traversing and rotating a probe. The arm shifting mechanism is used for making the mechanical scanner to keep out of obstacles such as nozzles and brackets.

By using such automatic scanner, all welds in the RPV can be inspected and the personnel's radiation exposure can be effectively reduced. The manual scanner (Fig. 13.13) used to inspect straight pipe to elbow welds can perform scanning in axial and circumferential directions of the pipe and all the data of ultrasonic echoes and their locations can be automatically recorded in floppy diskettes.

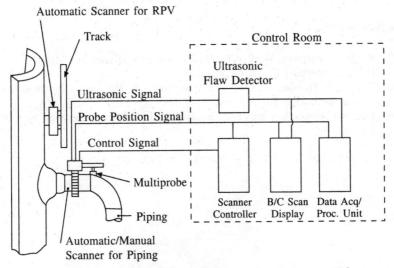

Fig. 13.13   Automated Scanner for reactor pressure vessel

13.4.8   Remote Operated Vehicles (ROV): A Driving Force for Reduced Outages

Originally, the driving force behind industry's move to utilise remote operated vehicles and other robotic devices was to replace humans in hostile nuclear environments wherever possible. Safety authorities have further promoted its adoption for performing inspections. Today, the level of safety standards and regulations are such that there is no alternative to robotics in carrying out inspections (as per the required ASME codes) while satisfying the ALARA (as low as reasonably achievable) concept and also for providing many emergency response measures.

ROVs provide precision devices to inspect high radiation areas. They help to assess the condition of the reactors and their internals and in planning maintenance and repair works. These vehicles are generally modular units which perform visual inspection to the relevant safety codes in reactor vessels, spent fuel storage pools and other storage tank environments. Crawling and "flying" type remote robotic equipment is now regularly being used to perform ASME see XI inspection as well as a variety of other maintenance and repair tasks. The quality of these inspections is improving with developments in monitoring systems with high resolution and radiation tolerant CCTV video recording equipment.

As robotic techniques continue to develop, experience and confidence in operating them increase. Utilities are now able to realize many objectives including reducing radiation dose to workers, shortened outage times, reduced man power requirements, improved cost-effectiveness, elimination of operator fatigue, improved reliability etc. Another potentially valuable advantage is the capability to work in high temperature environments and in inaccessible areas. With a well trained and experienced team, robotic equipment adds to the capability of inspection industry.

Further reading

32. Hartley, J. Robots at Work, A Practical Guide for Engineers and Managers, North Holland Publishing Co., Amsterdam, 1983.
83. Takeha, H., Hamada, K., Oda, M. and Sugiyama, S. Automatic Ultrasonic Testing System for Nuclear Power Plants.
101. Industrial Robots, Summary and Forecast EO$_2$, Tech. Tran. Corporation, Naperville, Illinois, 1983.

Chapter 14

Computers in Weld Inspection Technology

Computer technology has revolutionised the field of fabrication in recent years. In welding fabrication, presently, computers have been put into many important applications such as design, engineering analysis, process modelling, control of welding process parameters, prediction of residual stresses and HAZ micro-structures, development of expert systems, quality control and testing. Among these, computer technology has been exploited well in the field of design and engineering analysis as it is well suited for treating complex phenomena associated with welding.

14.1 ANALYSIS OF WELD DESIGN
Among the various stages of any weldment problem, the detailed design stage is highly amenable for analysis using computers. The detailed design stage includes the judicious selection of stiffeners to have adequate rigidity, selection of appropriate joint design and location of welds and selection of the weld metal to have adequate load carrying capacity.

14.2 SIZING OF WELDS
The most important step in the design of weldments is the sizing of the welds that are used for joining different parts of a component. It is imperative to select an optimum weld size, since it is likely to adversely affect the economics if oversized and the load carrying capacity if undersized. The weld size in general depends on the thickness of the members being joined, the nature and magnitude of the stress that the welds are subjected to and the strength of the consumables used for welding. Although certain thumb rules do exist, the "Allowable force" and the "allowable stress" method are the two widely used ones for sizing the welds. Of the two, the former is more rigorous while the latter is based on trial and error, even though both are amenable for computerisation.

The program based on "allowable force" method can be written in BASIC language on a Personnel Computer. The program is very user friendly having illustrated input facilities. The program can be used to determine the weld size for both static and dynamic types of loading conditions, for various types of direct as well as combination of loads and all commonly encountered types of weld configurations. The inputs for the program such as the selection of appropriate weld configuration, the magnitude, the sense and the location at which the loads are acting and the nature of analysis required are fed through easily operatable input display features.

The program based on "allowable stress" method involves computation of the section properties of the cross section of the assembly which is under consideration for analysis. Once the section properties are evaluated, the actual stress acting on the weld can be computed using the maximum resultant load acting on the cross section, the assumed weld size to start with and the strength of the weld metal. Comparing it with that of allowable stress, the weld size is either incremented or decremented till the size becomes optimum. This program can also be developed in a Personal Computer incorporating all standard user friendly features.

14.3   OPTIMISATION OF STIFFENERS

Very often stiffening or ribbing of plate panels is resorted to for achieving economy by reducing plate thickness of tanks, at the same time achieving higher rigidity. The type, the amount and the spacing of stiffeners mainly depend on the loads acting on the panels, the unsupported length that can be tolerated for a given extent of deflection and material strength. Optimisation aims at arriving at the minimum amount of stiffening and optimum spacing for a given type and shape of stiffener selected to withstand the loads with minimum bending.

A software can be developed in BASIC language on a Personal Computer. The program can handle three most widely used shapes of stiffeners such as rectangular, C-section and L-section, two styles of stiffening viz. diagonal and orthogonal should be capable of analysing all the three types of loads commonly come across such as concentrated, hydrostatic and uniformly distributed.

14.4   ANALYSIS OF WELD SEQUENCING

One of the most practical methods of minimizing weld distortion is by the application of welding in a sequential manner. This is a very useful shop floor technique, especially for complete welded structures. Even though sequencing apparently looks simple, it can become difficult to analyse in complicated geometries. To predict the weld sequence to obtain minimum distortion, a computed software can be developed. This approach will enable any technologist to analyse the effect of sequencing on distortion and will help one to arrive at the optimum sequence that is associated with minimum distortion.

The program basically consists of three parts. First part involves generation of the geometric configuration (cross section) of the assembly under consideration. Second part involves the evaluation of the various section properties such as area of cross section, moment of inertia in two mutually perpendicular axes and the size and the position coordinates of the welds. The third part involves computation of the distortion due to each weld and the resultant distortion. Finally the sequence of welds and the expected degree of distortion are determined. The program can be developed using BASIC language on a personal Computer and can incorporate all *user friendly* features for making it simple for analysis.

14.5   ANALYSIS OF RESIDUAL STRESSES

Prediction of residual stresses due to welding involves analysis of complex material behaviour at elecated temperatures. Either analytical methods in combination with computers or numerical methods are the most common means of evaluating residual stresses. To compute the thermal residual stresses that are induced during welding, a rigorous computerised method of analysis can be developed that performs an analysis of the stresses. It can incorporate variations in important physical properties with temperature and effects of plastic deformation. Computer technology in the field of design and engineering analysis of welded structures has great potential and wide scope.

14.6 COMPUTER BASED NDT SYSTEMS

To respond to the growing need for accurate and timely inspection on cost effective basis, computer based NDT systems have come in the usage. Industry demands automated measurements, defect size calculations and characterisation, storage of data and image display on the screen for qualitative and quantitative examination of components. Compact digital equipments that are simple to use, with fully featured performance capabilities, with a comprehensive internal data logger, with menu driven facility are available now especially for in-service inspection of components.

Weld inspection, weld root corrosion, fatigue and stress corrosion cracking, corrosion, erosion and the early detection of hydrogen damage are just some of the applications where computer aided NDT equipments are able to give both fast and accurate information. This has made plant life management more efficient.

Further reading

78. Shyamsunder, M.T. and Rao, B.P.C. Recent Advances in ECT, Seminar on NDT and QS, Vol. 1, Interline Publication, Bangalore, 1992.
79. Sing, G.P. and Udpa, S.S. The role of Digital Signal Processing in NDT, NDT International, 1986.
83. Takeha, H., Hamada, K., Oda, M. and Sugiyama, S. Automatic Ultrasonic Testing System for Nuclear Power Plants.
93. Yen Fwn Chew, Automatic Crack Detection with Computer Vision and Pattern Recognition of Magnetic Particle Indications, Proceedings of 11th WCNDT, Vol. 1, 1985.
100. P-Scan System for Ultrasonic Weld Inspection, British Journal of NDT, 23(3), 1981.

Chapter 15

Intelligent Welding

The ability to monitor materials and manufacturing processes in an adaptive control mode and perform an inspection in real time is of wide spread interest in many industries such as chemical, aerospace, automotive, nuclear, shipbuilding etc. Development of advanced materials and manufacturing processes with close tolerances is currently limited by the inability to properly monitor and control the processes. "Intelligent" computer-aided process control systems are essential for obtaining products with high quality and desirable properties and also to ensure reproducibility, reliability and cent % acceptability. Intelligent Processing of Materials (IPM) technology aims at on-line assessment of quality through nondestructive characterization with a provision for use of physical, nondestructive testing (NDT) or other suitable parameters for control of the process parameters through feedback loop. This is an important and advanced technology which when effectively implemented results in products with improved quality, reduced scatter in properties, reduced scrap and cuts down in energy requirements. Validation of theoretical models with the experimental interpretations obtained through smart sensors is the crucial and important component of this technology. Thus, the heart of the IPM technology is the development of techniques suitable for in-process quality assessment and feed back control.

15.1 PERSPECTIVE

Intelligent welding (IW), as the name implies, combines welding equipment with intelligent sensing and control, knowledge of human experts, and artifical intelligence to improve joining efficiency. Occurrence of weld defects can be reduced by developing smart or intelligent welding machines. A smart welding machine is the one equipped with sensors, artificial intelligence (AI) and actuators to sense and control welding operations in real time. The smart welder is differentiated from a mere mechanized or preprogramed welder in that it controls the quality of the weld directly rather than simply maintaining the welding parameters within specified limits of the values based upon general experience and/or trial welds. Fudamental efforts have concentrated on the static and dynamic characteristics of the welding arc, in particular, disturbances and the interaction between the arc and the molten pool. Initial control work has centered on closed-loop control of penetration for root pass welds where complete melting of the root is required.

Intelligent sensing and control is a multi disciplinary approach that attempts to build adequate sensing capability, knowledge of process physics, control capability, and welding engineering into the welding system such that the welding machine is able to analyse the state of the weld and knows how to correct the process to make a good weld. The sensing and control technology should reduce the burden on the welder and guide the welder to eliminate errors while providing the adaptability needed to accommodate the variability found in the production world. This approach, accomplished together with the application of AI techniques, breaks the tradition based on separation of procedure development methods from control technology.

Intelligent sensing essentially comprises of three modes: supervisory, performing error detection by sensor monitoring; diagnostic, determinations of underlying cause and effect of errors; recovery or compensation and generating actions to remedy the errors. The key to the success of these systems is thus the sensor or a combination of complementary sensors. Sensors play a significant role in changing the competitive nature of the industry. In most cases, these sensors are based on well-established technologies for measuring basic process parameters and product characteristics such as temperature, pressure, surface imperfections, thickness, and weight. However, for intelligent welding, specialized sensors are needed which represent a significant challenge. The chosen sensors must perform reliably in hostile manufacturing environments and provide data that permit accurate determination of temporal and spatial changes during the welding process. This requires that the sensors to be in intimate contact with the material to permit detection of changes reliably. It is also preferable that the sensors be made of the same material itself. To accomplish this, it requires an understanding of the material properties that have only recently become possible. Sensors are still the weak link of Intelligent Welding.

The multi-disciplinary character of welding technology and the variety of influencing parameters have made this technology data intensive and dependent on field experience. We may also say that the art of welding is ahead of the science and technology of intelligent welding. More and more welding engineers are using computerized methods to support their tasks. Mostly, relational data base is in use. A more intelligent access to welding data and decision criteria can be realized using expert systems. By coupling knowledge-based data with calculation and information systems, the capability and exploitation of experience can be further enhanced. Neural network techniques offer significant advantages for handling noise and complex data. Neural networks are a form of genuine artificial intelligence having analogy to the operation of biological neurons of the brain. They possess many useful properties such as the ability to learn, data characterization, generalisation and the ability to cope with noisy or chaotic signals. The technique uses netural networks to identify and measure the vital information about geometry of weldment. Once "trained", an expert system based on neural network can provide the fundamental information required for on-line positional and penetration control. This chapter explores the areas in which the concepts of intelligent welding have been tried till data. It should be emphasised here that automation in welding has already entered the era of intelligent robot based systems. Fully automated, intelligent arc welding robots have been developed which control the weld penetration and bead height simultaneously. The system essentially consists of a Charge Coupled Device (CCD) camera which monitors the molten pool and performs real time feedback adjustments. The system has been successfully used for butt welding of stainless steel cylindrical pressure vessels and liquefied gas storage tanks. Extensive work has been reported on the application of robots for arc welding processes.

A survey of literature indicates two schools of approach in intelligent welding. One is based on the acquisition and on-line evaluation of electrical signals like voltage, current and the dependent parameters such as power and resistance as time-functions followed by statistical signal analysis and intelligent signal processing. The other and newer trend involves the use of non-destructive evaluation sensors to monitor acoustic emission, X-rays, ultrasound and infrared radiation. Typical case studies highlighting these approaches have been outlined in this chapter.

15.2   PENETRATION SENSING AND CONTROL DURING ORBITAL TUBE WELDING BY WELD POOL OSCILLATION

One of the major problems in orbital tube welding is maintaining sufficient penetration. In many applications, a weld is immediately rejected when the penetration does not reach from the outside to the inside of the tube. Furthermore, it is required that both the inside and outside welded surfaces are as flat as possible. These requirements can generally be reached only after a large number of test welds and with a perfect process control. However, too often, welds are rejected because of small differences in material properties and seam preparation can also cause unacceptable weld bead appearance.

Several decades of welding research has resulted in a number of sensors that can detect weld penetration. Most of these sensors require access to the backside of the work piece, which is often not possible. A weld pool can be triggered into oscillation by an external force, for instance by a current pulse, superimposed on the normal welding current. The external force depresses the weld pool surface. After release of this force, the pool surface moves back to equilibrium in a damped oscillation. This surface oscillation causes a variation in arc voltage, the frequency of which can be calculated by means of Fourier analysis.

Research at the Laboratory of Materials Science and Engineering, Delft University of Technology, showed that the oscillation frequency of a weld pool in the case of partial penetration (mode 1) is considerably larger than that in the case of full penetration sensing (mode 3). This approach is based on the fact that the transition from partial penetration to full penetration (or vice versa) is accompanied by an abrupt change in oscillation frequency. Continuous measurement of the oscillation frequency during welding thus provides real-time information on the extent of penetration. For this, a penetration sensor, which is based on generating and sensing weld pool oscillation has been developed by Aendenroomer and Den Ouden. The sensor is simple, easy to use and can be applied in all welding positions. This sensor has been employed successfully for the pulsed current GTA welding which is being increasingly used as a quality welding process and is especially important in orbital tube welding.

In pulsed current GTA welding, the welding current alternates between a high level (pulse current I_p) and low level (base current I_b) with a duration of t_p (pulse time) and t_b (base time). The pulse frequency $f = 1/t$, where $t = t_p + t_b$. In the case of optimal penetration, the frequency distributions during the pulse time and during the base time are given by curve (A) and curve (B) respectively (Fig. 15.1a), in the case of under penetration by curve (C) and curve (D) (Fig. 15.1b) and in the case of over penetration by curve (E) and curve (F) (Fig. 15.1c).

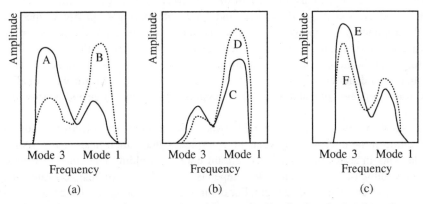

Fig. 15.1 **Schematic presentation of frequency distribution during the pulse time (solid line) and the base time (dashed line) for three different situations: (a) Optimal penetration, (b) Under penetration and (c) Over penetration**

A transition from curve (A) to curve (C) indicates that the penetration is becoming insufficient: the mode 1 peak during the pulse time has risen at the expense of the mode 3 peak. A transition from curve (B) to curve (F) indicates that the penetration is becoming too heavy: the mode 3 peak during the base time has risen at the expense of the mode 1 peak. Penetration control is thus possible in GTA welding by monitoring the two peaks in the frequency spectrum. This has been realised by the feedback control system in which the welding current is adjusted in small discrete steps. Thus, transition from curve (A) to curve (C) triggers the current control to increase the welding current, whereas the transition from curve (B) to curve (F) triggers a decrease in current.

15.3 FUZZY LOGIC CONTROL OF RESISTANCE SPOT WELDING

Resistance spot welding (RSW) is used for fabricating sheet metal assemblies. It is used extensively for joining steel components used for bodies and frames of automobiles, trucks, trailers, buses, mobile and motor homes, recreational vehicles, and railroad passenger cars, as well as office furniture, appliances, and many other products. In a typical Maruti Car, there are about 3000 spot welds and in a TV picture tube gun, there are about 90 spot welds. In a host of other industries, high strength low alloy steels, stainless steels, nickel, aluminium, titanium, and copper based alloys are also spot welded. The major advantages of RSW are high speed and adaptability for automation in high volume and/or high rate production. It can be readily incorporated into assembly lines with other fabrication operations and is robust in typical production environment. Spot welding is economical in shopfloor conditions because it is faster than arc welding or brazing and requires less skill to perform.

Despite these advantages, RSW suffers from a major persistent problem, i.e., inconsistent quality from one weld to another. This results from both the complexity of the basic process as well as from numerous sources of variation such as material composition, thickness, and types of coating (e.g. hot dipped or electroplated glavanizing); work piece surface roughness variations; assembly fit-up variations and errors; electrode deformation, contamination or wear etc. Any or all of these variations complicate the process of automation, reduce weld quality, and increase the cost. For this reason, ensuring uniform weld quality through process control has been and remains a major challenge and worthwhile goal.

RSW involves creating a bond between two or more workpieces by causing melting at the interfaces between the workpieces due to their heating as resistive elements in series in an electrical circuit between welding machine electrodes. The volume of the material melted depends on the amount of heat generated and directly affects the weld strength. For obtaining good quality weld and exercising control over process, it is essential to obtain a weld penetration of about 0.6 to 0.7 times of combined thickness of the sheets (to be welded). This means that the volume of the material to be melted must be controlled. The volume of the material that melts depends on the amount of heat, H (Joules) generated, as given in the following relationshp.

$$H = I^2 Rt$$

where I is the current between the electrodes (in Amps), R is the resistance to welding current across the work pieces (in Ohms) and t is the time of current passage (in sec). Controlling the process means controlling the total heat and thus the melted volume and the final weld nugget size. Many attempts have been made by numerous workers to develop an effective RSW control system. In recent times, control systems relying on the dynamic resistance curve which has been shown to reflect nugget formation and growth, have been used to advantage. Combining this with fuzzy logic and neural network, it is possible to achieve the desired control of the RSW Process. The fuzzy logic controller achieves control without involving complex mathematical computations as compared to conventional controllers, thus reducing computation time and power needs. Adjustment of control parameters is handled by a fuzzy rule based system, rather than by calculation of errors from the solutions of sets of differential equations which purport to define the RSW process, but have been impossible to develop so far. Further, the growth rate of the weld nugget can be controlled to avoid expulsion, that is undesirable. Thus, even in the absence of accurate mathematical model for the process, effective control can be implemented. The greatest challenge with a fuzzy logic controller is to adjust the fuzzy rules to obtain good performance. However, experimental data, knowledge of the process, and the experience of human operators all help to define the direction and the magnitude for adjusting the input through fuzzy rules.

At the Welding Research Institute (WRI), Tiruchirapalli, India, work on the use of fuzzy logic control technique based on dynamic resistance for RSW is in progress. It is well known that dynamic resistance and nugget diameter are two measurable output parameters in the RSW process that reflect the formation and growth of spot weld. Thus, these two parameters were employed as feed back signals to fuzzy logic controller. In the first phase of the study, two low carbon steel sheets of 1.6 mm thickness each were spot welded by making use of 45 kVA capacity portable spot welding machine. Spot welding trials were carried out at different welding conditions (representing struck weld, good weld and splash weld conditions) by adjusting the phase shift setting and the weld time. Variations in dynamic resistance during RSW for each cycle have been determined after each spot welding using the special instrumentation system developed at WRI. Nugget diameter, was measured for each weld by standard instrument. The quality of the spot welded joint is assessed by carrying out tensile shear test. For implementation of the fuzzy logic control, both nugget diameter and dynamic resistance were graded as small, medium and large with triangular membership function. The quality (output) is graded as very poor, poor, good and very good. Based on this classification, the following inference rule is used for fuzzy logic based evaluation.

Nugget diameter	Dynamic resistance	Quality
Small	Small	Very poor
	Medium	Poor
	Large	Good
Medium	Small	Poor
	Medium	Good
	Large	Very good
Large	Small	Good
	Medium	Very good
	Large	Good

Based on the software developed by Indian Institute of Technology, Madras (India), fuzzy estimator for the above experimental data has been arrived at. Systematic studies showed that the experimental value of quality index (i.e. tensile shear load) is in agreement with that predicted by the fuzzy estimator.

15.4 NDE SENSORS FOR PROCESS CONTROL

It can be observed from the above that different control methods have been used over the years to achieve good weld quality. However, the latest trend in intelligent welding control involves the use of nondestructive evaluation sensors to improve product quality. A number of approaches were utilised by various groups, but only two techniques, real-time radiography and ultrasonic monitoring have been found to be capable of direct measurement of the weld quality. The advantages of using NDT sensors include: (a) In the case of penetration control and seam-following device, some defects might occur during welding due to unpredictable factors and the complexities of the welding processes. If these defects could be detected as soon as they occur by employing on-line NDE based defect detection methodologies, it would be possible to rectify the defects by suitable repair procedure or avoid further occurrence of such defects through feed back control of the welding parameters. In this way, the weld quality would be greatly enhanced. The unacceptable defects are repaired immediately after halting the welding process. As a result, repair costs, which could be very significant in many cases, could be minimised especially when the defect is located in the root run of a thick plate multipass weld. Therefore, a real-time defect detection device is also significant for a multi pass welding quality control system, (b) Previous methods involved problems with time and space delays in extracting information on weld penetration. However, NDE sensors, due to their capability to provide online response in conjunction with control systems, can avoid such delays.

Real-time radiography has been used for in-process control of arc welding. The experimental system developed includes arc welding unit, welding manipulator, real-time X-ray imaging unit, and computerized image-processing and control unit. In this system, welding current is automatically controlled as a function of defect-feature extraction from computer processing of the weld images. Experiments have been conducted with the submerged arc welding process. In this process, the weld pool is covered by a thick layer of welding flux and therefore is optically unobservable. The depth of the weld pool, which characterizes the weld penetration, is a very important characteristic of the weld quality. This characteristic is measured in real time using an image intensifier system together with a X-ray source. Information on weld penetration in solidified areas extracted from real-time radiographic images and supplemented by sensor data on welding current and voltage is then used to control the weld power supply in a closed loop process. Particular attention has also been paid for distinguishing a specific weld defect. The defect identification method is based on artificial intelligence technology and employs two methods in conjunction for the categorization of the weld defects. One of them is based on the data base of the features of the defects, and the other is based on the knowledge base created from interviews with experts.

A system has been developed (Fig. 15.2) at the Department of Industrial Design at Brunei University, which is capable of tracking various steel weld geometries with considerable accuracy and reliability. The technique employs two ultrasonic transducers mounted on either side of the weld seam, and operates in pulse echo mode. Shear wave pulses are directed into the plate from the transducers at an angle of 45 deg. Some of the waves are reflected from the under-side of the plate towards the underneath of the weld pool where they are reflected back to the transducer as an echo. As a direct result of ultrasonic beam spread, the signal is not only reflected from the weld bead but also from the top and bottom edges of the plate immediately in front of the molten weld pool. The timing of these echoes provides information on the position of the liquid/solid interface and plate edges. This information is then used for penetration and positional control. The problems involved in monitoring molten weld pools with ultrasound are significant, as the liquid/solid interface does not provide a very stable reflecting surface and thus the returning signals are extremely erratic. Not only does the amplitude varies enormously and rapidly but also the shape of the reflected pulse changes continuously. The elevated temperatures in and around the weld pool affect the velocity and amplitude of the ultrasound and cause practical problems in probe design. Computational analysis of incoming signals is therefore a highly complex task involving a high degree of filtration and software manipulation before the necessary penetration and control data can be extracted. Built-in safety checks and "educated" responses to unusual or conflicting data readings need to be incorporated in the software design. For this reason, an alternate method of analysis was sought and neural network techniques were found to help in handling such noisy and complex data. The technique uses neural networks to identify and measure the position of interfaces and defects. Once "trained", the system provides the fundamental information required for on-line positional and penetration control. Ultrasonic techniques have also been used to detect incomplete sidewall fusion, porosity and weld bead geometry in molten steel pools formed during gas metal arc welding of T-joints and single-bevel V grooves. A dual-element, piezoelectric transducer mounted on the base metal (e.g. carbon steel) transmits ultrasonic pulses into the region at the base of the weld pool. The returning echoes are indicative of the geometry of the pool and of the presence of incomplete fusion and porosity. Two analysis methods, based on ray tracing and transducer field calculations, have been used to confirm experimental results. An expert system would analyze the returning echoes and provide information about the weld pool to an intelligent controller that controls the welding process parameters to obtain welds of acceptable quality.

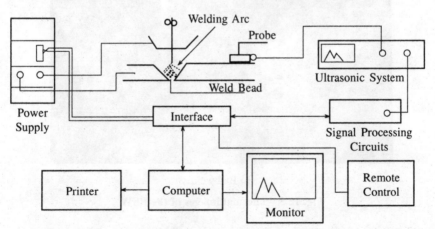

Fig. 15.2 Schematic diagram of computer controlled experimental system

NDE techniques such as thermography and acoustic emission (AE) have been employed for the study of resistance spot welding and end cap welding processes used for critical nuclear fuel sub-assembly components. Experiments have been carried out at WRI, and Nuclear Fuel Complex (NFC), Hyderabad, on the use of these techniques for monitoring narrow gap welding, resistance spot welding, spacer pad welding, endcap welding and calandria seam welding. In the case of resistance spot welds, analysis of the thermal images with respect to nugget diameter and the acoustic emission data (total counts) has revealed that it is possible to distinguish the good welds from the bad ones. Figure 15.3 shows the thermal image of a good spot weld and a spot weld made with reduced current. The variation in the nugget diameter is clearly revealed by thermography.

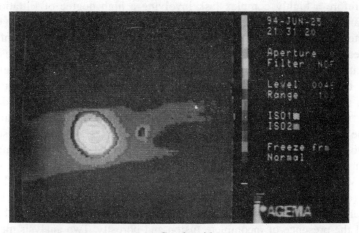

(a) Good weld

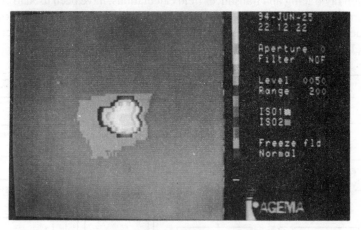

(b) Bad weld

Fig. 15.3   Thermal images of the RSW

Figure 15.4 indicates the root mean square (RMS) voltage of the AE signal with time for a good weld and for a spot weld made with reduced current. Integrity of the end cap welds of Pressurised Heavy Water Reactor fuel pins is quite important. Any failure of these can result in the escape of radioactive fission gases/products into the primary coolant system. On-line acoustic emission

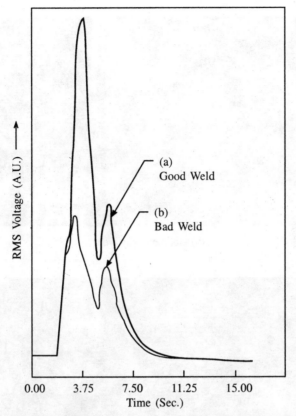

Fig. 15.4 **Variation in RMS voltage of the AE signal with time**
for: (a) good weld and (b) bad weld

monitoring during the end cap welding was carried out at NFC. A number of elements without fuel pellets and with fuel pellets were welded. Imperfections such as end squareness and ovality of tubes, graphite impurities etc. were introduced and the AE data was acquired during welding. Thermal imaging was also carried out on these elements immediately after the welding process was completed. Analysis of the AE data has indicated that it is possible to detect formation of defects during welding process due to different imperfections. Analysis of the cooling patterns and evaluation of the rate of cooling from thermal images have indicated that it is possible to detect very confidently the imperfections such as graphite impurities and sparking during the welding process. A comparison of the thermal imaging data with the results obtained from the subsequent UT and metallography studies has confirmed these predictions. Figures 15.5 and 15.6 show the thermal images and the AE total counts respectively for a good weld and a tube welded with a coat of graphite impurity. Figure 15.5(a) shows the thermal image of good weld indicating a thermal pattern with uniform isothermal width, while Fig. 15.5(b) indicates a thermal pattern with non-uniform isothermal width. Further, a hot spot can also be observed in the thermal image due to sparking during the welding process.

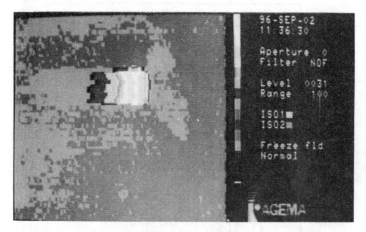

(a) Good end cap weld

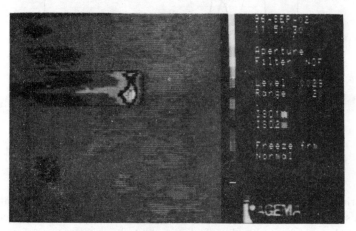

(b) End cap weld with presence of impurity

Fig. 15.5   Thermal images of endcap welding (White - Max. Temp. and Black - Min. Temp.)

Figure 15.6 depicts variations in AE count rate with time for a good weld and for a defective weld. It can be inferred from Fig. 15.6 that the total AE counts for tubes welded with impurities (graphite) are much higher. Thus, the results on the use of NDE sensors are very meaningful and encouraging. Image processing of thermal images and signal analysis of AE signals, would enhance the capability of these techniques and lead to development of intelligent feed back controllers for controlling critical welding processes.

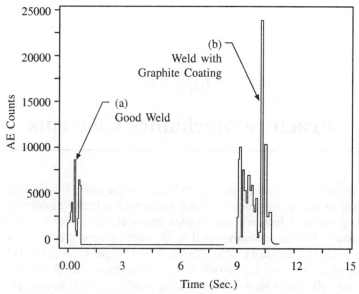

**Fig. 15.6   Variation in AE count rate with time for (a) good weld and
(b) weld with presence of impurity**

Further reading

88. Venkataraman, B., Baldev Raj and Jayakumar, T. Intelligent Welding, Proceedings
     of International Conference on Recent advances in Metallurgical Processes, IISc.,
     Bangalore, New Age International Publishing, New Delhi, Vol. 2, 1997.

Chapter 16

Fracture Mechanics Concepts

Fracture mechanics plays a vital role in assessing the safety of a structure. It is necessary to answer the question that for a particular loading system existing, whether potential defects will start to grow and/or at what defect sizes, failure of the structure under consideration will occur. Such process of crack growth will occur only under continued loading conditions and the crack can suddenly become unstable after the crack has grown to a certain critical size. Stable growth of cracks may also occur under cyclic loading conditions. This growth process is called fatigue crack growth. Here the important question is to know the extent of crack growth that takes place with each load cycle, so that it can be determined after how many cycles, a crack with critical size would be developed.

In order to understand the mechanisms of crack growth itself, it is necessary to consider the dynamic phenomena occurring at the tip of a crack on a microscopic level from a metallurgical view point. In addition, it is also necessary to determine the influence of the applied loading system on the mechanical state at the crack tip. This causes the need for applying structural mechanics techniques in order to be able to determine the structural response of arbitrary structures containing defects under a particular loading system.

Over the past three decades, an intensive research effort has been devoted to the problem of understanding crack growth phenomenon. This combined wisdom of both metallurgical and applied mechanics research workers has resulted in a new engineering discipline, which is known as "*Fracture Mechanics*". The main goal of the field of fracture mechanics is to establish parameters which characterize the crack growth phenomenon. The basic approach to be followed in practical situations consists of making a judgement under which circumstances certain fracture mechanics parameters, which are to be calculated from the mechanical response of a structure, will reach critical values that are valid for the material under consideration. The fracture mechanics parameters have to be determined by means of well standardized experiments. Due to the limited availability of analytical solutions to fracture related problems, numerical techniques such as finite element methods are usually applied to analyze the mechanical behaviour of cracked structures.

Earlier, fracture mechanics techniques were, in general, restricted to those structures for which it is of utmost importance that no structural failure by fast fracture is allowed to occur. Examples of this class of structures are amongst others: nuclear pressure vessels and air planes. Nowadays, fracture mechanics is being used in a large variety of engineering disciplines. This wide spread use is mainly due to the suitability of linear elastic fracture mechanics (LEFM) parameters for the prediction of brittle fracture and economic savings in the case of components designed on the basis of fracture mechanics concepts.

16.1 FATIGUE LIFE PREDICTION OF WELDED JOINTS IN STEEL STRUCTURES

In the real structures, cracks often develop within the weld and HAZ regions. The reason for this is inherent, due to the nature of the welding process and to the location of the welds. Some of the characteristics, which distinguish a welded structure from a non-welded structure are: (a) weldments usually cause geometrical discontinuities and do have inhomogeneous material properties, (b) welding process introduces residual stresses and (c) weld inhomogeneities may act as crack initiators.

16.1.1 Weld Toe Discontinuity

At the weld toe, there is generally an angle between the base material and the weld material. The notch root radius can be very small and therefore the local stress and strain range can be very high. In general, fatigue cracks start at the weld toe. Depending on the loading mode and geometry, the crack will grow into the parent material or into the weld material.

When predicting the life time of a welded joint in a steel structure, the designer is not only interested in the crack growth period but also in the initiation period of the fatigue cracks. In the initiation period, a micro crack is initiated at the location of stress concentration and grows to a macro crack. The crack growth of the macro crack can be calculated with normal fracture mechanics approaches. The classical definition of a macro crack is that the crack is large enough to be seen with the naked eye. A more realistic definition is that a crack is called a macro crack when the crack size is sufficiently large to be stated that local surface conditions responsible for crack initiation no longer affect the crack growth. A third definition could be: A crack is a macro crack as soon as fracture mechanics is applicable. Another important application of fracture mechanics is the "fitness for purpose" approach of a steel structure with a weld defect larger than normally accepted. Fracture mechanics based calculation of the remaining life can show if repair welding is necessary or not.

16.1.2 Initiation Period

In genral, a fatigue crack initiates at a notch root. For the calculation of the fatigue crack initiation period, a theoretical model can be used assuming that the behaviour of the material at a notch root is similar to the behaviour of a smooth specimen under cyclic strain controlled loading. Consequently the notched member and a smooth specimen having the same strain range will have the same initiation life. The calculation procedure will take into account the cyclic stress-strain relation of a smooth specimen, theoretical elastic stress concentration factor (k_t), fatigue notch factor (k_g), stress and strain range at the notch root and the number of cycles for crack initiation.

16.1.3 Crack Growth Period

During the crack growth period, a macro-crack propagates from an initial small size to a final large size. The most simple crack growth model is the Paris relation.

Fatigue crack propagation rate (mm/cycle)

$$\frac{da}{dN} = C(\Delta K)^m$$

where C is the environment constant, ΔK the stress intensity factor range and m the material constant.

16.1.4 Influence of Weld Geometry

The stress raising effect due to the presence of the weld will also affect the stress intensity factors. This is taken into account by multiplying the stress intensity factors by a magnification factor M_k. The M_k values determined, should be based on the local weld angle. A simple crack growth model for a weld joint (example, a tubular joint) based on fracture mechanics can be developed. This assumes the following factors:

1. The crack at the weld toe location is semi-elliptical.
2. Stress intensity factors for depth and length directions are calculated using formulae available in literature.
3. For the crack propagation, the Paris relation is applied in two directions.

This crack growth model can be verified by comparing the results with actual crack growth in a fatigue tested tubular joint.

16.2 FITNESS FOR PURPOSE

The above said information is based on LEFM concepts. The mathematical treatment of static conditions to localized cracks or other sources of stress concentration is called "linear elastic fracture mechanics" and is based on elastic analysis which assumes that stress is proportional to strain. It is based on the work of Griffith and Irwin. They make a "fitness for purpose" analysis possible when the initial defect is known. This initial defect can be a weld irregularity defect. Usually the stresses are well below the yield stress of the material when fatigue is considered and the crack tip plastic zone is so small that LEFM can be applied. Difference has to be made between "acceptance levels" and a "fitness for purpose" approach. The former gives tables with admissible weld irregularities. The later can be used, when weld irregularities are more severe than specified in the tables with admissible weld irregularities, to show that welds are acceptable for performing their function in the structure. The "fitness for purpose" approach can lead to the decision on the need for immediate repair or postpone the repair. This may lead to financial advantage or safer structures since the integrity of a structure can decrease due to repair. Not every repair means an improvement in the structure.

16.3 ACCEPTANCE LEVELS

If weld irregularities do not violate a certain acceptance level, further analysis is not necessary and a fitness for purpose approach is superfluous. For structure under static loading, several acceptance levels are given in the codes. For structures under fatigue loading, no generally accepted acceptance level exists. Thus, the combined analysis and experimental approaches become important to predict the performance.

16.4 DEFECT SCHEMATISATION

With the LEFM techniques, a fitness for purpose analysis can be carried out when the initial defect is known. In LEFM, the initial defects usually are elliptical or round shaped. Therefore, weld irregularities have to be schematized. First of all, weld irregularities have to be analysed using NDT methods. Then the weld irregularities have to be projected on the area perpendicular to the principal stress direction. The important dimensions of some planar defects are:

1. for through thickness defect, the required dimension is "length"
2. for embedded defects, the required dimensions are length, thickness and projected angle
3. for surface defects, the required dimensions are length and thickness (distance from surface)
4. for defects at toe of fillet welds, the required dimensions are length and thickness
5. for defects such as holes, the required dimensions are length and radius.

The length and width of these defects are the long and short axes respectively of an ellipse. If the largest dimension of a defect is in the direction of the plate thickness, then the defect is schematized as a circle.

16.5 DETERMINATION OF CRITICAL DEFECT SIZE

The following singlistic procedure as a first approximation can be used to determine whether a crack is critical or not. The final crack length, as calculated using the Paris equation, can be transformed to an equivalent through thickness defect by calculating the stress intensity factor of the elliptical defect and by taking this stress intensity factor equal to the following equation:

$$K = \sigma \sqrt{\pi a}$$

Now the equivalent half crack length a of a through thickness defect can be calculated. The equivalent crack length a has to be compared with the admissible crack length for cracks under static loading conditions.

Further reading

15. Dijkstra, F.H., de Raad, J.A. and Boumen, T. TOFD and Acceptance Criteria, A perfect Team,. INSIGHT, Vol. 39, No. 4, 1997.
17. Edward, A. and Fenton, Terms and Definitions, AWS Committee on Definitions and Symbols.

18.   Farrar, J.C.M. and Dolby, R.E. Lamellar Tearing in Welded Sreel Fabrication, The Welding Institute, Abrington, 1972.

102. The Application of an Engineering Critical Assessment in Design Fabrication and Inspection to Assess the Fitness for Purpose of Welded Products, - Appendix 6 (Experts), International Institute of Welding, SST 1141–89.

104. The Significance of defects in Welds, Proceedings of the 2nd conferrence, The Welding Institute, London, May, 1968.

Chapter 17

Weld Related Failures: Case Studies

The process of failure analysis plays an important role in the design, development and testing of every product that is being produced. Finding the cause of failure was a fascination of humans from the very beginning of history and the ability to learn from mistakes is one of the driving forces behind the progress of civilization. For many years, the work in this field was restricted to a few laboratories or universities. Recently, more companies are taking advantage of the benefits resulting from the investigations of the causes of failiures. These benefits are reflected in safer products, increased productivity and probably a cleaner environment.

When a failure analysis is initiated, the strategy or methodology must be rooted in common sense. Thus, even before examining the failed component, a detailed service history must be established. This extra time for documenting, observing and studying can help in developing potential hypothesis and determining the analytical techniques that can directly prove or disprove the possible hypothesis. For example, if the component is found to have a deposit, then an analytical technique that includes identifying the composition of the deposit and establishing the corrosion agent is necessary. Furthermore, once a component is sectioned, such as for metallographic preparation, deposits can be damaged, contaminated or lost. Premature sectioning can also compromise the documentation. Finally, only when a minimum quantity of the deposit is available, definitive analysis can be performed. Once the observations have been documented and related to the service history, the strategy for the failure analysis can then be formulated.

A failure investigation and subsequent analysis should determine the primary cause of a failure and based on the determination, corrective action should be initiated that will prevent similar failures. Frequently, the importance of contributory causes to the failure must be assessed and new experimental techniques may have to be developed. A complete accident investigation usually requires the services of experts in several branches of engineering and physical sciences as well as metallurgy.

Welding constitutes an important part of fabrication of most of the components and structures. Performance of a welded component in service depends upon a number of factors like workmanship, joint design, residual stresses, pre and post weld heat treatment, use of suitable welding consumables etc. Presence of weakness in one or more of these factors may lead to unforseen failures. This message is clearly brought out by presenting a few systematically analysed failures related to welds/welding procedures in the following typical case histories.

17.1   FAILURE ANALYSIS OF AN AMMONIA REFRIGERANT CONDENSER TUBE

Catastrophic failure of an ammonia refrigerant condenser tube was noticed within three hours of its operation. Firure 17.1 shows the failed component in as-received condition. The concerned component was a 370 mm diameter pipe (with wall thickness of about 11 mm) with its end welded to a hemispherical dished end (with maximum wall thickness of about 15.9 mm near the weld). The welded component formed the dead end on the pipeline. During its brief operating life, the component was filled with ammonia and the internal pressure dropping from 0.1 MPa to 0.04 MPa and the temperature correspondingly decreasing from 270 to 241 K. It was reported that the concerned pipe was welded to the dished end by SMAW process using AWS E 6013 electrodes. The welded pipe was hydrostatically tested at a pressure of 3.2 MPa before putting it into operation. No radiographic examination was carried out on the welds. The materials of construction of the concerned pipe and the dished end were reported as API 5L Gr. B and A 234 (WPB) [equivalent to A 106 Gr. B] respectively. The nominal chemical composition of these materials (in weight %) is:

Pipe : 0.25 C/0.95 Mn/0.06 S_{max}/0.05 P_{max}
Dished end: 0.3 C/0.29-1.06 Mn/0.058 S_{max}/0.048 P_{max}

Fig. 17.1   Failed ammonia refrigerent condenser tube

Examination Techniques and the Results: Visual examination of the failed component revealed that the pipe to dished end weld was associated with non-uniform penetration. X-radiographic examination of the welded component revealed the presence of lack of fusion area almost throughout the length of the weld. The weld joint was poorly designed as the tapered transition provided at the joint between sections of different thicknesses (3 mm) was short of the minimum specified limit of 1.5 mm. Presence of inadequate taper at the weld joint would result in stress concentration in the weld region. Fractographic examination revealed brittle fracture associated with well defined Chevron marks, indicating the direction of crack propagation. The crack nucleation region, as indicated by chevron marks, revealed the presence of a sharp lack of penetration area. Near the crack nucleation site, fracture surface was found to be intergranular in nature (Fig. 17.2). Metallographic examination of the specimens taken out from the weld region clearly indicated that the failure had started from the lack of penetration

Fig. 17.2   Intergranular nature of fractured surface

area of the weld (Fig. 17.3). The crack was intergranular in nature (Fig. 17.4). This region also exhibited microcracks emanating from inclusion sites and decohesion of inclusion/matrix interface. These features are characteristic signs of hydrogen embrittlement. Impact testing of sub-size Charpy V-notch specimens taken out from the weld region revealed a ductile to brittle transition temperature

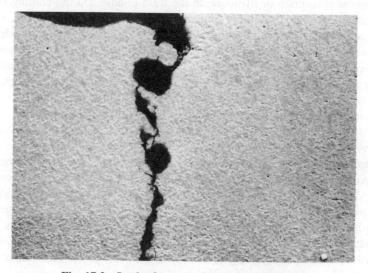

Fig. 17.3   Lack of penetration area in the weld

(20 J criterion for standard Charpy specimen) of about 265 K as compared to 228 K for base metal.

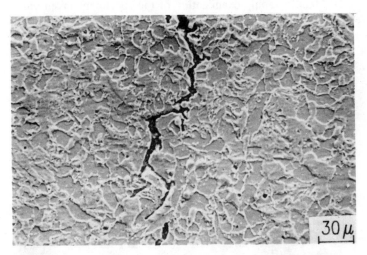

Fig. 17.4   Intergranular nature of crack

Cause of Failure: In the light of the evidence gathered during the investigation, it is clear that the failure of the condenser tube had started from the lack of penetration area of the pipe to the dished end weld. Hydrogen absorbed at the time of welding had helped in initiating the crack under the possible influence of weld residual stresses. Welding with AWS E 6013 electrode containing large amount of cellulose in its coating was primarily responsible for formation and subsequent absorption of hydrogen in the weld puddle. During cooling of the weld metal, hydrogen solubility in matrix drops abruptly and hydrogen, in the supersaturated state, diffuses to the regions of high stress concentration where it can initiate a crack. Lack of penetration area of the poorly designed weld is believed to be the stress concentration site which in turn would have been the favourable region for hydrogen induced cracking to occur. This is believed to have taken place during storage of the component after welding. Poor weld toughness at the low temperature facilitated easy crack growth during start up. Once the crack length reached the critical crack length, it resulted in a catastrophic failure.

Recommendations: To avoid similar failures in future, it was recommended to improve the workmanship to avoid weld defects. Use of low hydrogen electrodes (like AWS E 6016, 6018 etc,) for pipe to dished end weld was recommended to improve low temperature toughness of the weld metal as well as to reduce the risk of hydrogen embrittlement. Proper design of the weld joint was also recommended to avoid stress concentration. Radiographic examination of the welded component would help to detect weld defects in the fabrication stage itself, thus facilitating corrective action, if required.

17.2 FAILURE ANALYSIS OF CARBON DIOXIDE BRANCH LINE IN A UREA PLANT

A few failures of carbon steel (A 105 grade) pipe fittings of high pressure carbon dioxide line tapping (branch line) were reported in an urea plant. In the urea plant, carbon dioxide gas is passed to urea reactor through a pipe line at a pressure of 15.6 MPa. The main pipe line has been provided with 3/4 inch (18.75 mm) or 1/2 inch (12.5 mm) tapping lines for pressure and flow measurements. The temperature and flow rate of the gas in the pipeline are 377 K and 29,000 to 33,000 Nm^3/h. respectively. Branch line fittings were socket welded to the main line by using SMAW process. Additional supports were provided to the valve to reduce vibrations on the branch line. After about two years of service, the branch lines started falling one after the other. The failures were noticed in the form of leakage of carbon dioxide from the branch lines. Detailed investigation was carried out on the failed component to ascertain the cause of the failure and to suggest remedial measures to avoid recurrence of similar failures in future.

Examination Techniques and Results: Visual examination of the failed components, revealed two circumferential cracks passing through the additional support welds and a longitudinal crack. Out of the two circumferential cracks, one was found to have extended through the wall thickness. Metallographic examination carried out on the component revealed a typical ferrite-pearlite microstructure. The cracks were almost straight and transgranular in nature.

In order to examine the fracture surfaces, formed by the propagation of the crack, the two mating fracture surfaces were separated by cutting the component longitudinally till the through and through crack was approached. The two fracture surfaces were found to be covered with thick layer of corrosion products. Attempt made to clean the fracture surfaces resulted in partial success. Fractographic examination of these surfaces at low magnification revealed a semicircular region with its center at the outside. Presence of a weld defect was also noticed on the outside surface near the centre of the semi-circular region. The weld defect was filled with red coloured corrosion products. The semicircular region was heavily corroded while the surface was relatively smooth. Other important fractographic features observed were: (i) beach marks in a localised zone inside the semi-circular region and radial lines below the semi-circular region. Fractographic examination under SEM was hampered by the presence of thick layer of corrosion products on the surface. However, evidence of crack nucleation from the outer surface was noticed in a localized region.

It was found that the weld defect was open to outside environment and had penetrated quite a long distance along the length of the weld. In order to examine the condition of surface inside the weld defect, the weld crown was ground off. The surface under the weld was covered with thick layer of corrosion product. The surface cleaned by replication did show evidence of corrosion inside the weld defect. Metallographic examination of the longitudinal cross-section of this region revealed the presence of corrosion pits and micro cracks starting from the corroded surface (Fig. 17.5).

Cause of Failure: Evidence gathered during the course of investigation indicated that the corrosion under the weld defect in the support weld (acted as a crevice) was primarily responsible for crack initiation. Development of irregular corroded surface and/or pits under the weld defect provided favorable site for crack nucleation. The cracks thus nucleated had propagated by fatigue loading (manifested by traces of beach marks on the fracture surface), as the pipe was experiencing high flow induced vibrations transmitted from the main pipe through the supports provided.

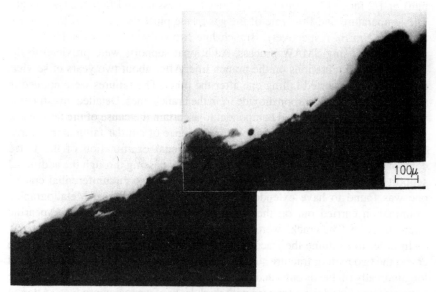

Fig. 17.5   Corrosion pits and microcracks from the corroded surface

Recommendations: In order to avoid similar failures in future, it was recommended that the support to the branch pipeline should be given from some rigid base and not from the main pipeline, experiencing high vibrations. Workmanship should be improved to avoid formation of weld defects. Wherever possible, weld crowns should be ground off. Use of proper NDT methods to check the quality of the welds was also recommended.

17.3   FAILURE ANALYSIS OF A STAINLESS STEEL REDUCER

The failure of a stainless steel reducer (AISI type 316 stainless steel), used in a pipeline carrying mixture of vaporized naphtha, hydrogen and steam at a pressure of 1.75 MPa, was reported in a chemical plant. The temperature of operation was 783 K. After about 2.5 years of operation, a leak was noticed in the seamless pipe welded to the similar diameter end of the eccentric reducer. The leak site was very close to the pipe to reducer weld. Subsequently, failed portion of the pipe was replaced by a fresh one. After 4 to 5 months of operation, leak reappeared in the reducer portion close to the weld. An attempt made to arrest the leak by repair welding resulted in cracking of the component. The cracked reducer section was used for failure analysis.

Examination Techniques and Results: The failed component exhibited three welds on its outer surface (Fig. 17.6) viz. (i) two circumferential welds at the junctions of reducer to cylindrical portions and (ii) a partly ground longitudinal repair weld. Upper circumferential weld exhibited non-uniform penetration at the inside surface. A large defect was also noticed near this weld on the inner surface of the component. Dye penetrant testing (DPT) on the outside surface of the component revealed fine cracks in the ground region of the repair weld. It was noticed that dye applied on the outer surface had penetrated through the wall thickness of the component. Application of developer on the inside surface of the component revealed a crack network starting from the defect region. *In-situ* metallographic examination of the inner surface showed a network of intergranular cracks and cracks emanating from the pits (Fig. 17.7). The cracks started from weld defects. Regions close to the upper circumferential weld exhibited normal microstructure while the microstructure of the regions away from the weld were found to be sensitized. Metallographic examination of the cross-section of the upper circumferential weld revealed a region of incomplete fusion at weld interface and also a sharp opening at the interface. In addition, cracks starting from a lack of fusion area were also noticed. The carbon content of the material of construction of the failed component was found to be 0.095% which is higher than the maximum limit specified for AISI type 316 material.

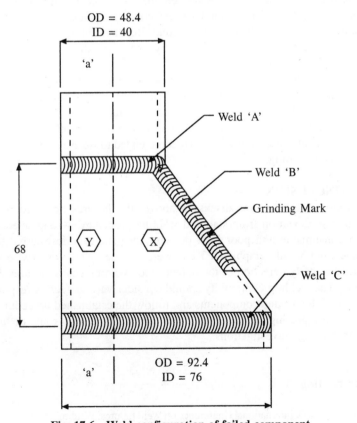

Fig. 17.6 Weld configuration of failed component

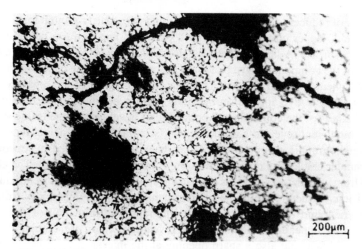

Fig. 17.7 Network of intergranular cracks at the inner surface

Cause of Failure: High carbon content of the material of construction of the reducer facilitated sensitization of the material during operation of the component at 785 K. In the presence of corrosive environment, sensitized microstructure facilitated nucleation of intergranular stress corrosion cracking from a point of stress concentration (like lack of fusion area). Repair welding of the component induced further stresses in the material thereby leading to extensive stress corrosion cracking of the component.

Recommendations: In order to avoid such a failure in the future, it was recommended to use low carbon variety of stainless steel to avoid sensitization of the material. Welding procedure should be standardized to achieve 100% penetration. Adequate NDT procedures like DPT, X-radiography etc. should be used to detect weld defects. It was also recommended to stress relieve the reducer section before welding.

17.4 CONCLUSION

In the weld related failures discussed above, the failures occurred by poor workmanship, deviation from standard welding procedure, wrong selection of welding consumable and poor joint design. Adequate non-destructive testing techniques like X-radiography, DPT etc. were not used which otherwise would have aided in early detection of the defects and avoiding costly failures during operation. The welding community should consider various factors responsible for quality of the welded components and follow the established procedures and should avoid repeating the mistakes learnt through the costly route of failures and their thorough investigations.

Further reading

34. Harrison, J.D. International Conference on Weld failures, Welding Institute, London, 1988.

39. Ivan Dickson, J. Failure Analysis Techniques and Applications, Conference Proceedings, The Materials Information Society (ASM), 1992.
67. Pal, T,. Kand Mitra, M.K. Monogram on Weld. Failures, Jadavpur University, Calcutta, 1996.
71. Rakesh Kaul, Muralidharan, N.G., Kasiviswanathan, K.V., Jayakumar, T. and Baldev Raj, Weld Related Failures—A few case studies, Proceedings of National conference on Failure Analysis for Safety and Reliability in process equipments, FAIL 95, Ooty, Sept. 95.
72. Raghu, N., Muralidharan, N.G., Jayakumar, T. and Kasiviswanathan, K.V. In-situ Metallography for Damage Assessment and Life Extension in Power Plants-A Few Case Studies, Proceedings of 14th World Conference on NDT, Oxford Press, Dec. 1996.

Chapter 18

Quality Control in Production Welding

Any weldment should possess a sufficient level of quality or 'fitness for purpose' to provide required reliability throughout its life. Weld quality relates directly to the integrity of the weldment. It underlines all of the fabrication and inspection steps necessary to ensure that a welded product will be capable of serving the intended function for the design life. Quality is a relative term. Specifying high quality can lead to high costs with no benefits, while low quality weldments lead to high maintenance costs and loss of service. Therefore, the aim should be to specify optimum quality level which leads to 'fitness of purpose'.

For any job, optimum quality level requirements should be thought at design stage itself. With the increase in quality level, the cost of quality assurance increases but the loss due to scrap, rework or repair decreases. The point of intersection of these two curves on quality vs cost gives the optimum level (Fig. 18.1). The curve of total costs descends gradually up to optimum level and there onwards it ascends. One should realise that it is difficult to maintain quality exactly at optimum point but, to be economical, it should be maintained in optimum range that is nearer to optimum level.

To maintain quality, stage inspection is an effective tool. The number of inspection stages required is a function of materials to be welded, welding processes required and the criticality of the job with respect to end use. The selection of welding process for a particular application depends upon many factors such as materials, thickness, welding position, over all dimensions of the job, accessibility, quality and finally cost. Once the material to be welded and the welding process are selected, quality plan has to be drawn indicating the number of quality assurance stages and the agency responsible for each stage, to ensure smooth functioning and flow of work with quality.

18.1 QUALITY ASSURANCE

Quality can be defined as the "totality of features and characteristics of a product or service that bears its ability to satisfy a given need". Quality Assurance (QA) is a term related to the efforts of manufacturer in order to create confidence in the client that the manufactured product will perform intended service satisfactorily over the period of design life. The term QA can be defined as all those well planned and systematic actions taken by a manufacturing or service organisation to instil confidence in the mind of the buyer that the product or service is made as per a standard and it serves the purpose well.

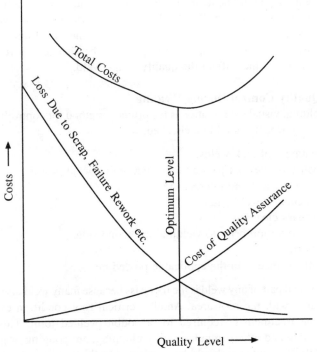

Fig. 18.1   Quality level vs costs

In pursuance of QA in the fabrication of welded structures, the following activities are to be carried out by the manufacturer:

1. Approval of detailed designs by the client.
2. Approval of raw materials and consumables by client.
3. Calibration of testing equipments.
4. Qualification of welding consumables, welding procedure and welder performance.
5. Qualification of NDT Personnel.
6. Quality Control during production welding.
7. NDT of welds.
8. Quality Control during Post Weld Hear Treatment (PWHT).
9. NDT after PWHT.
10. Hydraulic testing or load testing of welded structures.
11. Leak testing of welds.
12. Documentation.

18.2   QUALITY CONTROL

18.2.1   Quality Control Before Welding

Examination of the base metal prior to fabrication can detect conditions that tend to cause weld defects. Scabs, seams, scales, or other harmful surface conditions may be found by visual examination. Plate laminations may be seen on cut edges. Base metal should be identified by type and grade. Corrections should be made before work proceeds. Before the parts are assembled for welding, the edge preparations should be checked for root face and bevel angle. After the parts are assembled for welding, the fit-up should be checked for root opening and misalignment which affect the quality of the weld.

18.2.2   Quality Control During Welding

During welding, visual examination is the primary method for controlling quality. The following aspects should be checked:

1. Treatment of tack welds.
2. Quality of the root pass and the succeeding weld passes.
3. Proper preheat and interpass temperature.
4. Sequence of weld passes.
5. Interpass cleaning.
6. Root condition prior to welding on second side.
7. Distortion.
8. Conformance with the applicable procedure.

The most critical part of any weld is the root pass because many weld discontinuities are associated with the root area. Another critical root condition exists when second stage treatment is required for a double welded joint. This includes removal of slag and other irregularities by chipping, arc gouging or grinding to sound metal. The root gap should be monitored as the welding of the root pass progresses. Special emphasis should be placed on the adequacy of tack welds and clamps designed to maintain the specified root gap to assure proper weld penetration and alignment. Inspection of successive layers of weld metal usually concentrates on bead shape and interpass cleaning. The weld parameters like arc voltage, arc current and welding speed are to be recorded for each bead for computing heat input. To ensure weld quality as work progresses, each weld layer should be visually checked by the welder for surface irregularities and adequate interpass cleaning to avoid subsequent slag inclusion or porosity.

18.2.3   Quality Control After welding

The following are checked by visual inspection after welding:

1. Final weld appearance.
2. Final weld size.
3. Dimensional conformance.
4. Amount of distortion.
5. Post weld heat treatment.

Discontinuities on the surface of a completed weld like crack, undercut, overlap, surface porosity and slag inclusions, unacceptable weld profile and irregularities in the weld faces can be found by visual examination. A fabrication standard may permit limited amounts of undercut, concavity and porosity but lack of penetration, cracks, incomplete fusion and unfilled craters are generally not acceptable. Undercut, overlap and improper weld profile act as stress raisers under load and cracks may develop at these locations under cyclic loading. The conformity of weld size and contour may be determined by the use of suitable weld gauge. In general, the weld surface appearance should meet the requirement of the specification.

18.3   STATISTICAL QUALITY CONTROL

In this era of competition, it has become necessary for component manufaturer to keep a continuous watch over the quality of the products produced. Although the need for maintaining and improving quality standard is growing with increasing competition, the idea of quality control is not a new one. What is new about quality control is the use of statistical techniques which are helpful in maintaining and improving quality standards and hence the term statistical quality control. Statistical quality control (SQC) involves the statistical analysis of the inspection data and such analysis is based on sampling and the principal involved is normal curve. These techniques were developed by W.A. Shewhart in America. The problem he solved was that of checking on the consistency of manufacture of a very large number of components. The idea that statistics might be instrumental in controlling the quality of manufactured products goes back to 1920s and 1930s but its value was fully appreciated during World War II. Nowadays, SQC is used to some extent virtually in every kind of industry. Infact, it has become an integral and permanant part of management controls.

The term 'quality' in statistical quality control is usually related to some measurement made on the items produced. A good quality item is one which conforms to standards specified for the measurement. Quality does not always imply the highest standards of manufacture, for the standard required is often deliberately below the highest possible. It is almost always consistency of manufacturer which presents the most desirable situation rather than the absolute standard that is maintained.

The need for quality control arises because of the fact that, even if quality standards are specified, some variation in quality is unavoidable. The variation in quality characteristic can be classified as chance variation and assignable variation.

18.3.1   Chance Variation

Chance variation is the variation which results from many minor causes that behave in a random manner and produce slight difference in product characteristic. For example, slight changes in temperature, pressure, metal hardness etc. causes slight variation in product quality. This type of variation is permissible and is inevitable in manufacturing. There is no way in which it can be completely eliminated. When the variability present in a production process is confined to chance variation, the process is said to be in a state of statistical control.

18.3.2   Assignable Variation

Assignable variations are those variations that may be attributed to special non-random causes. Such variation can be the result of several factors such as a change in the character of input raw material, improper machine setting etc.

Assignable variations can be detected and corrected. Infact these variations are often detected before the product becomes defective. The two ways of controlling the quality of a product are through:

1. 100% inspection
2. Sampling technique or use of statistical quality control.

The 100% inspection is not desirable because it is too expensive and is not always reliable as it becomes too much routine for those inspecting, resulting in fatigue of the inspector who may label defective pieces as good. The inspection done at the end of the manufacture cycle provides few controls over the manufacturing process. Hence, even 100% inspection is not adequate.

Statistical quality control is a statistical method for finding the extent of quality goals that are met without necessarily checking every item produced. It only indicates wheteher or not the variables occurring are deviating from normal expectations. The statistical method applied in process control is the 'control charts'. The principle objectives of process control are: (a) to keep the manufacturing process in control so that the proportion of defective units is not excessive and (b) assisting in determining whether a state of control exists. Acceptance sampling is the inspection of materials to determine their acceptability whether they are in raw, semi-finished or in a completed state. The object of acceptance sampling is to evaluate a definite lot of material that is already in existence and about whose quality, a decision must be made. This is done by inspecting a sample of the material using definite stastical standards to infer from the quality of the sample whether the whole lot is acceptable.

18.3.3   Control Charts

A control chart is a statistical device principally used for the study and control of respective processes. It is a method to be used in specification, production and inspection. It is essentially a graphic device for presenting data so as to directly reveal the frequency and extent of variations from published standards or goals. It consists of three horizontal lines: (a) A central line to indicate the desired standard or level of the process, (b) Upper control limit and (c) Lower control limit. The outline of a control chart is given in Fig. 18.2. From time to time, a sample is taken and the data are plotted on the graph. As long as the sample points fall within the upper and lower control limits, there is nothing to worry as in such a case the variation between the samples is attributed to chance or unknown causes. It is only when a sample point falls outside the control limits it is considered to be a danger signal indicating that assignable causes are causing the variations. In that case, necessary corrective action has to be taken. Thus, if all dots are found between the upper and lower control limits, it is assumed that the process is 'in control'.

The basis of control chart is the setting up of upper and lower control limits. Control limits are established by computation based upon data covering past and current production records and statistical formulae whose reliability has been proved in practice.

Types of control charts: These are control charts of: (a) variables and (b) attributes.

Variables are those quality characteristics of a product which are measurable and can be expressed in specific units of measurement such as thickness of weldments, tensile strength of parent material, temperature of the electrodes etc. Attributes, on the other hand, are those product characteristics which are not amenable for measurement. Such characteristics can only be identified by their presence or absence from the product. For example, defects in weldments.

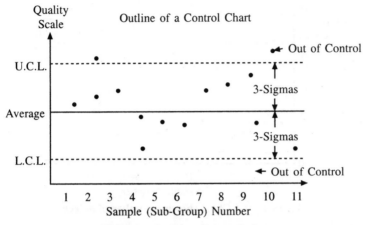

Fig. 18.2 Outline of control chart

Control procedure: In establishing basic procedure for the operation of a quality control programme, the manufacturer must take the following steps:

1. Select the quality characteristics that are to be controlled.
2. Analyse the production process to determine the kind and location of probable causes of irregularities.
3. Determine how the inspection data are to be collected and recorded.
4. Choose the statistical measures that are to be used in the charts.

There are X, R, C and P control charts. The 'X' chart is based on the distribution of sample means. It is used to determine if variations in a product dimension are random and to detect assignable variations. The 'R' chart is used to show the variability or dispersion of the quality produced by a given process is a companion to 'X' chart. Both are usually required for adequate analysis of the production process. 'C' chart is designed to control the number of defects per unit. The 'C' chart is based on the Poisson distribution and is very popularly used in statistical work. Control chart 'C' is used in situations wherein the opportunity for defects is large while the actual occurrence tends to be small. Such situations are described by the Poisson distribution. Let C stand for the number of defects occurred in one unit of a component and $\overline{C}$ for the mean of the defects counted in several such units, the central line of control chart for C is $\overline{C}$ and the sigma control limits are:

$$\overline{C} \pm 3\sqrt{\overline{C}}$$

This formula is based on a normal curve approximation of the Poisson distribution. The use of 'C' chart is appropriate if the opportunities for a defect in each production unit are infinite but the probability of a defect at any point is very small and is constant (Fig. 18.3). Uniform sample size is highly desirable while using 'C' chart.

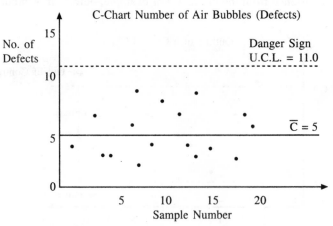

Fig. 18.3   'C'-Chart showing number of defects

'P' chart is designed to control the percentage or proportion of defects per sample. Since the number of defectives (C) can be converted into percentage expressed as a decimal fraction merely by dividing C by the sample size, the 'P' - chart may be used in place of the 'C' chart. The 'P'-chart has at least two advantages over the 'C' -chart.

1. Expressing the defectives as a percentage or fraction of production is more meaningful and more generally understood than would be the statement of the number of defectives. The latter concept must be related in some way to the total number produced.

2. Where the size of the sample varies from sample to sample, the 'P' -chart permits a more straightforward and less cluttered presentation.

Acceptance sampling: The control charts cannot be applied to all types of problems. They are useful only for the regulation of the manufacturing process. Another important field of quality control is acceptance sampling. Inspection for acceptance purposes is carried out at many stages in manufacturing. There is inspection of incoming materials and parts, process inspection at various stages of welding, final inspection by the manufacturer and ultimately inspection of the finished product by purchaser. Much of the acceptance inspection is carried out on a smapling basis. The use of a sampling inspection by a purchaser to decide whether or not to accept a shipment of product is known as Acceptance Sampling.

Acceptance sampling is very widely used in practice for the following reasons:

1. It is less expensive than 100% inspection.

2. In many cases, it provides better outgoing quality. It is generally agreed that good 100% inspection will remove only about 85 to 95% of defective material. Very good 100% inspection will remove 99% of the defective items.

Because of the effect of inspection fatigue involved in 100% inspection, a 'good sampling plan' may actually have better quality assurance than 100% inspection. In modern manufacturing plants, acceptance sampling is used for evaluating the acceptability of components at various stages of processing.

18.4 TOTAL QUALITY MANAGEMENT

Total quality management (TQM) represents a comprehensive procedure, methodology and approach towards Quality Assurance and Management, that transcends the barriers of materials, processes, countries, time and space, in order to satisfy the customer right from the introduction of any product or service in the market, through its evolution and use, till the complete phasing out of the product or service, only to be replaced by a better one. TQM is the highest destination in the ladder with steps of Quality Control, Quality Assurance, Quality Audit, ISO 9000, Quality Improvement and TQM. The TQM is related to the character of the company, vision of the leader, an ideal (rarely realisable) and guaranteed profits through customer delight, brand status, commitment of the employees and the employer to a common focus, policy of the company through quality circles and quality improvement etc.

In a way, TQM is the sum total of all these small, yet important aspects. Strict control, documentation and updating of data in the following areas are mandatory for TQM: (a) Choice of raw materials, (b) Processes, (c) Final Product, (d) Marketing, (e) Services (with respect to both Spatial Efficiency and Temporal Efficiency), (f) Product Support; Customer Support, (g) Product Upgradation, (h) Education to the customer about the product or the service, (i) Gradual phasing-out of any product and its related services, (j) Gradual re-introduction of the new product and (k) the beginning of the next equivalent cycle leading to a better product or service.

The concept of zero-defect (100% quality assurance) should be accorded prime importance as part of the TQM by incorporating suitable non destructive testing methods in the total chain of TQM. The adoption of the technology of intelligent processing of materials (IPM) with provision for feedback control to the process based on on-line measurements and of course understanding the vital correlations between measured parameters, process variables and quality specifications is another step towards achieving TQM. Multi-sensor data fusion and integration can be defined as the synergistic use of information from multiple sources to assist in the accomplishment of a task with TQM. One of the emerging possibilities to effectively utilize the multi sensor data together with the knowledge explosion is to explore the concepts of artificial intelligence (AI) wherever applicable. Successful implementation of AI concepts in the form of verified and validated knowledge based systems and knowledge based inference mechanisms are currently being developed for various specific problems.

The conventional approach tends to advocate a single technique at a time, for achieving a single or a few objectives. Results from the application of this first technique are normally used for planning subsequent tests (also applied sequentially). However, in most cases, results from the previous campaigns are not fully utilised in planning the subsequent campaigns. The volume of data collected during each inspection campaign is quite high and correlating the results and making effective decisions become tedious. Moreover, many a time, different inspection personnel will be carrying out the condition assessments, at different stages of the life of the plant. However, carrying out the inspection with identical or comparable sensitivity and reliability and proper utilization and interpretation of data and results from previous campaigns are essential for the success of the inspection objectives. Constraints on time for carrying out the assessments, add another source of possible errors. In order to carry out effective and reliable condition monitoring, it is thus necessary to utilise a number of modern approaches including tandem application of techniques, data fusion, improved storage, management and presentation of data, and use of automation in inspection.

18.5 TAGUCHI CONCEPTS IN QUALITY CONTROL

Dr. Genich Taguchi from Japan has introduced some new concepts in statistical quality control, and they are named after him. Taguchi methods involve application of designed experiments for evaluation of quality during various stages i.e. design, production and service of a product's life cycle.

18.5.1 Basic Concepts

Designed experiment: An experiment where one or more variables (called independent variables) that are believed to have an effect on the experimental outcome are identified and manipulated according to a predetermined plan. Data collected from a designed experiment can be analyzed statistically to determine the effect of the independent variables. An experimental plan must also include provision for dealing with extraneous variables, that is, variables not explicitly identified as independent variables.

Quality: Quality is defined as the loss imparted to the Society from the time a product is shipped. Taguchi divides quality control efforts into two categories: on-line quality control and off-line quality control.

On-line quality control involves diagnosis and adjustment of the process, forecasting and correcting the problems, inspection and disposition of product, and follow-up action on the defectives shipped to the customer.

Off-line quality control methods are the quality and cost control activities conducted on design and process stages of the product during the product development cycle. Three major aspects of off-line quality control are as follows.

(a) *System design*: The process of applying scientific and engineering knowledge to produce a basic functional prototype design. The prototype model defines the initial settings of product or process design characteristics.

(b) *Parameter design*: An investigation conducted to identify settings that minimize or at least reduce the performance variation. A product or a process can perform its intended function at many settings of its design characteristics. However, variation in the performance characteristics may change with different settings. This variation increases both product manufacturing and life time costs. The parameter design comes from an engineering tradition of referring to product characteristics as product parameters. An exercise to identify optimal parameter settings is therefore called parameter design.

(c) *Tolerance design*: A method for determining tolerances that minimize the sum of both product manufacturing and lifetime costs. The final step in specifying product and process designs is to determine tolerances around the nominal settings identified by parameter design. It is still a common practice in industry to assign tolerances by convention rather than scientifically. Tolerances that are too narrow increase manufacturing costs, and tolerances that are too wide increase performance variation and the lifetime cost of the product.

Expected Loss: Expected loss refers to the monetary losses and arbitray user of the product is likely to suffer at an arbitray time during the product's life span because of performance variation. Taguchi advocates modelling the loss function so that the parameter design can be made more accurate. Noise is the term used to describe all the variables except the design parameters that cause performance variation during a product's life span and across different units of the product. Sources of noise are classified as either external or internal. External sources of noise are variables external to a product that affect the product's performance. For example, the performance of a perfectly designed pump can be affected by external factors such as vibration from other sources, high ambient temperature etc. Internal sources of noise are the deviations of the actual characteristics of a manufactured product from the corresponding nominal settings.

Performance Statistics: It estimates the effect of noise factors on the performance characteristics. Performance statistics are chosen such that maximizing the performance measure will minimise expected loss. Many performance statistics used by Taguchi include various 'signal to nose ratios' which account jointly for the levels of the parameters and the variation of the parameters.

Further reading

6. Baldev Raj, Jayakumar, T. and Thavasimuthu, M. Practical Non-destructive Testing, Narosa Publishing House, New Delhi, 1997.

Chapter 19

Welding Codes and Standards

19.1 CODE

Code is a comprehensive document relating to all aspects like design, material, fabrication, construction, erection, maintenance, quality control as well as documentation for specfic industrial sectors like pressure vessels, aircrafts etc. Codes are prepared by professional bodies or government agencies on a specific subject. For some activities like design calculation, material qualification, NDT etc., codes may refer to standards which are independent and parallel documents. As for NDT, the codes should clearly indicate when and what NDT methods should be applied, what is the intent of NDT and what are the acceptance limits.

19.2 STANDARD

The codes will often refer to standards which are more specific documents giving the details of how a particular operation is to be carried out. These standards take into account the available technological levels and operational skills of the operators. To take an example, with regard to radiographic testing or any other NDT, test results are greately dependent on the person's skill. Hence, the procedures for testing and evaluation must be standardised in detail so that the test results will be least affected by the differences in the personnel skill.

Standards are documents prepared by a body of professionals or a government agency in a specific subject. As the name implies, standards attempt to standardise material or activity. The standards making body takes into account industrial requirements and prepare standards in such a way that a few standards can fit in for a large variety of industrial applications. Codes in turn find it convenient to make use of these ready-made standards. Standards relating to NDT of welds are given in Appendix I.

19.3 SPECIFICATIONS

The document that prescribes in detail, the requirements with which the product or service has to comply is the Specification. The specifications are of paramount importance in the acheivement of quality. The specifications may be either evolved by national bodies or by the manufacturer through his own experience. Appendix II gives the list of ASTM materials specifications where NDT is mandatory/non-mandatory.

19.4 ASME BOILER AND PRESSURE VESSEL CODE

The ASME Boiler and Pressure Vessel Code was initially enacted in 1914. It was established by a committee set up in 1911 with members from utilities, states insurance companies, and manufactures. Whether or not it is adopted in the USA is left to the discretion of each state and municipality. In any event, its effectiveness in reducing human casualities due to boiler accidents since adoption is widely recognised.

ASME Boiler and Pressure Vessel Code has 11 sections of which Section V deals with NDT. It is divided into subsections. Sub-section A contains the code articles in the various methods of NDT whereas sub-section B deals with the various standard practices of testing. These standards become mandatory when they are specifically referenced in whole or in part in sub-section A. After initial establishment, ASME issued revisions once every three monts. One of the features of the ASME code is that partial revisions are issued twice a year, the summer addenda (July 1st) and the winter addenda (January 1st). These addendas are effective immediately upon issuance. Any question about interpretation of rules may be submitted to the committee in a letter of inquiry and answers from the committee are published as 'code cases' from time to time.

19.5 CONSTITUTION OF ASME CODE

Rules for non-destructive examination are collectively prescribed in Section V. Other sections for each component (Section I, II, III, or VIII) refer to Section V or other applicable rules for examination methods and SNT-TC-1A (ASNT Recommended Pracice) for qualification of non - destructive examination personnel. Acceptance criteria are specified in each Section or in some cases these are quoted from ASTM.

ASME Boiler and Pressure Vessel Code

Sections

I. Rules for construction of power boilers

II. Material specifications
    Part A: Ferrous materials
    Part B: Non - ferrous materials
    Part C: Welding rods, electrodes and filler metals,
    Part D: Properities

III. Sub-section NA-general requirements for Divisions 1 and 2
Division 1

Subsection	NB	Class 1 components
Subsection	NC	Class 2 components
Subsection	ND	Class 3 components
Subsection	NE	Class MC components
Subsection	NF	Component supports
Subsection	NG	Core support structures

Division 2   Code for concrete reactor vessels and containments

IV. Heating boilers

V. Non-destructive examination

VI. Recommended rules for care and operation of heating boilers

VII. Recommended guidelines for care of power boilers

VIII. Division 1: Rules for construction of pressure vessels

Division 2: Alternative rules

IX. Welding and brazing-qualifications

X. Fibre-reinforced plastic pressure vessels

XI. Rules for inservice inspection of nuclear power plant components.

19.6 STRUCTURAL WELDING CODE

American Welding Society (AWS)

American National Standard Institute (ANSI)
The AWS welding handbook first appeared in 1938. Basically it was a collection of papers on welding subjects. It was the beginning of an effort to produce a standard work on welding which would fill the need for a guide and reference on welding materials, processes and practices. The second edition was published in 1942. The third edition came in 1950. The sixth edition came in 1970. The seventh edition came in 1978 and the eighth in 1987.

The American Welding Society Handbook consists of five sections covering the following aspects of welding:

Section 1. Fundamentals of welding

Section 2. Welding processes; Gas, Arc, and Resistance

Section 3. Special welding processes and cutting

Section 4. Metals and their weldability

Section 5. Applications of welding

The NDT procedures, as described in this code have been in use for many years and provide reasonable assurance of welding integrity. User of the code should become familiar with all the limitations of non - destructive testing methods to be used, particularly the inability to detect and characterise planar defects with specific flaw orientation. This code has taken reference from ASTM for procedures and acceptance criteria for many of the NDT methods to be used for evaluation of weldments.

19.7 APPENDIX I: COMPILATION OF STANDARDS ON WELD TESTING

Radiographic Testing		
Organisation	Standard No.	Title
ASTM	E 390	Reference radiographs for steel fusion welds.
	E 1032	Method for radiographic examination of weldments.
ASME	Sec. I/PW II	Radiographic and ultrasonic examination of boilers fabricated by welding.
	Sec. II/PW 51	Acceptance standards for radiography of boilers fabricated by welding.
	Sec. III (1)/NB 2553	Radiographic examination of seamless and welded (without filler metal) tubular products and fittings.
	Sec. III (1)/NB2560	Examination and repair of tubular products and fittings with filler metal.
	Sec. III (1)/NB 5320	Radiographic acceptance standards for welds.
	Sec. VIII (1)/UW 11	Radiographic and ultrasonic examination of pressure vessels fabricated by welding.
	Sec. VIII (1)/UW 51	Radiographic examination of welded joints in pressure vessels fabricated by welding.
	Sec. VIII (1)/UW 52	Spot examination of welded joints in pressure vessels fabricated by welding (spot radiography).
BSI	BS 499/Part 3	Terminology and abbreviation for fusion weld imperfections as revealed by radiography.
	BS 2600	Methods for radiographic examination of fusion welded butt joints in steel.
	BS 2910	Methods for radiographic examination of fusion welded circumferential butt joints in steel pipes.
BIS	IS: 1182	Recommended pracice for radiographic examination of fusion welded butt joints in steel plates.
	IS: 2953	Glossary of terms used in radiographic inspection of castings.
	IS: 4853	Recommended practice for radiographic inspection of fusion welded butt joints in steel plates.
	IS: 7810	Code of practice for radiographic examination of resistance spot welds of aluminium and its alloys.
ISO	ISO/R 947	Recommended practice for radiographic inspection of circumferential fusion welded butt joints in steel pipes upto 50 mm wall thickness.
	ISO/R 106	Recommended practice for radiographic inspection of fusion welded butt joints for steel plates upto 50 mm thick.
	2407	Recommended practice for radiographic inspection of fusion welded butt joints for steel plates of 50 to 200 mm thick

(Contd)

	2437	Recommended practice for X-ray inspection of fusion welded butt joints for aluminium and its alloys and magnesium and its alloys of 5 to 50 mm thick.
	3777	Recommended practice for radiographic inspection of resistance spot welds for aluminium and its alloys.
DIN	DIN 54/11/Part I/II - 73	Testing of welds of metallic materials by X-rays or gamma rays.

Ultrasonic Testing

Organisation	Standard No.	Title
ASTM	E 164	Recommended practice for ultrasonic contact examination of weldments.
	E 273	Ultrasonic inspection of longtudinal and spiral welds of welded pipe and tubing.
ASME	Sec. I/PW 11	Radiographic and ultrasonic examination of boilers fabricated by welding.
	Sec. I/PW 52	Acceptance standards for ultrasonic examination of boilers fabricated by welding.
	Sec. III (1)/NB 2552	Ultrasonic examination of seamless and welded (without filler metal) tubular products and fittings.
	Sec. III (1)/NB 2560	Examination and repair of tubular products and fittings welded with filler metal.
	Sec. III (1)/NB 5330	Ultrasonic acceptance standards for welds.
ASME	Sec. VIII (1)/UW 11	Radiographic and ultrasonic examination of pressure vessels fabricated by welding.
	Sec. VIII (1)/W 53	Technique for ultrasonic examination of welded joints in pneumatically tested pressure vessels.
	Sec. VIII (1) Appendix U	Non-mandatory appendix, ultrasonic examination of welds.
	Sec. VIII (2) Appendix 9, Article 9-3	Mandatory appendix-Non-destructive ultrasonic examination welds.
BSI	BS 3923	Methods for ultrasonic examination of welds.
	Part 1	Manual examination of fusion welded butt joints in ferritic steels.
	Part 2	Automatic examination of fusion welded butt joints in ferritic steels.
	Part 3	manual examination of nozzle welds.
BIS	IS 4260	Recommended practice for ultrasonic testing of butt welds in ferritic steels.
	IS 7343	Code of practice for ultrasonic testing of ferrous welded pipes and tubular products.
ISO	ISO 2400	Reference blocks for the calibration of equipment for ultrasonic testing of welds in steel.

(Contd.)

Eddy Current Testing

Organisation	Standard No.	Title
ASTM	E 426	Recommended practice for electomagnetic (eddy current) testing of seamless and welded tubular products of austenitic stainless steel and similar alloys.
	E 1033	Recommended practice for eddy current examination of Type F - continuously welded ferromagnetic pipe & tubing above curie temperature.
ASME	Sec. III (1) NB 2554	Eddy current examination of seamless and welded (without filler metal) tubular products and fittings.

Magnetic Particle Testing

Organisation	Standard No.	Title
ASME	Sec. III (1) NB 2555	Magnetic particle examination of seamless and welded (without filler metal) tubular products and fittings.
	Sec. III (1) NB 2560	Examination and repair of tubular products and fittings welded with filler metal.
	Sec. III (1) NB 5340	Magnetic particle acceptance standards for welds.
BSI	BS 4397	Methods for magnetic particle testing of welds.
BIS	IS 5334	Code of practice for magnetic particle flaw detection of welds.

Liquid Penetrant Testing

Organisation	Standard No.	Title
ASME	Sec. III (1) NB 2556	Liquid penetrant examination of seamless and welded (without filler metal) tubular products and fittings.
	Sec. III (1) NB 2560	Examination and repair of tubular products and fittings welded with filler metal.
	Sec. VIII (2) AF 228	·Liquid penetrant examination of welding joints.
BSI	BS 4416	Methods for penetrant testing of welded or brazed joints in metals.

19.8   APPENDIX II: ASTM MATERIAL SPECIFICATIONS FOR WELDED COMPONENTS WITH NDT REQUIREMENTS

No	Reference	Description	NDT Requirements	
			Man-datory	Non-mandatory
1.	A 381	Specification of metal arc welded steel pipe for high. Pressure transmission systems.	RT	
2.	A 422	Specification for butt welds in steel tubes for refinery service.	RT	
3.	A 557	Specification for electric resistance welded carbon steel feed water heater tubes.	UT/ECT	
4.	A 587	Specification for electric welded low carbon steel pipe.	UT/ECT	
5.	A 672	Specification for electric fusion welded steel pipe for high pressure service at moderate temperatures.	RT	UT/LPI/MPI
6.	A 688	Specification for welded austenitic stainless steel feed water heater tubes.	UT/ECT	
7.	A 691	Specification for carbon and alloy steel electric fusion welded pipes for high pressure service at high temperatures.	RT	UT/LPI MPI
8.	B 338	Specification for seamless and welded titanium and titanium alloy tubes for condensor and heat exchanger tubes.	UT/ECT	
9.	B 353	Specification for wrought zirconium and zirconium alloy seamless and welded tubes for nuclear service.	UT	
10.	B 464	Specification for seamless and welded Cr-Ni-Fe, Mo-Cu-Nb stabilised alloy tubes.	UT/ECT	
11.	B 467	Specification for welded Cu-Ni pipes and tubes.	RT/Other NDT	
12.	B 515	Specification for welded Ni-Fe-Cr alloy tubes.	UT/ECT	
13.	B 543	Specification for welded copper and copper alloy tubes.	ECT	
14.	B 58	Specification for welded brass tubes.	ECT	

References

1. Alers, G.A., Huebschen, G., Maxfield, B.W., Reblinger, W., Salzburger, H.J., Thomson, R.B. and Wilbrand, A. Electromagnetic Acoustic Transducers-Non-destructive testing handbook, ASNT, Columbus, OH 1991.
2. Badalyan, V.G. The use of Acoustical Holography in Non-destructive inspection (Review), Plenum Publishing Corporation, 1987.
3. Baikee, et al. Ultrasonic Inspection of Austenitic Welds-Proceedings of International Conference on Non-destructive Examination in Nuclear Industry, ASM, Tests 1978.
4. Barat, P., Baldev Raj, Subramanian, C.V., Bhattacharya, D.K. Estimation of ultrasonic beam skewing in thick austenitic stainless steel weldments—A comparative study, Proceedings of 12th WCNDT, Navada, 1988.
5. Baldev Raj, Subramanian, C.V., Bhattacharya, D.K. An Overview of Status in Testing Measurement and Control of Welds-Report of Commission V of Indian Institute of Welding, INC 1987.
6. Baldev Raj, Jayakumar, T. and Thavasimuthu, M. Practical Non-destructive Testing, Narosa Publishing House, New Delhi, 1997.
7. Baldev Raj, Venkataraman, B. Ionising Radiations for Non-destructive Evaluation, Indian Society for Radiation Physics, ISRP (K) TD-11989.
8. Bernd Rohloft. NDT methods, The South African Mechanical Engineer, Vol. 4, 1994.
9. Birnbaum. Eddy current characterisation of Materials and Structures, Free editors, SSP77, ASTM.
10. Boniface, E. and Rossi. Welding Engineering, McGraw-Hill Book Co, NY, 1954.
11. Bruce, J. and Nestleroth. Remote Field Eddy Current Detection of Stress Corrosion Cracks in Gas Transmission Pipelines, Review of progress in Quantitative Non-destructive Evaluation, Vol. 10A, Edited by Thomson, D.O. and Chimenti, D.E. Plenum Press, NY, 1991.
12. Davies, C. The Science and Practice of Welding, Vol. 12, 8th edition, Cambridge University Press, 1984.
13. Davies, A.C. The Science and Practice of Welding, Cambridge University Press, London, 1967.
14. Devine, T.M. Intergranular Corrosion Behaviour of Wrought and Weld Deposited 308 SS, Proceedings of the Vth Balton Landing Conference, AWS.
15. Dijkstra, F.H., de Raad, J.A. and Boumen T., TOFD and Acceptance Criteria. A perfect Team, INSIGHT, Vol. 39, No. 4, 1997.
16. Dutli James, W., Gerhold, H. and Tenney. A preliminary Investigation of the Radiographic Visualisation of Cracks, Non-destructive Testing, Vol. 12, No. 2, 1994.
17. Edward, A. and Fenton. Terms and Definitions, AWS Committee on Definitions and Symbols.
18. Farrar, J.C.M. and Dolby, R.E. Lamellar Tearing in Welded Steel Fabrication, The welding Institute, Abrington, 1972.

19. Farlay, J.M., Thomson, J.L. and Dikstra, B.J. Non-destructive Testing to Avoid Weld Failure, International Conference on Weld Failures, London, Edited by Harrison, J.D. The Welding Institute. 1988.

20. Furner, Pand Kuntny, M. Residual Stress Measurements in Welded Aluminium Alloys, Proceedings of Vth Balton Landing Conference, ANS 1978.

21. Gebhardt, W., Banity, F. and Woll, H. Defect Reconstruction and Classification of Phased Arrays, Materials Evaluation, Vol. 40, 1994-95.

22. Gebhakdj, W., Schwaz, H.P., Bonitz, F. and Woll, H. Application of Phased Arrays in Basic and In-Service Inspection, 6th International Conference on NDE in the Nuclear Industry, 1983.

23. George Dieter E. Mechanical Metallurgy, 2nd edition, Mc Graw Hill International Book Company, USA, 1984.

24. Ghosh, J.K., Panackkal, J.D. and Roy, P.R. Inspection of End Closure Welds of Fast Reactor Fuel Elements, Afro Asian ·Conference on Welding and Metals Technology, 1978.

25. Giachino Weeks and Jhonson, Welding Technology, 2nd edition, American Technical Society, Chicago, 1977.

26. Gourd, L.M. Principles of Welding Technology, Edward Arnald Publishers, 1980.

27. Goswami, G.L. An Introduction to Acoustic Emission Technology for In Process Inspection of Welds, BARC Report 1216, Commission J, Doc V, 806, 1987.

28. Green, Jr. RE, Ultrasonic Measurements of Mechanical Properties, Practice on Materials Science and Technology, Academic Press, 1973.

29. Halmshaw, R. Industrial Radiography Theory and Practice, Applied Science Publishers, London, 1982.

30. Halmshaw, R. and Hunt, C.A. Can Cracks be found by Radiography, British Journal of NDT, 1975.

31. Halmshaw, R. Non-destructive Testing, Metallurgy and Materials Science Services, Edward Arnold, London, 1992.

32. Hartely, J. Robots at work, A Practical Guide for Engineers and Managers, North Holland Publishing Co., 1983.

33. Harry Udin Edward Funk, R. and Jhon Wulff, Welding for Engineers, Jhon Wilay and Sons, London, 1994.

34. Harrison, J.D. International Conference on Weld failures, Welding Institute, London, 1988.

35. Hicks, J.G. Welded Joint Design, BSP Professional Books, 2nd edition, Oxford, 1987.

36. Hould Croff, P.T. Welding Processess Technology, Cambridge at the university Press, 1967.

37. Hubschen, G., Salzburger, H.J. and Kroning, M. UT of Bimetallic Welds by Shear Horizontal Waves and electromagnetic Ultrasonic (EMUS) Probes. 12th International Conference on NDE in Nuclear and Pressure Vessels Industries.

38. Irwin, G.R. Analysis of Stresses and Strains near the end of a Crack traversing a plate, ASME Journal of Applied Mechanics, Vol. 24, 1957.

39. Ivan Dickson, J. Failure Analysis Techniques and Applications Conference Proceedings, The Materials Information Society (ASM), 1992.

40. James, A. Welding, The Magran Hill Foundation Series, Pender, 1968.

41. Jackson, M.D. and Charless, Welding Methods and Metallurgy, Griffin Co. Ltd, London, 1967.

42. James, W., Dulti Gerhold, H. and Tenney, A. Preliminary Investigation of the Radiographic Visualisation of Cracks, Non-destructive Testing, Vol. 12, No. 2, 1994.

43. John Whittle, Non-destructive Testing—The View from Albuquerque, Nuclear Engineering International.

44. John, Fand Harver, P.E. Theory and Design of Pressure Vessels, CBS Publishers and Distributors, 1987.

45. Kenyon, W. Welding and Fabrication, Pitman Engineering Craft Series, 1972.

46. Kenneth Easterling, Introduction to the Physical Metallurgy of Welding, 2nd edition, Butterworth Henemann, 1992.

47. Kenyon, W. Welding and Fabrication Technology, Pitman Books Ltd., 1982.

48. Koichi Masubuchi, Analysis of Welded Structures, International Series on materials Science and technology, Vol. 33, Pergamon Press, Oxford, 1980.

49. Kohutek, T.L. Fundamentals for a procedure for Non-destructive determination of position, shape of flaws in Welds by Radiometric Measurements.

50. Krzywosz, K. and Dau, G. Comparison of Electromagnetic Techniques for Non-destructive inspection of Ferromagnetic tubing, Materials Evaluation, No. 48, Jan. 1990.

51. Mcnab, A. and Thomson, J. Eddy Current Array Instrument for Fixed Position Scanning, Proceedings of the 12th World Conference on NDT, Amsterdam, 1989.

52. McElory, J.W. AE Inspection of Buried Pipelines, Symposium on AE Monitoring of Pressurised Systems, ASTM, SPP 697, 1979.

53. Milner, D.N. and Apps. R.L. Introduction to Welding and Brazing, Pergamon Press, 1981.

54. Milewski, J.O. and Hmelo et. al, Using Synchrotron X-ray Micro Tomography to detect defects, Welding Journal, 73 (2), 1994.

55. Milewski, J.V., Hmelo, A.B. and Amico, D. Characterizing Laser Fusion Welded Aluminium using Synchrotron X-ray Microtomography, The Minerals Metals and Materials Society, USA, 1993.

56. Morials, J.N. Welding Principles for Engineers, 1951.

57. Moorthy, V., Vaidyanathan, S., Jayakumar, T. and Baldev Raj, Evaluation of Post Weld Heat-treatment in 2.25 Cr-1 Mo Steel Tube to Tube Sheet Welded Joints using Magnetic Barkausan Noise Measurements, Material Science and Technology, Vol. 13, July, 1997.

58. Moorthy, V., Vaidyanathan, S., Laha, Jayakumar, T., Bhanushankar Rao and Baldev Raj. Evaluation of Microstructures in 2.25 Cr-1 Mo Steel Weldments using Magnetic Barkhausen Noise, IWC, 1996.

59. Monty, H. and Cornor, P. Phased Array Eddy Current Inspection of Expansion Transition Zones in Steam Generator Tubing, Eng-ECT Report R 8605.

60. Muller, W., Schmitz, V. and Schafer, G. Reconstruction by the Synthetic Aperture Focussing Technique, Nuclear Engineering and Design, North Holland, Amsterdam, 1994.

61. Murugan, S., Kumar, P.V., Baldev Raj and Bose. M.S.C. Residual Stress Analysis in Weldments-Theoretical Approach, Indian Welding Journal, Vol. 29, No. 4, Oct. 1996. Commission V, DOC 1014-93.

62. Newton, K. et. al., A New Eddy Current Instrument for weld Inspection-Operational Experience, IRM 90.

63. Nichols, R.W. Residual Stresses in Welded Construction and their Effects, International conference, The Welding Institute, Vol. 12, London, Nov. 1977.

64. Noyar, I.C. and Cohen, J.B. Residual Stress Measurements by Diffraction and Interpretation, Springer Veriag, New York, 1987.

65. Palanichamy, P., Joseph, A., Sanjay Rai, Jayakumar, T., Bhattacharya, D.K. and Kasiviswanathan, K.V. Non-destructive Measurement of Residual Stress in Carbon Steel Weld Joints, Indian Welding Journal, Vol. 27, No. 4, Oct. 1994.

66. Palanichamy, P., Joseph, A., Jayakumar, T., Sanjay Rai, Moorthy, V, Vaidyanathan, S. and Baldev Raj. Evaluation of Residual Stresses in Weldments using NDT techniques, Proceedings of SOJOM, Sept. 1996.

67. Pal, T. Kand Mitra, M.K. Monogram on Weld Failures, Jadavpur University, Calcutta, 1996.

68. Palaniappan, M., Subbaratnam, R., Leak testing, Pressure teting and Field exprience, Course on Welding Metallurgy, Technology and Quality Assurance, IIW, Kalpakkam, 1996.

69. Paul, EMix. Introduction to Non-destructive Testing—A Training Guide, A Wiley Inter Science Publication, John Wiley & Sons, New York, 1987.

70. Rajagopal, C.S. and Mohan Babu, M. In-service Ultrasonic Examination for Flaws in BWR Feed Water Nozzles-Case Study, Proceedings of National Symposium on Advances in NDT, BARC, 1980.

71. Rakesh Kaul, Muralidharan, N.G., Kasiviswanathan, K.V., Jayakumar, T. and Baldev Raj. Weld Related Failures—A few case studies, Proceedings of National Conference on Failure Analysis for Safety and Reliability in process equipments, FAIL 95, Ooty, Sept. 95.

72. Raghu, N., Muralidharan, N.G., Jayakumar, T. and Kasiviswanathan, K.V. In-situ Metallography for Damage Assessment and Life Extension in Power Plants—A Few Case Studies, Proceedings of 14th World Conference on NDT, Oxford Press, Dec. 1996.

73. Rao, B.P.C., Shyamsunder, M.T., Baburao, C., Bhattacharya, D.K. and Baldev Raj. Eddy Current Imaging of Surface Defects, 4th Asia Pacific Conference on NDT, Shanghai, China, 1995.

74. Rao, B.P.C. Internal Report No. 980133-TW, Frunhofer Institute for NDT-Saarbrucken, Germany, March, 1998.

75. Rao, P.N. Manufacturing Technology-Foundry Forming and Welding, Tata Mcraw Hill Publishing Co. Ltd., New Delhi.

76. Ramesh, A.S., Subramanian, C.V., Joseph, A., Jayakumar, T., Kalyanasundaram, P. and Baldev Raj. Internal Rotary Inspection System (IRIS)—An useful NDT tool for Tubes of Heat Exchangers, Journal of Non-Destructive Evaluation, Vol. 19, Nos. 3-4 Dec., 98.

77. Sanjay Rai, Sujith, S., Jayakumar, T. X-Ray Diffraction based Residual Stress Analysis of Repair Welds, Preoceeding of the 14th World Conference on NDT, Oxford Press, New Delhi, 1996.

78. Shyamsunder, M.T. and Rao, B.P.C. Recent Advances in ECT, Seminar on NDT and QS, Vol. 1, Interline Publication, Bangalore.

79. Sing, G.P. and Udpa, S.S. The role of Digital Signal Processing in NDT, NDT International, 1986.

80. Smith, J.H., Dood, C.V. and Chitwood, L.D. Multi Frequency Eddy Current Examination of Seam Weld in Steel Sheath, Materials Evaluation, Vol. 43, No. 12.

81. Song, H. Half A Century of Magnetic Particle by SEI, 11th WCNDT, Vol. 1, 1985.

82. Subramanian, C.V., Thavasimuthu, M., Rajagopalan, C., Kalyanasundaram, P. and Baldev Raj. Ultrasonic Test Procedure for Evaluating Fuel Clad Endcap Weld Joints of PHWRs, Materials Evaluation, 1995.

83. Takeha, H., Hamada, K., Oda, M. and Sugiyama. S. Automatic Ultrasonic Testing System for Nuclear Power Plants.

84. Takeshi, Kanazava and Albert, Kobayashi, S. Significance of Defects in Welded Structure, Proceedings of the Japan-US Seminar, University of Tokyo Press, 1974.

85. Troifskii, A.V., Shevehenko, I. Ye and Baldakov, Automated UT of Pipeline Weld Joints, Commission V of IIW, Doc. V 897–89.
86. Troifskii, V.A., Bondarenko, Yu. K. and Eskov, Yu. B. The Increase in Efficiency of the automation Ultrasonic Inspection.
87. Venkataraman, L., Subramanian, C.V. and Balaramamoorthy, K. Ultrasonic Examination of Austenitic Stainless Steel Welds, NDT News, Vol. 4, No. 1, Dec 1979.
88. Venkataraman, B., Baldev Raj and Jayakumar, T. Intelligent Welding, Proceedings of International Conference on Recent Advances in Metallurgical Processes, IISc, Bangalore, New Age International Publishing, New Delhi, Vol. 2, 1997.
89. Votava, E. and Jax, P. Inspection of Nuclear Reactors by means of Acoustic Emission during Hydrotest, Symposium on Acoustic Emission Monitoring of Pressurized Systems, ASTM, STP-697, 1979.
90. Wadley, H.N.G., Scruby, C.B. and Speake, J.H. Acoustic Emission for Physical Examination of Metals, International Metals Review, No. 249, 1980.
91. Willingham, D.C. Weld Decay in Austenitic Stainless Steels. The Welding Institute, 1975.
92. Yan Dawei. A New Composite Magnetization Method, Proceedings of 7th Asian Pacific Conference on NDT, China, APC NDT, 1993.
93. Yen Fwn Chew, Automatic Crack Detection with Computer Vision and Pattern Recognition of Magnetic Particle Indications, Proceedings of 11th WCNDT, Vol. 1, 1985.
94. Yokota, O. and Ishii, Y. Crack Detectability by Radiography, International Journal of NDT, Sep. 1979.
95. Weld Imperfections, Proceedings of a Symposium at Lockheed Palo Alte Research Laboratory, California, Sept. 1966.
96. Welding Handbook, Vol. 1, Chapters 11, 12 and 15, American Welding Society, 550, N.W. Lejeune Road, Miami, U.S.A., 1976.
97. American Society of Metals Hand Book, Vol. 6 and Vol. 11, ASM International, The Materials Information Society, Materials Park, Ohio, U.S.A., 1993.
98. Handbook in the Ultrasonic Examination of Welds, The Welding Institute, Cambridge, 1979.
99. Specifications for Image Quality Indicators for Industrial Radiography, BS 3971, 1980.
100. P-Scan System for Ultrasonic Weld Inspection, British Journal of NDT, 23 (3), 1981.
101. Industrial Robots, Summary and Forecast EO2, Tech Tran Corporation, Naperville, Illinois, 1983.
102. The Application of an Engineering Critical Assessment in Design Fabrication and Inspection to Assess the Fitness for Purpose of Welded Products—Appendix 6 (Experts), International Institute of Welding, SST 1141-89.
103. Considerations on Ultrasonic Testing of Austenitic SS Weld Joints, Doc. V 704–81, Commission V of IIW, Welding in the World.
104. The Significance of defects in Welds, Proceedings of the 2nd Conference, The Welding Institute, London, May, 1968.

Index